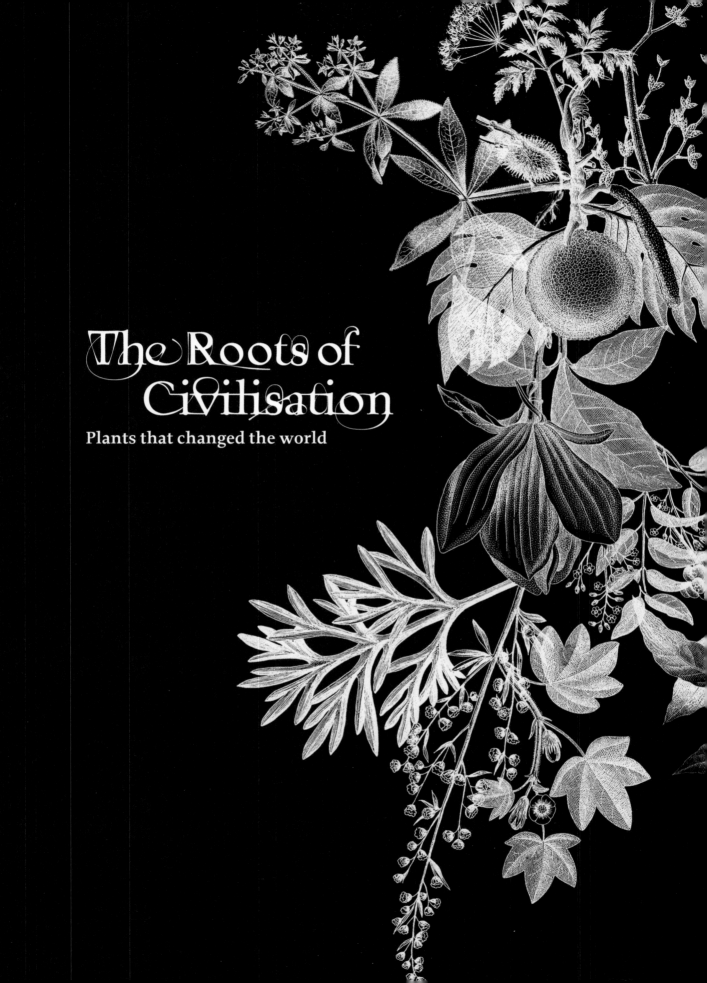

The Roots of Civilisation

Plants that changed the world

The Roots of Civilisation

Plants that changed the world

John Newton

PIER
9

Contents

Introduction

They were here long before we were. If the Big Bang that produced our universe went off between ten and twenty billion years ago, and Earth is about 4.5 billion years old, they—plants, or at least the first signs of organic life—appeared about 3.5 billion years ago. As theoretical chemist Leslie E Orgel wrote in *The Origins of Life on Earth*, 'When the earth formed, it was a lifeless, inhospitable place; a billion years later, it was teeming with organisms resembling blue green algae'. These single-cell organisms spread rapidly throughout the planet's seas. As they grew, they began to produce oxygen, filling the atmosphere with it and providing the environment for other types of organisms to grow, from the mighty trees of the rainforest to the mysterious fungi on and beneath the forest floor.

This book looks at what happened next, when the very first hominoids— the Australopithecines—appeared in the African Rift Valley between four and five million years ago, and began their long and, until recently, mutually beneficial relationship with the plant kingdom.

That relationship still continues, but the immense and intricate plant kingdom is now under threat from the very species it has grown alongside for hundreds of thousands of years.

During all that time we have relied on plants for food, shelter, clothing, medicine, to change our consciousness, to clean the air that we breathe and to sustain the life of our planet. We have used them to poison our enemies and to control our fertility, to navigate the oceans and to build houses and bridges. They are the most important elements in the cycle of life.

We breathe oxygen given off by plants. Through the process known as photosynthesis, plants take energy from the sun, carbon dioxide from the air and water and minerals from the soil, and give off water and oxygen. Humans and other animals take part in this process through respiration. By breathing, they absorb oxygen to release energy from food, and liberate energy in the form of carbon dioxide and water. It is this cycle of photosynthesis and respiration that helps maintain the natural balance of the Earth's oxygen, carbon dioxide and water.

But beyond these dry—but vital to our survival—scientific facts, there is the drama of humanity's association with the plant kingdom. And that is what this book is about: our long and often turbulent relationship with the mantle of green that covers the Earth.

Plants have been central to human evolution in quite intriguing ways— for example, helping us, through the symbiotic relationship of our primate ancestors with tropical fruits (see page 88), to literally see more clearly. But as soon as we stopped living among them, in their shadow, gathering and working in harmony with them, we began to dominate them. It started with agriculture, the invention of which has been described by evolutionary biologist Jared Diamond as a 'catastrophe'. This may be so, but it was also central to the birth of human civilisation. Farming taught us about property, showed us the way to both wealth and poverty, and allowed us to settle and eventually to gather in villages that grew into cities. And it is those cities that are the cradle

of culture. Once we began to sow and reap, New York and Paris, Rembrandt and Picasso, Shakespeare and James Joyce, Bach and the Beatles were just down the evolutionary track.

Along the way, and in the race to find and control the sources of desirable plants (such as rare flowers, spices or medicinal plants) we have enslaved, conquered, explored and devastated whole ecosystems. But we have also nurtured and created useful, beautiful and domesticated versions of wild plants.

The twin miracles of life on Earth are its flora and fauna. This book offers a guided tour of the intersection of the two in all their complexity and variety, with all the wonders and woes that we have experienced along the way.

CLASSIFICATION

Although this is not primarily a book of science or botany, a little background will be useful.

All plants (and animals) are classified according to biological criteria. Let's take a look at the process, using the tomato as an example.

First is the species (abbreviated to sp, or spp in the plural)—in the case of the tomato, *Solanum lycopersicum*. In most cases, or after the first mention, it will be referred to as *S. lycopersicum*.

Similar species group together to form a genus, *Solanum*. The convention is that the genus name is capitalised, the species name (*lycopersicum*) is not, but both are italicised. The plural of genus is genera.

Third comes the family. In the case of the tomato, this is Solanaceae. Plant families often include members that appear to have little to do with each other. The Solanaceae family includes such disparate members as tobacco, petunias, chillis and capsicums, potato, eggplant, the poisonous deadly nightshade and datura. There are sometimes alternative names for families. In this book, we've stuck to the most commonly used.

Often, you'll find the addition of a cultivar name: for a tomato, that might be *S. lycopersicum* cv. 'Beefsteak', 'cv.' being the abbreviation for cultivar (which is a variety or strain produced by horticultural or agricultural techniques, not normally found in the natural population).

Above that, and for the serious student of botany, there is, in ascending order of magnitude:

Order (Solanales);
Subclass (Asteridae);
Class (Magnoliopsida);
Division (Magnoliophyta);
Subkingdom (Tracheobionta); and
Kingdom (Plantae).

These classifications are, mostly, outside the scope of this book.

History of classification

Human beings love to classify, and nothing has been so carefully classified as the plant and animal kingdoms.

The first task was to classify classes of plants as opposed to animals—the animals being generally and broadly defined as the ones that moved. Aristotle (384–322 BC) was the first to attempt classification, and, although not without its errors, it was a major project for the times.

But it was the Swedish botanist, physician and zoologist Carl Linnaeus (1707–1778) who was the first in modern times (but not the last) to attempt a carefully codified classification of both kingdoms. It is to Linnaeus that we owe the eminently sensible 'binomial' (two name) system of naming species, although some refining of his original system has since been necessary to accommodate discoveries in, for example, molecular biology and virology. Five subsequent groupings have appeared since the 1960s, all of which have followed a new system of grouping according to an evolutionary history, now called a phylogenetic tree.

Because of this, at the time of writing a new code of nomenclature is being nutted out by a group of about seventy systematic and evolutionary biologists from eleven nations, as a result of the First International Phylogenetic Nomenclature Meeting, which took place in Paris on 6–9 July 2004. What they are working on is a PhyloCode, designed to name the parts of the tree of life by explicit reference to phylogeny (the classification of organisms). This PhyloCode (see under Websites in the bibliography) will go into operation in a few years, with the exact date yet to be determined. It is also, at the present time, unclear how the PhyloCode and the Linnaean system can coexist.

Solanum lycopersicum (tomato)

Plants for containers

Plants for containers

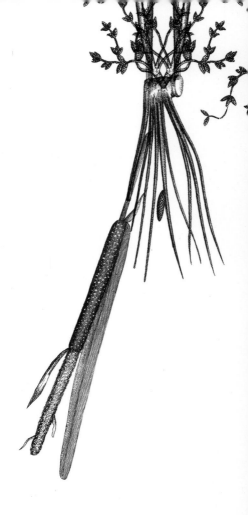

'And the Lord God took the man, and put him into the garden of Eden to dress it and to keep it.'
Genesis 2:15

Humans are toolmaking animals. Other animals may eat their prey where it falls, and drink from rivers and streams, but humans, from their very beginnings in Africa's Rift Valley, made tools. The evidence is in the fossil deposits in the Olduvai Gorge, and we can be pretty sure that these tools included containers.

Those containers would have been as simple as the remnant skin of a cooked animal, the shell of a mollusc, gourds or leaves. Later, they were fashioned from natural materials such as hollowed logs, woven grasses and animal organs—in Spain, until quite recently, wine was transported in a goatskin bag. Later came pottery made from the earth, and even later, glass, from sand.

Plants provided many of human-kind's containers. Beginning in Africa, humans noticed that when dried, the gourd (a vegetable) provided a hollow and waterproof shell. In Asia, the most common, and the fastest-growing plant, bamboo, was used for everything.

And all across the planet, wild grasses and reeds were woven and fashioned into all sorts of containers. Most famously, the baby Moses was found floating on the Nile in a basket made from the reeds that grew along the edges of that river. Until recently, olives were crushed in flat baskets woven from esparto grass—there is even a flavour in oil called 'esparto', the flavour being imparted by the fresh esparto grass baskets used in the oil's extraction.

Twigs were also used. The Roman soldier and writer, Marcus Cato, known as The Elder (234–149 BC), mentions the word *crates* (twigs) four times in his manual on farming, *De Agricultura*. Wicker—also a kind of twig, made from split cane or rattan—is used for baskets as well as furniture.

At first, these containers crafted from vegetable matter were plain and utilitarian but, inevitably, decorations were added. Today, decorated baskets, gourds and bamboo containers are highly sought after by collectors.

GOURDS

'Sugar in the gourd, honey in the horn,
I was so happy since the hour I was born.'
Anon.

Luffa acutangula (angled luffa)

The problem of how to transport liquids in prehistoric times was neatly solved by the discovery of the dried gourd—in most cases, any member of the genus *Lagenaria*, most often *Lagenaria siceraria*, a cucurbit (as are the pumpkin, melon and luffa). We can guess it was an accidental discovery. A sharp-eyed member of the post-Pleistocene population in Africa probably saw that the bottle-shaped vegetable, when left to dry in the sun, transformed into a hard, shiny, watertight vessel containing only seeds.

Whether gourds were first cultivated as containers or food is not known, but about 10,000 years ago small wild gourds were first used in Africa, most likely as fishing net floats. These gourds, tangled in net remnants—thus helping to identify their use—drifted downstream and even, it is hypothesised, across the Atlantic to South America, where they have been recorded dating from about 9000 BC. It is known that a gourd can float with its seeds intact for more than 300 days.

By 7000 BC, gourds had spread as far north as central Mexico and were being used not just as net floats but also as bottles (one type is even called the bottle gourd) and eating utensils. They also spread overland from Africa into Asia, and have been used throughout temperate and tropical zones since then—and not just to hold liquids. Musical instrument of all kinds are made from gourds, including drums, rattles and, most notably, maracas. Originally (and often still) a gourd filled with its dried seeds and attached to a stick, maracas are used in Latin music. The hinnari, a southern Indian wind instrument, is made of two hollow gourds hung from a string. A gourd was also used to make the original banjo.

In the highlands of New Guinea, some tribesmen will go naked except for a penis gourd. The currency of Haiti is called the *gourde* (French for gourd); in the early nineteenth century, gourds were declared currency by the governor (and later self-proclaimed king) Henri Christophe because, although there was little cash in the country, there were plenty of green gourds. In early Peruvian civilisations, pieces of gourd were used to replace broken skull during primitive head surgery.

Throughout the world, gourds have been decorated so that the functional is also beautiful—indeed, there are gourd collectors dedicated to the provenance of these fascinating objects. As we turn to glass, plastic and aluminium for our containers, only these preserved, decorated gourds will remain to remind us of their versatility and utility throughout the ages.

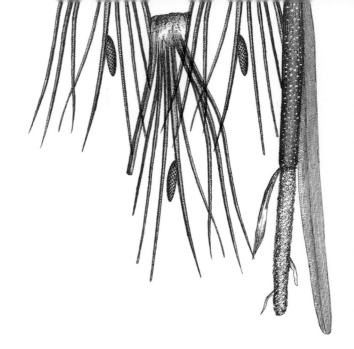

BAMBOO

'The bamboo is my brother.'
Vietnamese folk saying

Anyone who has battled with bamboo in their home garden will not be surprised to learn that it is the fastest-growing plant on the planet and that can take just two months to grow to its mature and maximum size: instances of bamboo growing over a metre a day have been recorded. They may, however, be surprised to learn that it flowers once every hundred years—and then dies.

It is this ferocious will to survive and grow that has made bamboo one of the most useful plants known to half of humanity—the eastern half. The way in which bamboo permeated every aspect of life in the East was described in an 1862 travel book, *Niphon and Pe-Chi-Le*, by Victorian adventurer and author Edward Barrington de Fonblanque:

What would a poor Chinaman do without the bamboo? Independently of its use as food, it provides him with the thatch that covers his house, the mat on which he sleeps, the cup from which he drinks and the chopsticks with which he eats. He irrigates his field by means of a bamboo pipe; his harvest is gathered in with a bamboo rake; his grain is sifted through a bamboo sieve, and carried away in a bamboo basket. The mast of his junk is bamboo; so is the pole of his cart. He is flogged with a bamboo cane, tortured with bamboo stakes, and finally strangled with a bamboo rope.

One could add to this bamboo fences and gates, indeed even entire houses built of bamboo. Today in China, bamboo is also used as scaffolding in the building trade. Some species are even eaten as bamboo shoot. The insides of the shoots are used as food, after cutting away the rough outer leaves, and boiling for several hours to remove the toxic hydrocyanic acid—another example, if one were needed, of the genius of the Chinese people at finding food anywhere in their many times of need.

It is not just in the East that bamboo is used in building. On the Balearic island of Mallorca, a species of bamboo that grows in the dry riverbed is picked, dried and used to weave the base of a ceiling which is then covered with plaster.

For many years there have been arguments over bamboo's classification, with some botanists classifying it as a grass, others as a kind of rice. Today, it is accepted that it is unique, the family—Bambusaceae—being characterised by the structure of its canes, its rapid growth and that centennial flowering.

Again, anyone who has had problems with the rampant nature of bamboo will probably know that there are two kinds—clumping, or sympodial, and running, or monopodial—with the monopodial kind causing the most havoc. It is not uncommon for an untended bamboo grove of this type to eventually demolish a house. Clump growing (sympodial) is the best type to choose for a garden, but even then it is wise to contain the clump with a sturdy border—bricks or underground sheets of glass are often used.

Bamboo could arguably win a contest as the most useful plant known to humanity; a catalogue of its uses could fill this entire section. But we will record just one more—in some parts of China, the tradition of cutting the umbilical cord with a bamboo knife blade is retained.

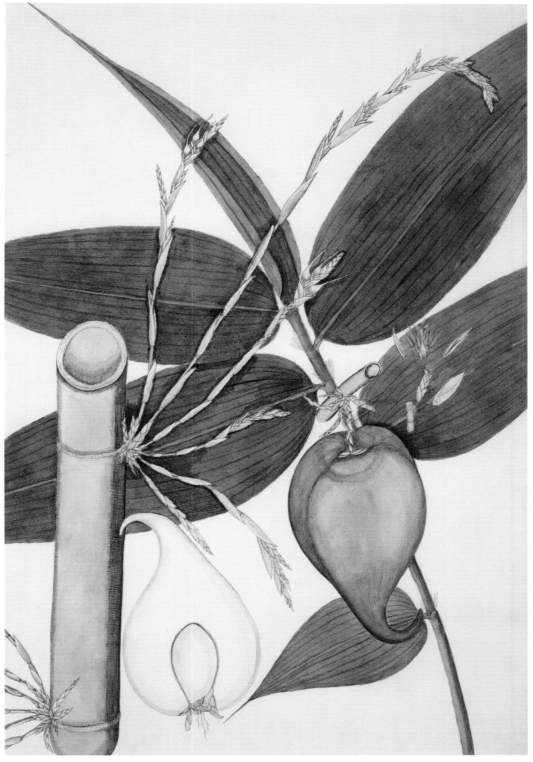

Melocanna baccifera (berry bamboo)

REEDS, GRASSES AND WEAVABLE LEAVES

'And when she could no longer hide him she took for him an ark of bulrushes
and daubed it with slime and with pitch and put the child therein.'
Exodus 2:2

When humans—especially women—first saw reeds and grasses growing, they began to weave them together to make baskets and boats, winnowing grain, carrying babies, catching fish, even making houses.

Presumably baskets, and basket designs, moved around the world with the people carrying them. One weaver might see the design of a foreign basket and emulate it, which would explain, for example, how the hexagonal weaves of Asian baskets appear in Europe and how European designs found their way to the Americas.

Reeds and grasses used for baskets vary round the world. In the Punjab in India, baskets are made from *sarkanda*, a wild swamp grass. Kashmir is famous for its willow baskets. The baskets made at Buka, on the island of Bougainville in Papua New Guinea, are famous worldwide for the closeness of their weave and the beauty and intricacy of their designs.

Indigenous Australians make many beautiful baskets from reeds, grasses and baskets. The fibres are taken from plants and trees, soaked and dried or split or steamed, and chewed to remove the starches. Their intricate patterns are either woven in, using different coloured materials, or painted on.

Perhaps the best-known form of Australian indigenous basket is the dilly bag, a coiled 'string' bag woven from various natural fibres such as the leaves of the pandanus plant or the bark of the kurrajong tree. The fibres are dyed in oranges, yellows, reds, blacks and purples using the roots of various plants. Although no longer made for traditional use, beautiful baskets and dilly bags are still made for sale, as is the case for most traditional baskets around the world.

Until the middle of the twentieth century (and still in some remote places), baskets made of esparto grass were used in extracting the oil from olives. Crushed olives were placed in flat baskets made of esparto, and then squeezed until the oil ran out. The grass used to make these baskets grows in Spain and North Africa, and was known to the Romans for its durability and longevity. It is also used to make sturdy cestas, or baskets, all over Spain.

The many techniques for weaving baskets include coiling, or winding the material like a snake and regularly stitching it, a technique perfected by the Native Americans of the south-western states of America; coiling with sweetgrass, a West African technique imported to America with the slaves; and splint weaving, or weaving with flat materials such as reed and cane, especially rattan (from *Calamus rotang*, the rattan palm), which grows in the rainforests of Indonesia, and much of which is exported to China.

The basket is still with us. Metaphorically, we learn not to 'put all our eggs in one basket', and describe one another as 'basket cases'; physically, we still use wastepaper baskets and play basketball. It's been a long journey, and the basket has carried us all the way.

Calamus rotang (rattan palm)

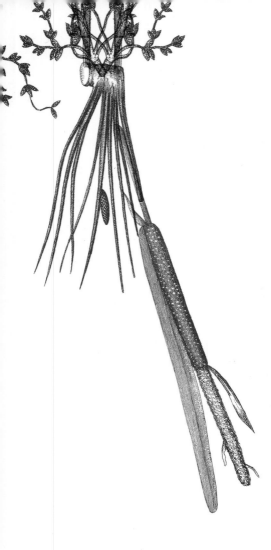

WICKER

'…new straining bags, old straining bags, cord, a cushion, lamps,
1 hide, two wicker strainers, 1 "meat-rack", one pair of steps.'
Cato the Elder (234–139 BC), from a list of equipment for the press room of a vineyard

Wicker is best described as 'anything made with twigs', a modest description for the elaborate wicker furniture beloved of the Victorians. The term derives from two words of Scandinavian origin, *wika* (to bend), and *vikker* (willow). Dried, treated willow and rattan vine are the main materials used to make wicker furniture today.

The first known example of wicker is a round stool seen in a Syrian sculpture dating from 2600 BC, and many examples of wicker furniture have been found in Egyptian archaeological excavations, dating back to about 3000 BC. Later, Cato the Elder mentions wicker in his manual on farming: as a protective covering for harvested grapes, as a basket for figs, and for carrying manure.

Wicker was used in Europe for furniture, in Japan for shoes and rainsuits, and in China to make hearses. It had its heyday in nineteenth-century Europe, where it was used in elaborate chairs and sofas, as surroundings for wall mirrors, for baskets, and especially for baby carriages.

In 1927, modernist architect and designer Mies van der Rohe designed one of his MR chairs with a wicker seat and back on a base of curved mirror-chromed steel tubing.

Today, wicker is still a useful, relatively inexpensive, long-lasting material for outdoor and indoor furniture, although some Victorian pieces now sell for extravagantly high prices.

Salix (willow tree)

THE MARSH ARABS

The marshlands of southern Iraq have been claimed as the original site of the Garden of Eden, and were home to tribes of Arabs for 5000 years, still using the materials used by the Sumerians in 3000 BC. Before they were devastated by the forces of Saddam Hussein, marshes covered the southern part of the Tigris–Euphrates delta in Iraq, an area of 30,000 square kilometres (11,600 square miles). Known as *al Hor* (the marshlands), they supported some 250,000 Ma'dan, or Marsh Arabs, and were made up of a myriad shallow lakes and narrow waterways winding through dense thickets of reeds. Water buffalo, wild boars, otters, geese, ducks, herons, coots and many other water birds lived in and among them.

In October 1950, the British explorer and writer Wilfred Thesiger (1910–2003), accepted an invitation to go duck hunting in the marshes, and discovered for himself this mysterious part of the world. 'It was unexpected and delightful and the marsh people seemed quite untouched by Western civilisation ... I went there for a spot of duck shooting and stayed for eight years.' His 1964 book, *The Marsh Arabs*, brought the people and their lives to the attention of the world.

Of particular interest were their buildings. They lived and congregated in houses and public buildings made of reeds. The principal building in each village was the beautiful cathedral-like *mudhif*, a meeting house, courtroom and guesthouse. The *mudhif* was about 45 metres (150 feet) in length, and supported by bundles of tall reeds arched over to meet at the top, the spaces filled in with thatched reeds. Inside, reed mats were laid on the ground and brocade cushions lined the walls. There were also smaller houses, about 6 metres (20 feet) long and 2 metres

(6 ½ feet), called *raba*, and one-roomed structures called *bayt*; all were made of reeds and mud. The cattle and water buffalo herds were also housed in structures of reed. These reed dwellings dotted the vast marshes and straddled the waters on floating islands built from layers of reed matting and mud.

The marshlands were one of the major food-producing areas, not just for Iraq but for the whole region. Fishing from their wooden and reed canoes using spears, the Marsh Arabs caught enough fish to sell far and wide. From their cattle they produced dairy products for the whole of Iraq.

But from the middle of the twentieth century, the outside world began to encroach on this fragile ecosystem. In 1951, British engineers working for the Iraqi government of the time designed a proposal to drain the marshes and to channel the waters for use in irrigation. Construction of the grand canal began in 1953, then was interrupted until the 1960s, when further construction began. Construction began anew during the first Iraq war in the 1980s, with Saddam Hussein's engineers using the original British plant to continue draining the marshes.

Towards the end of the sixties, the Iraqi government had begun a program to remove the Ma'dan Sheikhs, which resulted in disruption of their management of the fragile marshes, and poverty.

The marshes had always been a refuge for anyone at odds with the authorities, from British colonial times onwards. They would simply break dams, cut bridges and hide on the islands.

But when the Shi'ite Ma'dan joined a revolt against the Sunni rulers in 1991, retaliation was swift and cruel. Saddam Hussein's soldiers burned and bombed marsh villages, while his regime's engineers completed the massive system of dykes and canals to divert the flow of the Euphrates away from the marshes. By 2000, satellite images showed that the marshes had all but disappeared.

By 2003, the environmental effects were thought to be irreversible, with the sparse water remaining contributing to extensive salinisation. In the same year, Human Rights Watch estimated that of the original 250,000 Ma'dan, only 4000 were living in their homeland; the rest had been executed or scattered to refugee camps in Iran and other parts of Iraq.

But there is hope for both the environment and the Ma'dan. Soon after the demise of the Saddam Hussein regime in 2003, a number of organisations began work on restoring the marshlands. In 2005, the UN's Environment Program said that the latest satellite imagery now showed that almost 40 per cent of the marshlands were beginning to recover.

And, while there are still political, environmental and financial obstacles to be overcome—not the least of them massive dam-building projects in Turkey, Iran, Syria and upstream in Iraq—for the first time in many years, there is some hope for the future of both the Ma'dan and their unique, beautiful and productive homeland.

Dye plants

Dye plants

From the sympathetic magic of cave paintings to the intricate, exquisitely coloured patterns of oriental rugs, humans have used dye to colour the world to their own liking and to reproduce images of that world. Dyeing ranges from the simple soaking of a bark cloth in a mixture of ochre and water to the complex secrets of extracting madder red from the madder plant. Black, yellow and red pigments from cave paintings have been dated to 15,000 BC, and textile fragments dyed with woad have been dated to 100 BC.

A dye is most simply described as any coloured substance with an affinity to the ground (such as cloth, bark or rock) to which it is applied. Many thousands of plants are used for dying—including vegetable plants such as *Brassica oleracea* (red cabbage), flowers such *Haemodorum coccineum* (scarlet bloodroot) and the bark from trees such as *Quercus* (oak). The dye is mostly applied in an aqueous solution and may need a mordant (a chemical used to fix the pigments) to improve its colour fastness.

Dyeing seems to be an almost universal human practice, although it is difficult to be absolutely sure of this in the absence of written records, and because remnants usually do not survive geological disturbances and the rigours of time and climate.

Although here we are only concerned with vegetable dyes, other sources of dyes have included cochineal insects and the female shield louse which produced red colours, and species of *Purpura* and *Murex* shellfish which produced the famous Tyrian purple of the Mediterranean, obtained from their mucous gland.

Dyeing is also one of the original complex chemical processes known to humans. The Greek Stockholm Papyrus (c. 300–400 AD) details dyestuffs and techniques as practised in Egypt in such intricate and intimate detail that scholars surmise the knowledge it contains is the result of thousands of years of practical application.

And in spite of a nineteenth-century surge in the production of synthetic dyes, there is a revival of the natural vegetable dyes, thanks to the persistence of chemists like German scientist and rug scholar Harold Bohmer, who initiated the DOBAG project (see page 26), and craftspeople who have never lost sight of the depth and brilliance of the real thing. The quest for colour and beauty is a human constant.

Haemodorum coccineum (scarlet bloodroot)

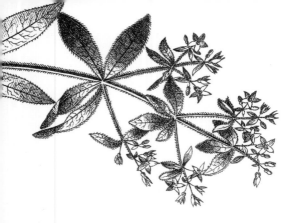

MADDER

'When I look at madder red, my eyes are excited before I know what I'm seeing.'
Robert Chenciner, **Madder Red,** *2000*

No dye illustrates the dictum that the history of colour follows the history of civilisation more than madder, the matured and fermented root of the native European madder plant *Rubia tinctorum.* For the ancients, and right up to the middle of the nineteenth century, madder was simply the finest and reddest of red dyes. It was used to dye the skirts portrayed in the paintings of the Minoan first period (1500 BC), by rug makers all through the Middle East, and by the tartan makers of Scotland. It was used to dye cotton, wool, leather and silk.

There are words for the wild and cultivated madder plant in Babylonian, Pharaonic Egyptian, Khotanese, Chinese, Turkish (it was also known as Turkish red) and all the European tongues. The English word 'madder' comes, it is said, from the Old English *mædere*, whose meaning and origins are so ancient they are lost to the historians of the language.

Growing the plant and extracting the dye from its root were both extremely complex processes; it was said that a farmer who could cultivate madder really had mastered a mystery of nature. The freshly dried root, which took twenty months of growing to contain a significant amount of red dyestuff, had

first to be matured, then fermented, then chemically treated to release its magic— all in all, a thirty-step process. The French scientists who eventually unlocked the secrets of Turkish red in the mid-nineteenth century were puzzled as to how dyers with no scientific knowledge had mastered such a complex process. That they were skilled artisans who had worked their way through the discovery process patiently, perhaps for centuries, did not occur to them.

When the secret of Turkish red was unlocked, the plant was cultivated in Spain, France and Lombardy. A boom in madder-dyed textiles went hand in hand with the mechanisation of industry. The French and the Dutch dominated the trade, and the Russians began extensive plantings in the early 1860s. It was at that point that a scientific breakthrough put an end to the ancient madder trade.

The French chemist Pierre-Jean Robiquet isolated the two colouring agents in the madder root, alizarin and the not-so-colour-fast purpurin in 1826. After that, it was only a matter of time before science found a way to make synthetic alizarin. In 1868, Carl Graebe and Carl Leibermann, who worked for the German chemical company BASF

(Badische Anilin Soda Fabrik), duplicated it using anthracene, derived from coal tar.

This was followed by the synthetic reproduction of all vegetable dyes, and the development of what were known as the aniline dyes, derived from benzene. Overnight, oriental rug makers began using the new dyes. The results varied from average to abysmal. Chemists were 'playing God'.

But real madder would not go away. Synthetic madder just did not have the depth. The red achieved using the plant extract consists of the random application of twenty-five micro-colouring agents, of which alizarin is only one. The effect of madder red is similar to the colour scheme of a pointillist painting.

True craftsmen recognised this. As researcher Robert Chenciner wrote in *Madder Red,* 'Master dyers, pigment makers, painters and weavers ... knew what was required and the second rate was rejected. The quest for eternal quality proved irresistible'.

The English designer, writer and socialist William Morris attempted to revive the production of madder for his fabric designs. But it wasn't until 1978 that the German scientist Harold Bohmer, working in Turkey, reintroduced the art and craft of vegetable dyes—including madder—by analysing the dyes in old rugs using thin-layer chromatography and then manufacturing and using the dyes in making carpets for his DOBAG project. (DOBAG is a Turkish acronym that stands for National Dye Research and Development Project.)

In 1981, Bohmer introduced the women of Ayvacik in western Turkey to his rediscovered methods, and by the end of the year, twenty families had made twenty carpets using original vegetable dyes—including madder. Today, rugs from this project are available around the world and their most striking qualities are the clarity, depth and harmony of the colours. Now, to paraphrase Robert Chenciner, when we look at a DOBAG rug, our eyes are excited but we know what we are seeing.

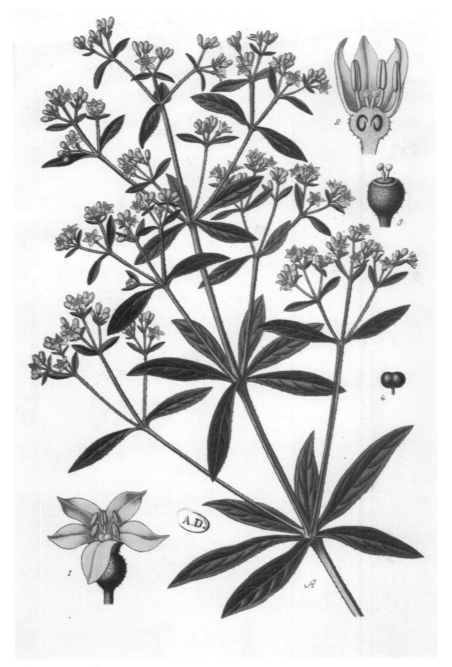

Rubia tinctorum (madder)

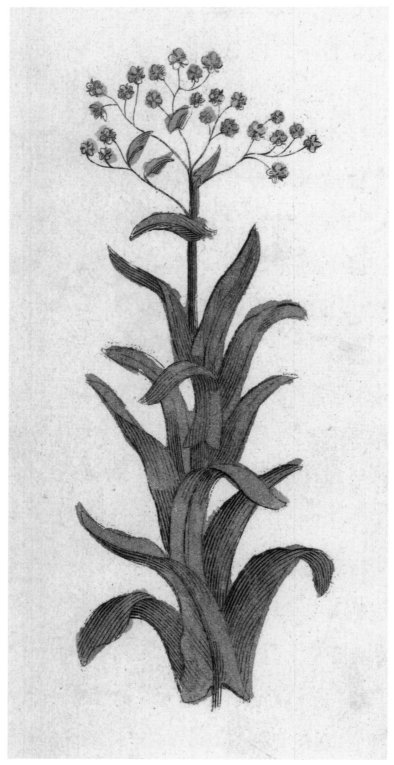

Isatis tinctoria (woad)

The Roots of Civilisation

INDIGO

'You ain't been blue, no, no, no
You ain't been blue till you've had that mood indigo …'
Duke Ellington, 'Mood Indigo'

From Ancient Egypt, to the Bayeux Tapestry, to the jeans you may be wearing now, indigo has been the colour of feeling, fashion and the supernatural for millennia. Its origins are embedded in numerous legends. In western Africa, it was said that wise women gained the secret of extracting the colour from a seeress who broke off a piece of blue sky to eat, after which the sky was pulled up out of reach. Capricious Krishna—the Hindu avatar of Vishnu, the Apollo of India, and adored by women—is always depicted with indigo skin.

The word 'indigo' refers to the blue colouring extracted from the leaves of various plants, including woad (the European plant *Isatis tinctoria*). The name comes from the Greek *indikon*, meaning 'from India', because for many years it was believed that this is where the dye came from. In fact it grew in several countries around the Middle East and Africa.

The colour could have been used, in the form of woad, as long ago as 6000 BC, but was definitely used in Tutankhamen's funerary robe (c. 1324 BC). In the medieval and Byzantine worlds, it is associated with divinity and humility. The New Age movement uses the term 'indigo children' (they have auras of indigo) to refer to children who, they say, are possessed of

paranormal attributes. And no colour expresses the blues more than indigo.

Indigo is different to the other important dye of ancient times, regal or Tyrian purple, by just one or two bromine atoms, and on the colour spectrum it is placed between blue and violet. The most widely exploited plant for indigo dye was *Indigofera tinctoria*. Before the late nineteenth century and the production of synthetic dye, indigo was cultivated at one time or another in El Salvador, Mexico, Brazil and the West Indies and extensively in India. It was also grown in Louisiana, and it is believed that the Dutch attempted to grow it near what is today New York City.

The cultivation of indigo was not easy. Producing a quality dye required vigilance at every stage and was labour intensive. For example, fresh seed was always needed to maintain dye quality and whole fields were set aside for that purpose. In some areas, like Yorubaland in what is today Nigeria, excellent indigo could be produced from wild plants, but this was not the norm.

Once grown and cut, fresh leaves were placed directly in the dye vat, the leaf mass was water fermented and the pigment was extracted as a blue, clay-like sludge. This was evaporated until it became a hard, dry lump, which then needed to be ground to a

powder to be used as a dye. Such a powder was easy to transport.

The production of synthetic indigo followed the discovery of aniline dyes in 1856, and the isolation of alizarin (see madder, page 26) by German chemists in 1868. In 1880 a German chemist by the name of Adolf von Baeyer first artificially synthesised indigo, with financial help from BASF. It took seven years and a considerable amount of capital to develop and launch the dye Indigo Pure. At the time, there were 3000 indigo factories in India—but not for long. The natural indigo market declined severely once the synthetic dye was introduced.

By the mid twentieth century, the synthetic dye was going the same way as the natural. And then along came blue jeans, garments that perfectly suited indigo's one fault: they faded unevenly. And so, 110 years after it first hit the market, synthetic indigo is in constant demand, thanks to the one billion pairs of blue jeans sold around the world every year. But once again, Harold Bohmer has come to the rescue of this beautiful dye, and today, in Sindh in Pakistan, in Laos, Indonesia and India, indigo is being grown and the dyestuff extracted for use in rugs and cloth and by artisan weavers. Indigo lives.

Plants for fibres

Plants for fibres

They clothe us, catch the wind to send us scudding across the seas, hold information, ideas and literature, form the ground for the paint that inspires us and adds beauty to our environment, and—depending on your viewpoint—help us achieve transcendence or send us into the depths of despair.

Plant fibres are among the most important aids and adjuncts to human civilisation. And one of them, hemp, has been sadly neglected for many years by politically inspired misinformation.

As we move out of the petrochemical age, we should start looking towards plant fibres to replace many of the products these chemicals have provided—hemp seeds and oil for varnishes and paint solvents; hemp waste for fertiliser; and flax and hemp as replacements for cotton, which, while a useful plant, is water and chemical intensive to produce.

But the story of fibres must begin with papyrus.

Cyperus papyrus (bulrush)

PAPYRUS

*'Papyrus of whatever grade is fabricated on a board moistened with
water from the Nile: the muddy liquid serves as the bonding force.'*
Pliny (23–79 AD), **Natural History**

The invention of a writing material made from the reed *Cyperus papyrus* (the bulrush of the Bible) in Egypt around 3000 BC must rank as one of the most important discoveries in human history. Before papyrus, stone, clay, wood and metal were used to record information. Now, knowledge could be written in ink with a reed pen, easily transported, and stored for—as it turned out—thousands of years. As a technological advance, it gave an important advantage to Egyptian civilisation.

The earliest papyrus roll (pages came later) dates from about 3000 BC and was found in the tomb of the high official Hemaka. Ironically, it was blank. Papyrus was definitely in use by Dynasty I (c. 3050–2890 BC), as there was a hieroglyphic symbol of a papyrus roll, which has been translated to mean 'book'.

In 1906, an Italian archaeological expedition at Thebes uncovered a 16-metre (53-foot) scroll representing the 'Book of the Dead' in the tomb of the chief workman Kha and his wife Merit, which dated from 1386–1439 BC, Dynasty XVIII.

Egyptian papyrus was also used by the ancient Greeks, and by the literati of the time for legal papers and affairs of state. Egypt went on to supply the Roman Empire with papyrus and for many years kept the secret of its making to themselves. By the second century AD, paper, first made from mulberry bark and bamboo fibres in China, began to move around the world. It proved the end for papyrus. The latest papyrus found was an Arabic document dated 1087 AD.

The Egyptians used papyrus for many other purposes besides making paper. Pliny noted that they used it to make boats and sails, and twisted it into rope. The stalks of the plant were even eaten, raw, roasted, boiled or baked, and used as chewing gum. No wonder the plant was used as a symbol for Egypt.

Cyperus papyrus, which can reach 5 metres (17 feet) in height, is a perennial freshwater plant that once grew widely over swamplands in central and east Asia and parts of West Africa. It doesn't grow naturally in the Nile Valley today; it is speculated that this is due to depletion by millennia of overuse.

Although the process of making papyrus was a jealously guarded Egyptian secret, archaeologists have been able to uncover some of the method of making it—fittingly, by reading papyri. The freshly cut stalks were soaked in water before the green rind was removed. The softened piths were split into finger-length strips and laid side by side on a damp board. A second layer was arranged on top of the first strips in the opposite direction. The two layers were pressed together then pounded with a mallet or a stone for several hours, after which they became naturally stuck together by a sticky substance in the pith. They were then left to dry, and sometimes polished with a piece of ivory, shell or smooth stone, although Pliny wrote that if it was polished too much 'the writing was apt to become scaly'—the highly polished papyrus was not so good at absorbing ink.

Papyrus was made thicker in the later Greco-Roman period, as the Greek reed pen (also used by the Romans) was sharper than the Egyptian rush pen and tended to puncture paper; Pliny claimed that it was the Roman Emperor Claudius who proclaimed an alteration in the thickness. The sheets were glued into a roll with a paste made from the finest flour, and the glued joints flattened with a mallet.

Egyptians wrote with carbon black ink, and red ink made by mixing oak galls (abnormal swellings of tree tissue as a response to a stimulus by insects to provide a home for their eggs) with iron sulphate.

From about the third century AD, the book (or codex) form of papyrus came into use. There is a fragment of a papyrus codex of Homer's *Iliad* in the British Museum, reckoned to be from the third century AD. Perhaps the most interesting of the papyrus fragments was found in 1897 at the old Roman settlement of Oxyrhynchus, in Upper Egypt. It is a leaf from what purports to be the gospel of Matthew, an apocryphal account which, on the Oxyrhynchus codex fragment, says: 'These are the hidden sayings that the living Jesus spoke and Judas who is also Thomas recorded. And he said, "Whoever finds the interpretation of these sayings will not taste death" '.

The great invention of the Egyptian civilisation, then, lasted long enough to record the words of the founder of a religion that flourished long after its collapse. The world had to wait for the discovery of the printing press for the next most important contribution to the spread of knowledge.

CCXCII.

E. B. 1357.

Linum usitatissimum.   Common Flax.

Linum usitatissimum (flax)

FLAX

*'We grew flax in our fields this summer; there are still enough sheep
to give us some wool; and so this winter we'll make our own clothes.'*
Russian peasant interviewed by Ernest Poole for his book The Village: Russian Impressions, 1918

Flax, *Linum usitatissimum* (also called linseed), is an annual herb with leaves along its entire stem, and bluish-violet flowers, cultivated for its oily seeds (linseed) and its fibrous stem. It is one of the two plants used for making linen, the other being hemp (see page 40). Both are bast fibres, bast being strong woody tissue from just beneath the bark. Flax is stronger than cotton but lacks elasticity; the best of it is used in damask and sheeting.

Early examples of flax cloth are rare, because it dissolves easily in acidic soil. The earliest example is a headpiece from the Nahal Hemar cave in Israel dating from 6500 BC. A later find was a brightly coloured linen woven by Swiss lake dwellers in 3000 BC, a piece of such complexity that it suggests long experience of using flax.

The Egyptians were great cultivators and utilisers of flax; indeed, the greater part of Egyptian fibres are linen, and the blue flowers of the plant appear on tomb paintings. It was sown in November, following the flooding of the Nile, and took three months to mature. When the flowers died, it was ready to harvest, and the plant was pulled up with its roots (another activity depicted in tomb decorations), the intention being to get as long and straight a stem as possible.

The seed heads were removed and the stems left in running water to rot the hard outer bark. This was then removed and the bast dried in the sun. Once dried, the stems were beaten or bruised to separate the fibres, which were then spliced and twisted together. Many methods of spinning were shown in tomb paintings, including support spindle, grasp spindle and drop spindle.

The cloth was woven with two or more sets of threads interlaced, then dyed with earth or plant dyes, such as indigo, woad and madder (see pages 26–9), and yellowish dyes, perhaps from either the pomegranate (*Punica granatum*) or the safflower (*Carthamus tinctorius*).

The Bible abounds with references to linen; according to Mark (15:46), when Joseph took the body of Jesus from the cross, 'he bought fine linen and wrapped him in the linen, and laid him in a sepulchre'. In medieval times, linen was used for ropes and utilitarian fabrics like tea towels (a usage continued to the present day).

Today, flax is still grown. In the United States, it is mostly an oilseed crop, but it is grown for textiles in France, Belgium, the Netherlands, Spain and Russia, among other nations. The estimated crop of the three major producers (France, Belgium and the Netherlands) in 2006 was 162,000 tonnes of long and short flax, not a lot compared with the 2004–2005 figure of 19,550,000 tonnes for world production of cotton, but reflecting the renewed fashion interest in linen, which peaked in the 1990s with the crumpled look, and could even increase as alarm at the environmental problems of cotton cultivation increase. Either way, flax gets a new lease of life.

But ultimately, in the battle for the supreme natural fibre, flax—along with hemp—fell by the wayside, beaten by King Cotton.

COTTON

'When I was a little bitty baby
my mamma would rock me in the cradle.
In them old cotton fields back home.'
Huddie (Leadbelly) Ledbetter, 'Cotton Fields'

T-shirts, jeans, business shirts, chinos—even in the age of synthetic materials, cotton is perhaps the most important material for clothing today. And no wonder; it is light, relatively cheap, easy to work and can be made into anything from the most humble clothes item to a high fashion garment.

The history of cotton is long, and it has been a contentious one. The farming of cotton, along with that of sugar, will forever be associated with the shame of slavery, especially in the American South.

More recently, the on and off controversies surrounding cotton have been ignited by the dangers posed by massive amounts of hazardous agrochemicals used to grow it in some of the poorer countries of the world. Although it provides much needed injections of cash, this is often at the expense of human and environmental health. And in a planet where each year water becomes scarcer, it is a very thirsty crop indeed (see Organic Cotton, page 38).

The cotton used today is mainly from *Gossypium hirsutum* and *G. barbadense*, two of the forty-nine different species of the genus *Gossypium* which is distributed throughout most of the planet's tropical and subtropical regions. The origins of cotton are not known, but DNA sequence suggests that the plant is between 10 and 20 million years old, and first grew after the breakup of Gondwanaland. Early in its evolution, there were four primary centres of diversity: Arabia, Africa, Mexico and Pakistan.

Although cotton was not native to the Americas, cotton bolls and fragments of cotton cloth found in caves in Mexico date back to 5000 BC. It was cultivated in the Indus valley in Pakistan in 3000 BC, and had clothed the people of India, Egypt and China since prehistoric times. Cotton was imported to Europe by Arab merchants around 800 AD, and Columbus found it growing in the Bahamas when he arrived in 1492.

In more recent times, it was known that the Hopi Indians had grown cotton in southern New Mexico for hundreds of years before the arrival of the Spaniards, who began growing cotton in Florida in 1556. The English planted it at Jamestown, Virginia. After the invention of the cotton gin in 1793, which made harvesting far easier and cheaper, cotton overtook hemp (see page 40) as the fibre crop of choice and took off all over the American South, where it is now cultivated in seventeen states.

In addition to cotton's use for textiles, cotton seeds are used in animal feed, pressed for cooking oil and used in the manufacture of margarine and other processed foods.

The cultivated species of *Gossypium* went through dramatic changes adapting to their various homes, and *G. hirsutum*, the dominant species in use today, has evolved from a sprawling perennial shrub bearing sparse, coarse hairs to a compact, annual plant with large, readily germinated seeds bearing a thick coat of strong white fibres.

Once processed (ginned) to remove residues, cotton consists of almost 100 per cent pure cellulose, a natural polymer, arranged in a way that gives it natural strength and durability. Each of its fibres contains up to thirty layers of cellulose coiled in a series of natural springs which, when the boll is opened, dry into an interlocked form that is ideal for spinning.

The latest controversy to engulf cotton involves genetic modification, which allows farmers to spray much larger quantities of herbicide in their fields, a development many see as being harmful to the environment. And, with the increasing awareness of the scarcity of water, especially in Australia, cotton farming is being singled out as a huge consumer of valuable resources.

Gossypium barbadense (pima cotton)

ORGANIC COTTON

Cotton is an example of a useful and benign crop turning toxic when farming practices changed after World War II to incorporate the intensive use of agrochemicals, since revealed as dangerous.

Until then, it was planted at low densities in rotation or in tandem with other crops with a view to maintaining soil health. Pests were taken care of by predators, or their cycles were taken into account when planting.

And then along came an arsenal of chemical weapons that allowed farmers to massively increase crop concentrations and ignore the checks and balances of working with nature. Today, according to global figures compiled by the Institute of Science in Society and others, more than 25 per cent of the world's insecticides and 10 per cent of pesticides are used in cotton farming.

Many of those pesticides are listed as possible carcinogens, some are known carcinogens, and one, Aldicarb, recently re-approved for use in Australia by the Australian Pesticides and Veterinary Medicines Authority, is classified by the World Health Organization as 'extremely hazardous'.

The United States uses only 5 per cent of its land area for cotton, but that one crop accounts for 55 per cent of the total US$355 million spent annually on pesticides. In Uzbekistan, it is estimated that 20–90 kilograms (45–200 pounds) of pesticide is used per hectare of cotton. The neighbouring Aral Sea has been drained of water for cotton production for many years, devastating ecosystems and traditional livelihoods. Médécins

Sans Frontières estimates that this results in 43 million tonnes of pesticide-laden dust blown through Central Asia every year, and the region suffers the highest incidence of throat cancers in the world.

In Australia it is claimed that the introduction of the latest version of Monsanto's genetically modified cotton, Bollgard2®, has reduced pesticide use by some 75 per cent. Bollgard2® uses two insecticidal genes from the soil bacterium *Bacillus thuringiensis* (Bt).

However, I-sis (the Institute of Science in Society) claims that 'although to date one fourth of American cotton is produced with genetically engineered Bt varieties, no significant reductions in the overall use of insecticides were achieved. In fact, those insecticides that could be replaced by Bt cotton make up a minor proportion of the insecticides used'.

Opponents of GM cotton also claim that the cost of the Monsanto seeds is prohibitive for farmers in developing countries, and point to the reported failure of crops and decreased yields in India, Indonesia and Africa.

They also point to a glut in cotton, making the use of such technology to continue to produce large crops of cotton counterproductive.

And this is where the push for organic cotton comes from. Like all organic crops, organic cotton uses farming techniques that maintain and regenerate soil fertility without the use of chemicals, toxins, fertilisers, pesticides, GM seeds or sprays.

Demand for organic cotton is rising and, although minuscule in the overall cotton market, sales increased to US$1.1 billion in 2006, up 85 per cent from the previous years.

Retailers such as Wal-Mart, Woolworths and Marks & Spencer, manufacturers like Nike, and fashion designer and organic cotton activist Katharine Hamnett are fuelling the trend.

Is it possible to turn King Cotton around to sustainability? We might not have any choice. To quote Bill McKibben from *Deep Economy*, 'our current economies are changing the physical world in horrifying ways. It's our greatest challenge—the only real question of our time—to see whether we can transform those economies enough to prevent some damage and to help us cope with what we can't prevent'.

HEMP

'May 12–13: Sowed hemp at Muddy hole by swamp.
August 7: began to separate the male from the female—rather too late.'
George Washington, diary, 1765

Poor old hemp. The tragedy is that such a potentially useful plant to humanity was sidelined by the clash of two events: an important technological breakthrough which came at a dramatic turning point in the efforts of a minor figure in American history to gain political advantage by vilifying it. As Robert Deitch wrote in *Hemp—American History Revisited*, humanity has 'exploited [the cannabis plant] in virtually every way for thousands of years'. As fuel, fibre, paper and food, Deitch writes, it could 'solve a number of environmental and economic problems we face today'. But because one of its uses involves pleasure, it has been sidelined by history.

Cannabis is a small genus of flowering annual dioecious plants (individual plants are either male or female), the two most important of which are *Cannabis indica* and *C. sativa*, whose distinctive serrated leaves that many a teenage gardener will recognise instantly.

Cannabis is another of those plants whose original home is unclear. Both Central Asia and Persia have been advanced, although some experts maintain that it began life in north and north-eastern China and south-eastern Siberia, where it is the only fibre plant of any importance.

Pieces of hemp cloth were found in Gansu in north-western China on the inside of a jar belonging to a Neolithic culture (2150–1780 BC). In Chinese, hemp is known as *ta-ma*, 'great fibre'. It was used for clothing, although the Chinese knew of its other properties from the first century BC, and, much later, the Taoists used cannabis as a hallucinogen with other ingredients in incense burners.

The plant grows wild in the hills and mountains of northern India, Asia, Africa and parts of Europe. In the fifth century BC, Herodotus wrote that it grew in Thracia (today an area stretching from southern Bulgaria to Turkey), where it was thrown on red-hot rocks and the fumes inhaled.

As an intoxicant, cannabis has been most widely used in India and the Middle East. The ancient Indian text the *Artharva-Veda* mentions cannabis as a herb that will 'release us from anxiety' and to the present day, cannabis is used by Hindu devotees in India as a part of religious ritual, and is the drug of choice in North Africa.

But cannabis has many other useful applications. In the second century AD, the Chinese surgeon Hua To developed an anaesthetic using cannabis and wine, which he called *ma yo*, to perform 'painless' surgery. In the late tenth century, Venice

became the first European principality to industrialise hemp for the production of fine cloth for garments, sails and rope. By the middle of the fourteenth century, Britain was a major producer of hemp, and the rise of the British navy depended to some extent on the country's production of hemp cloth for sails and ropes. In 1533, Henry VIII issued a law requiring British farmers to grow hemp; indeed, there were penalties for not growing it. The colonisation of India and America was seen as an opportunity to grow even more hemp; in fact the British first went to India in order to plant hemp.

Hemp had a real advantage over cotton as a fibre: its strands were longer and stronger. But in 1793, with the invention of the cotton gin by Eli Whitney, cotton suddenly became much cheaper to process than hemp. Cheap American cotton killed Britain's hemp industry, and devastated India's economy. The switch to cotton began, and cotton has reigned ever since.

But the final death knell for hemp sounded in America in 1937. For seven years, from his appointment in 1930, Harry J Anslinger, the director of the Federal Bureau of Narcotics, demonised marijuana as the 'killer weed', a campaign that culminated in the production of the cult classic film *Reefer Madness*. Finally, after resisting his efforts for those seven years, congress passed the *Marijuana Tax Act* and President Roosevelt signed it, not realising they were killing the hemp industry.

Before 1937, hemp seeds and oil were used as lubricants and in paints and varnishes—after the Act, they were replaced by petrochemicals. And in that same year, *Mechanical Engineering* magazine proclaimed hemp a miracle crop, pronouncing it the strongest of the vegetable fibres, giving the greatest production per acre, requiring less attention and not only not needing the use of herbicides, but acting as a herbicide itself. It is a crop, the magazine told its readers, that leaves the soil in splendid condition. In the same year, *Popular Mechanics* hailed hemp as 'the billion dollar crop', yielding three to six tonnes an acre, and told its readers that paper could be produced from hemp fibre without using sulphuric acid or dioxins, because the plant could be broken down simply with caustic soda. Hemp paper could be used everywhere that paper is used today, with much less cost to the environment. The reason for this praise being heaped upon hemp at the time was, ironically, the new method

Cannabis sativa (marijuana)

for cleaning hemp, the decorticator, which made it as cheap to produce as cotton.

The industrial use of hemp is slowly making a comeback. In 1995, Canada began allowing the cultivation, under license, of a kind of hemp growing to about 9 metres (30 feet), at which point there is hardly any of the psychoactive component of cannabis (tetrahydrocannabinol, or THC) present, and a maximum of fibre and cellulose. We can only hope that there is a return to sanity in society's attitude to this plant, surely one of the most useful on the planet. As for its psychotropic powers, let us end this

story of cannabis with a quotation from Michael Pollan's *Botany of Desire*, 2001:

Christianity and capitalism are both probably right to detest a plant like cannabis. Both faiths bid us to set our sights on the future; both reject the pleasures of the moment and the senses in favour of the expectation of a fulfilment yet to come—whether by earning salvation or by getting and spending. More even than most plant drugs, cannabis, by immersing us in the present and offering something like fulfilment here and now, short-circuits the metaphysics of desire on which Christianity and capitalism ... depend.

PAPER

'Youth and white paper take any impression.'
English proverb

The widespread adoption of the computer, we were told thirty years ago, would mean the end of paper. In *The Myth of the Paperless Office*, authors Abigail Sellen and Richard Harper remind us the reverse is true. For example, they say the use of email will cause a 40 per cent increase in paper consumption. Paper, they point out, is thin, light, porous, opaque and flexible, properties which give us the opportunity of grasping, carrying, folding and writing on it. Paper, as we know, is alive and well and piling up around us. Paper is indispensable to civilisation: where would we be without the book, the newspaper, toilet paper?

The Chinese claim that paper was invented by one Ts'ai Lun (Cai Lun), a eunuch and an official in the Eastern Han Dynasty imperial court, who used bamboo, bark and cloth to make the first paper around 105 AD. Whether he invented the process or recorded its existence is disputed, and of little real importance. Paper—that is, a matted or felted sheet or web of fibre formed on a fine screen from a water suspension—was first made and used in China.

That first paper was a mixture of bark and rag, mainly hemp. Perhaps the greatest Chinese invention using paper was paper money. Around 650 AD, the Emperor issued 'paper tokens'; by the ninth century, these were in regular use with merchants, and in general use one hundred years after that. The West had to wait until 1661, when Sweden issued the first paper money in Europe. America followed in 1690.

From China, paper found its way to Central Asia via the Gobi Desert to Samarkand (the second largest city in Uzbekistan today) and across the Hindu Kush. After the defeat of the Chinese by the Abbasid Caliphate (the second of the two great Muslim caliphates which ruled between 750–1258 AD) at the Battle of Talas in 751, paper was made in Samarkand; several paper makers were found in the losing side, and were set to work by the Arab victors. The secret was out, and papermaking began in the Abbasid capital of Baghdad.

In the West, the papyrus trade was drying up, and after about 600 AD parchment—a thin material made from the skin of calves, sheep or goats—was being used. But it was expensive, and writing on it was laborious—because of the cost, it needed to be used over and over again, and scraping off earlier texts was difficult.

The Arabs had abundant supplies of paper from Samarkand and Baghdad and used the woodblock printing technique to disseminate translations of the works of Ptolemy, Aristotle, Galen and other ancients. This was the underpinning of the intellectual and scientific supremacy of Arab civilisation in the Middle Ages: intellectual development in the West was hampered by a lack of paper.

It took 500 years for paper making to get to the Christian West. Paper documents began to turn up in Europe in the twelfth century, but the paper was almost certainly imported, and in many places, its use was prohibited for important documents because of its Islamic provenance. Roger II of Sicily forbade the use of 'Arabic paper'.

When paper was eventually made in Europe, it was in Spain, then still under Arab rule, the first mill being built in what is today Valencia. The oldest known document made of European paper is the Missal of Silos, dating from the eleventh century; it is still in the library of the monastery of Santo Domingo de Silos near Burgos in northern Spain.

At about the same time as the Spanish began making paper, the Italians learnt the technique in Palestine and took it back to Italy. Paper mills appeared in France in 1357 and Germany in 1390. In 1490, John Tate began making paper in England at Stevenage in Hertfordshire, and across the Atlantic, William Rittenhouse established the first paper mill in Philadelphia in the United States in 1690.

The invention of the printing press in 1450 had greatly accelerated the need for paper and by 1798 Nicholas-Louis Robert had invented the first papermaking machine, one sheet pressed at a time on a moving screen.

By the nineteenth century, vegetable pulps—mainly from trees—had replaced rags as the principal source of paper, although rag is still used for maximum strength. Paper can be made from any of the following fibres: hemp, flax, esparto grass, cotton rags, bamboo, sisal, sunflower stalks and many others. In more recent times, it has been made from recycled materials—waste paper and board are now important sources.

Paper is here to stay. But let's hope that as the twenty-first century progresses, it is made in sustainable ways, from sustainable materials, and doesn't come to our offices and home at the expense of the rapidly dwindling old-growth forests of the planet.

Agave sisalana (sisal)

Food plants

Food plants

If it is true that civilisation began with agriculture, it's also true that humans were eating plant foods long before the cultivation of crops. Before we planted, we gathered, and gathered with knowledge and discrimination.

Food gathering also helped with the development of tools. As noted by French historian Jacques Barrau, over half the wild food plants contain 'elements of an unattractive flavour which are more or less toxic'. Such plants—like bitter cassava—require elaborate preparation and often the use of numerous tools: stones for crushing or cutting, woven fibres, baskets for many purposes and wrapping materials. These could all be said to have led to the invention, eventually, of pottery.

How did the idea of cultivation take root? There are a number of theories, perhaps the simplest being that at first wheat, most likely einkorn (*Triticum monococcum*) and emmer (*T. dioccum*), was gathered wild, and then, perhaps, seeds dropped on the way back to the camp sprouted, giving the idea of planting and so gaining a more secure control of the food supply.

And if it is accepted that women were the gatherers, then perhaps they were the first planters. Certainly, the religious imagery that later grew up around planting—the Greek goddess Demeter and her Roman counterpart Ceres, for example—were feminine.

The other theories on the origins of agriculture include that of zoologists Wadley and Martin that cereals (and dairy foods)—have drug-like properties due to the presence of exorphins, and that these substances facilitated behavioural change, making people more tolerant of the crowded sedentary conditions that followed from the rejection of hunting and gathering, and helping them to play subservient roles in a new hierarchical social structure. Another theory put forward by ethnologist Brian Hayden suggests that it was the ability to produce beer that encouraged the cultivation of cereals. These are very interesting theories, but we'll stick with the dropped seed.

Once we began to plant, we stopped roaming the land looking for food. And once we settled, we began to build, to congregate first into villages, then cities. With agriculture came the idea of property, then wealth and poverty, trade, government, money, war, art, philosophy—the whole panoply.

Not all the results of agriculture have been good —evolutionary biologist Jared Diamond has written an article entitled 'The Worst Mistake in the History of the Human Race', in which he lays the blame for many social and human ills at the feet of agriculture. He points out that hunter-gatherers had more leisure time, not less, taking less time to gather sufficient calories to keep them alive, that our food choices narrowed with the cultivation of cereals, and that life expectancy decreased markedly with the adoption of agriculture. It is an interesting and seductive theory, but one which, ultimately, will have little impact on our lives. I don't think even Mr Diamond would expect us to revert to hunting and gathering. Agriculture has changed the planet and its human and animal inhabitants completely. Indeed, it has re-shaped the very landscape: the rice terraces of Asia, the olive terraces of Mallorca, the vast wheat fields of the American Midwest and the cornfields of Iowa are not so much landscapes as plantscapes.

With the spread of civilisation went the spread of food plants. Wheat broke out of the Fertile Crescent (present-day Syria, Iran, Iraq, Turkey, Jordan and Israel)

and headed west; the olive and the grape migrated west from the eastern shores of the Mediterranean with the Phoenicians; the Romans introduced carrots, garlic, onions, lettuce and much more to northern Europe; the Moors brought rice, oranges, lemons and eggplants (aubergines) from the East to Spain, and thence to the rest of Europe (although rice didn't reach Italy until the fifteenth century). And in the most interesting transfers of all—the Columbian Exchange between the New World and the Old—the Spanish brought the tomato, potato, maize, chocolate and much more to Europe and returned the favour by introducing rice, wheat, citrus and other food plants to the Americas. It's hard to imagine Italy without the tomato, Thailand without the chilli, Ireland without the potato, but those seemingly indispensable national foods only arrived in those countries after the fifteenth century.

Very few of the foods we eat bear much resemblance to their wild relatives. Centuries of hybridisation and selective breeding have changed them almost beyond recognition. The tiny, bitter red fruit that crossed the Atlantic with Columbus is nothing like the plump and juicy tomato we turn into sauce and slice for salads.

And, in more recent times, even more drastic changes have been proposed for our food plants. Genetic engineering, also known as genetic modification, involves forcibly inserting a foreign gene—often literally 'blasting it' into the DNA (an acid that contains the genetic code used in the development and instructions for all living organisms)—into a plant in order to 'improve' its characteristics. So far, genetic engineering has been used mainly to allow farmers to spray as much herbicide as they want on their crops.

As we become more and more urbanised, and more and more removed from the sources of our food, it is important that we remember how the corn in the can of sweet corn or the wheat in the loaf of sliced white bread got to us. In a small way, this chapter attempts to trace the journeys of some of the foods that we eat every day—the foods that have shaped our culinary lives, and the plants that not only give us enormous pleasure, but sustain us and keep us healthy.

Cereals

The word 'cereal' comes to us from Ceres, the Roman incarnation of Demeter, the Greek goddess of the harvest. All cereals are members of the grass family, which includes rice, wheat, barley, millet, oats, rye, maize and sorghum.

Civilisation began when wheat was cultivated around 10,000 years ago and, some might say, ended with the invention of the cornflake in 1894. Either way, cereals have been with us as bread, porridge, congee, couscous and pasta since we turned our back on hunting and gathering.

The planting, sowing and harvesting of grain were of great import to the ancients, with wheat, especially, holding deep religious significance. An ear of wheat became one of the symbols of Osiris, the Egyptian god of fertility and agriculture. Prince Millet was the celestial ancestor of the Chou Emperors of China, and the Dogon people of Mali believed that millet was stolen from the gods.

Grain eating was seen by the ancient Greeks as an essential activity of civilised life: the 'milled life' was their term for an ordered society, even though the milling—dirty, dangerous work—was done by women and slaves. They divided their diet into *sitos*, cereal, and *opsa*, animal.

One of the rites at the temple at Eleusis, centre of the cult of Demeter, consisted of contemplating grains of wheat. In Rome, bread was offered with the marriage contract, and in Macedonia, a loaf was shared by bride and groom to symbolise their union.

In Asia, there is a similarly profound relationship with their cereal, rice. In Bali, the legend is that Wisnu, the Lord of the underworld, raped Mother Earth to fertilise her, and she gave birth to rice.

For the Inca, Maya and Aztec peoples of pre-Columbian America, maize was their daily grain, with evidence of the first sowing of a crop dating back to 5500 BC from an archaeological dig in Tehuacán, in Mexico. The Aztecs sacrificed corn to Tlaloc, the rain god, in thanks for a good harvest. Maize was made into cakes, as it is today, but also porridge.

In both East and West, cereals were first eaten as gruel, or *pulmentum*, the Roman precursor to polenta (today made from maize), congee, pottage and other slurries of cracked grains with flavoured additives. Bread was a later invention; the early breads, Egyptian for example, were primitive, heavy and rather dry. A loaf of bread shaped like the eye of Horus, made from finely ground flour, was found at Dra Abu el-Naga (Thebes) and dated from the New Kingdom, around 1500 BC.

From the eleventh century on, bread was the dominant food in Europe. From this time we date the word *companaticum* (one who eats bread with another), the root of our word 'companion'; plots of arable land were known as bread lands and the kneading chest in which the bread was stored was the most important household item.

And wherever there was grain there was alcohol. Radiocarbon dating and chemical analyses of beer residues from a vat found in Hierakonopolis in Upper Egypt tell us that the beer was made around 3500 BC from wheat, barley, dates and grape pips. Since time immemorial, grains have been used to make alcohol, and, since the invention of distillation (either by the Chinese or the Ptolemaic Egyptians), to make spirits.

The importance of cereals to humankind cannot be overstated. 'No civilization worthy of the name', wrote natural historian Paul C Mangelsdorf in *The Scientific American*, 'has ever been founded on any agricultural basis other than cereals'.

RICE

'In the old societies of Asia, rice is a link between heaven and earth.
It shapes our landscapes, and the way we live, as it has done for centuries.'
Sri Owen, The Rice Book, 1993

Rice, *Oryza sativa*, in one or other of its over 80,000 forms (there are 40,000 rice cultivars, and over 80,000 types of rice when wild rices are included), is the staple food of half the world's population. It is another of those foods whose origins are difficult to pinpoint, although it is most likely that wild rice first grew in India and spread, initially with seeds being carried by birds, seas or river currents.

Wild rice growing in the Yangtze Valley, the first home of Chinese rice cultivation, has been dated to 2000 BC. Rice was not the first Chinese cereal; as discussed elsewhere in this book, wheat and especially millet were the major crops in the north. But it was the adoption of rice cultivation in the south that began the economic dominance of that region.

The deltas of the Yangtze, the Ganges and the Mekong rivers, and similar wetlands in the Philippines and Java, are rich repositories of their own varieties of rice, all being grown on flooded land using primitive methods that have changed little in 5000 years.

In China, the irrigated system of rice cultivation predominates. The rice is sown by being 'broadcast'—seeds are flung into the flooded fields (paddies), with the sower preceded by a draught animal or another human pulling a plank that flattens the soil and, more importantly, muddies the water so that the soil settles over the seed. Two or three days after sowing, the water is drained away, then, when the first leaves appear, the paddy is flooded again.

The cultivation of rice had a profound effect on many of the cultures adopting it as a staple, not the least of them China, of which Maguelonne Toussaint-Samat, author of the *History of Food*, 1992, wrote: 'rice was the making of Chinese civilisation which owed it, besides a meticulous cast of mind, that vast administrative apparatus that neither time nor revolution have changed'.

Another type of rice, mountain rice is grown in such places as Indonesia and northern Vietnam, utilising high rainfall. Rice-growing techniques will adapt to different climates and terrains. Another type of rice, dry or 'upland' rice, is mainly grown on hillsides, using slash-and-burn techniques on generally poor soils; most rice grown in Latin America today is cultivated this way.

Today, in rice-growing areas like Louisiana in America or New South Wales in Australia, germinated seed is sown from low-flying aircraft onto laser-levelled fields, which are then flooded.

The spread of rice to the West probably began with the Persians and Mesopotamians, who knew of it from around 500 BC, most likely through trading contacts between Darius, king of Persia, and the Chinese and Indians. In the next two centuries it reached Egypt, and arrived in Greece around 300 BC. Rice water was mentioned as a medicine by the Greek physician Pedanius Diosocorides in 100 AD. It was well known to the Arabs, and many rice recipes appear in medieval Arabic cook books. 'White rice with melted butter and white sugar is not of this world', said the writer Ibn Qutayba (828–889 AD); indeed, some traditions have this dish as the prophet Mohammed's favourite. The Moors introduced rice into Spain, where it is still grown in the deltas near Valencia. They were exporting it to Sicily by the tenth century, and by the late fifteenth century (and probably earlier) it was being grown in the Po Valley in Lombardy in Italy.

Rice was first grown in America in Carolina in the seventeenth century, when the grateful captain of a shipwrecked vessel carrying rice from Madagascar gave his rescuers several sacks of untreated rice. It is no longer grown in that state, but in Arkansas, California, Texas, Florida and along the Mississippi. America is the world's sixth largest producer.

Curiously, the French did not begin to grow rice until 1942, when returned Madagascan and Indo-Chinese troops in the French army began its cultivation in the Camargue region of Provence.

Rice is said to have been first grown in Australia by Chinese prospectors working on the goldfields of New South Wales and Victoria in the 1850s. Today, most Australian rice is grown in the irrigated Riverina region of New South Wales, although ongoing environmental and flow problems with the Murray–Darling River system may affect this.

Rice can be classified into three main types. Short grain rice (4–5 mm long) is now mainly grown in the Camargue, Italy and Spain. Medium grain rice (5–6 mm long) includes many cheap varieties, and is mainly grown in the United States, Japan, Thailand and Vietnam. Long grain rice (6 mm—1/4 inch—or more in length) has slender grains with a different starch. Its main producers are America, Thailand, Pakistan and India.

Other types of rice include sticky rice (*Oryza glutinosa*), used in Asia for making noodle cakes and 'sticky rice' dishes; the red rice of the Camargue, a relatively new natural hybrid between short grain and wild red rice; and American native wild rice (*Zizania aquatica*), which is not botanically a rice.

Although the bran (the outer layers) contains valuable vitamins, nearly all rice-eating nations and groups (with the exception of the hippie tribes) remove it and leave the rice either white or 'polished'. The reason for this is not so much aesthetic as practical: removing the oil-rich bran extends the storage life of rice—with the bran on, it would rot and be infested by insects.

'Paddy' is rice that has been cut but not threshed, or at least not husked. At the mill, the husk is first removed, revealing

Oryza sativa (rice)

the seed-coat or bran; this is known as brown or whole rice. In the next stage, the bran is rubbed away to expose white rice, which is then polished.

There are almost as many ways of cooking rice as there are rice varieties. The Chinese, Japanese, Indians and Pakistanis use the absorption method. The Chinese also love 'rice gruel'—congee or *jook*—mixed with savoury or sweet foods, mostly at breakfast. In the Middle East, most rice is steamed as pilaf; the Iranians love to slightly burn the base of rice in special rice cookers. The Spanish also prize a little burnt rice (known as *soccorat*) in the base of the paella pan; to

achieve this, they do not stir the rice once the stock has been added. When making risotto, the Italians stir incessantly. Both the English and the Greeks still prefer their rice sweet, in puddings, although the English do occasionally also eat rice at breakfast, as kedgeree. This dish, which includes smoked haddock and eggs, began life in India as *khichri*, and returned with retired members of the Raj, along with that odd dish called 'curry'.

WHEAT

'The farmer puts the grain into the ground, as if burying the dead,
and it is reborn as a plant which itself bears grain.'
Maguelonne Toussaint-Samat, History of Food, 1992

In many ways, as discussed previously, agriculture created civilisation, with all its attendant goods and evils. And although barley was the first of the cultivated crops, wheat—a grass of the *Triticum* genus—was and is the most important. Evidence of the cultivation of two varieties of primitive wheat, emmer (*T. dioccum*) and einkorn (*T. monococcum*), has been found near Jericho, in present-day Jordan.

In its spontaneous or wild form, emmer grew in dry, chalky soil in the semi-arid regions from north-eastern Turkey to western Iran, and was probably native to the southern Syrian area. Other wild wheats included spelt (*T. spelta*). Einkorn, one of emmer's mutations, dating from Neolithic times, spread to central and eastern Europe and as far north as Denmark and Bohemia.

Emmer gradually gave way to the so-called 'hard' wheat, *T. aestivum*, which was—and still is—cultivated for bread making. Whether this hybrid of the cultivated forms of einkorn and emmer was created by accident or design is not known.

In the case of *T. aestivum*, 'hard' means high in gluten, the protein that gives bread its structure. Another kind of hard wheat—hard in that its grains are glassy and split into chips when crushed—is *T. durum*, popular for cracked wheat dishes and for making pasta. It is thought to be a natural hybrid of emmer and wild grass (*Aegilops squarrosa*), emanating from Abyssinia (somewhere between present-day Sudan and Ethiopia).

The earliest mention of wheat is in a list of taxes in the Babylonian Code of Hammurabi from about 1800 BC, and wheat is depicted in Egyptian tomb paintings. One such mural, in the Louvre, shows a manual wooden plough in use, while another shows a plough yoked to oxen. The Egyptians were also among the first breadmakers.

Wheat arrived in China about the fourth century BC, their grain of choice until then being millet, a plant that thrives in dry soils (and still feeds a third of the Earth's peoples). China's severe winters presented cultivation problems in the hard ground, which were solved in many unusual ways. One agricultural treatise in the first century BC prescribes soaking the wheat seed overnight in a mixture of mashed peas and silkworm excrement before sowing it at dawn with help from the dew.

Although first following the Greeks in using barley as their staple, the Romans soon became dependent on wheat and began planting it throughout and importing it from their empire, mainly because Roman landowners were not interested in growing it; wheat; was not as profitable as other crops, such as olives. And so the wheat for Rome came from Sicily, North Africa and even Britain.

Bread was not the only way to eat wheat. Porridge or *pulmentum* was standard fare, and a recipe from Apicius calls for crushed cooked spelt. *Far* (crushed emmer) was at first coarse but became more refined with time and with the improvement of milling technology. In modern Italy it is eaten as *farro*. Polenta, originally wheaten (and an ancestor of *pulmentum*), was made with maize (corn) not long after it arrived from the New World (see page 56). In China, soft noodles of flour and water were made; a similar product called *laganum* or *lagana* was made in Italy and sometimes cut into long strips; this was mentioned by both Horace and Cicero, pre-dating any possibility that Marco Polo brought pasta from China.

The fall of the Roman Empire was to a certain extent the fall of the empire of wheat, for the Saxon invaders of Britain brought with them their own native rye. Wheat recovered in the Middle Ages, and

subsequently there arose class divisions in bread—white (pure) wheat bread for the rich, and coarser mixed-grain breads for the poor.

By the early sixteenth century, the Spaniards were growing wheat in Mexico, and as the North American continent opened up to European expansion, wheat moved north and began to carpet the Midwest area of the United States. It was also grown extensively in Argentina and Canada. Australia was planted with wheat soon after its colonisation in 1788.

When harvested—originally by scythe—the grain has to be threshed, which separates the seeds from the husk and the rest of the ear. Freshly harvested ears are dried, and then, in ancient times, were flailed, often by driving oxen over the wheat so their hooves could do the threshing, or by dragging a spiked sledge over it. Later, the chaff was winnowed, or blown away from the heavier grain, either by wind or fans. Now the whole process takes place inside a combine harvester.

The threshed grain to be made into flour is coated in several layers of bran. Inside is the endosperm, the wheat grain. This accounts for about 85 per cent of the mass, bran another 13 per cent, and wheatgerm 2 per cent.

The threshed grain is first graded to get rid of cracked grains or weed seeds, then conditioned—water is added to soften the grain and it is then milled. If the bran and germ are sieved off, the result is white flour; if they are left and crushed, that is wholemeal flour.

An interesting sidelight in the history of wheat is the research of food historian Clifford A Wright into the provenance of dried pasta, which is 'the generic term for all dried alimentary pastes cooked in broth or water'. Dried pasta, Wright reminds us, was only made possible by the arrival of *Triticum durum*, the high-gluten, low-moisture wheat which was, he asserts, imported into Italy and Spain by Moors, who themselves imported it from what was then called Abyssinia.

This development was extremely important. Dried pasta is transportable, can be stored and thus becomes an industrial product. One of the first mentions of dried pasta is in the twelfth century, by the great Arab geographer Al-Idrisi. Even at that time, it was being manufactured in Sicily and exported to Calabria.

A little later, in Spain, an anonymous thirteenth-century Arabic cookbook uses the word *al-fidawsh* to describe dried

pasta, from which came the Spanish *fideos*, a thin dried pasta used most commonly in Catalonia. Crushed durum wheat, or semolina, is also the basis of North African couscous.

It is interesting to note that in the past 10 years, artisan bakers have begun using the ancient wheats—einkorn, emmer and especially spelt—and have revived the pre-industrial yeast method of using a fermented starter to make what is today known as sourdough bread.

RYE

'Sing a song of sixpence, a pocket full of rye,
four and twenty blackbirds, baked in a pie.'
Traditional nursery rhyme

In its cultivated form, *Secale cereale*, rye, was a blessing in times of hardship. Easy to grow on poor soil, hardy rye was known to the Anatolian peasants as the 'wheat of Allah': when the main crop failed, rye was there to fall back on. It grows wild in wheat fields, and sprouts when bad weather kills the wheat.

Rye's wild ancestor, *S. montantum*, mountain rye, was native to mountainous regions of the Middle East, the Caucasus and North Africa.

It was developed into cultivated form probably around 3000 BC, somewhere in the highlands of Eastern Turkey, in a harsh climate unsuitable for barley or wheat. It was poorly regarded in southern Europe; the Romans regarded it as a weed, and Pliny wrote it off as a 'very poor food [which] only serves to avert starvation'. But in the north, it was much loved and revered. When the Saxons invaded Britain, they brought their rye bread with them and overthrew wheat for some time. It is the standard cereal for bread in Russia, where it is also used to make a fermented alcoholic drink, *kvass*.

A fascinating quality of rye—and something that must have proved a real problem before it was fully understood—is that, when spoilt (when it becomes damp, for example), it grows a puzzling mass of fungal species and strains named ergot. Historians have traced mass outbreaks of delusions and hallucinations to unwitting ingestion of this fungus, and they were not wrong. On 16 April 1943, Dr Albert Hofmann, working in the Sandoz laboratories in Basel, Switzerland, accidentally absorbed some LSD-25, which he had previously synthesised from ergot alkaloids, through his fingertips. He bicycled home accompanied by what he described as 'not unpleasant (hallucinations) accompanied by extreme activity of the imagination'. Hofmann went on to experiment further with LSD, for which he had a high regard, calling it 'medicine for the soul'.

OATS

'A grain which in England is given to
horses, but in Scotland supports the people.'
Dr Johnson's Dictionary

Avena sativa is the cultivated form of the grass *A. sterilis*, which grew in the Fertile Crescent. About 1000 BC it began to be cultivated in Central Europe. No one seemed all that keen on oats until they arrived in Scotland. The Egyptians despised them, but used them for making a gruel called *psitanes*; the Greeks and the Romans fed them mainly to animals, but the Romans encouraged their cultivation in Britain, where they were taken up by the Welsh and especially the Scots.

Oats are not suitable for making bread because of their almost total lack of gluten, but they make a fine porridge—which in Scotland is usually eaten with salt. In Yorkshire they are mixed with broth, gravy and butter to make browiss. Scottish oatcakes are made by mixing the oats with salt water and a little fat. Most famously, oats are an important ingredient in haggis, that Scottish parcel of sheep offal boiled in sheep stomach and traditionally eaten at New Year.

There was a craze for oat bran in the 1980s as it was believed to lower LDL (low density lipoprotein), the 'bad' cholesterol, and also to provide fibre in the diet.

Next page: *Triticum aestivum* (wheat), *Secale cereale* (rye), *Hordeum vulgare* (barley) and *Avena sativa* (oat)

MAIZE/CORN

'The corn is as high as an elephant's eye,
An' it looks like it's climbin' clear up to the sky.'
From Oklahoma, words by Oscar Hammerstein II, music by Richard Rodgers

Maize (*Zea mays*), known as corn in North America and Australia, is one of the world's most important and, in more modern times, most controversial foods. It originated in Central and South America, and was first cultivated around 5500 BC. The primitive form of the grain had very small ears, but the ears, or heads, of the modern maize plant are larger than those of any other grass used as grain—up to 60 centimetres (24 inches) long, with the grains set in rows along a central cob. Modern maize must be sown by humans, as it is incapable of self-propagation—if left, the ears merely rot.

Being the staple food of these American civilisations, the preparation of maize was important. The raw kernels were boiled in water and white lime (calcium carbonate), which boosted the levels of the available amino acids, calcium and niacin. Without this preparation, a diet heavy in maize leads to malnutrition and the disease known as pellagra, caused by a deficiency in niacin (vitamin B3).

Maize was central to the religious cultures of the Inca, Maya and Aztec peoples. In the town of Copán Ruinas in western Honduras, there is a Mayan temple which represents the birthplace of the sacred maize plant. In Aztec culture, the gods Xilonen and Cinteotl and the goddess Chicomecoatl were the principal maize deities, and an ear of corn was used for the zero symbol in Aztec mathematical calculations.

The nutritional importance of maize was as a source of carbohydrate energy. When combined with beans (which provide protein, iron and minerals), pumpkin (squash) (which contains vitamins A and D and fibre), and chilli peppers (for all the essential vitamins), it contains almost everything required for human survival. With fresh fruit and some animal protein, it is the basis of a rich, multifaceted diet.

The cultivation of maize took several thousand years to spread from central Mexico to the American Southwest, where it is now one of the most economically important crops in America and, as it has turned out, a mixed blessing.

Although it is generally accepted that maize first left the Americas with Columbus, there is some evidence to suggest that it appeared in Asia, Africa and Europe before 1492. Whether this is the case or not, it was planted on the Iberian peninsula not long after Columbus' return, and, by the early sixteenth century, had appeared in Castile,

Andalucia and Catalonia before spreading to southwestern France and then to the Veneto, in northern Italy, where its cultivation took hold in the 1530s.

At first, it was planted as fodder or experimentally, but perhaps its popularity increased with the Italian peasant farmers because as a novel crop, it didn't attract taxes like the other grains. It began to take off when landowners saw the profits in this new high-yield crop, and gradually replaced all other grains except wheat, although there was peasant resistance against the landlords who wanted to take it out of small production in the vegetable garden and turn it into a more intensively planted field crop.

The die was cast in the middle decades of the eighteenth century, when a severe famine saw the hardy maize, now eaten as polenta, become an indispensable item in the rural peasantry's survival in Italy. But as we have seen, this soon turned into a health problem.

As part of a diet, maize is fine, but on its own without the white lime treatment, it led to severe outbreaks of pellagra. The disease was first seen in Spain in the 1730s, and then spread through southern France, the Po Valley and into the Balkans. Peasants all over these regions couldn't afford the meat and wheat bread needed to supplement their maize diet. Only in the first decades of the twentieth century was this problem overcome, with improvements in diet made possible by seriously improved economic conditions.

But corn has also become a problem in America, where four corporations control the seed corn market, and the vast bulk of corn grown—about ten billion bushels a year—is fed to cattle. It has been estimated that if all the corn fed to cattle in America was instead eaten by people, it would feed 800 million.

The other problematic use for this ancient grain is in industrial foods, most commonly as high-fructose corn syrup, a product synthesised by Japanese scientists in the 1970s, which accounts for 530 million of those ten billion bushels. The large amounts of high-fructose corn syrup have been implicated in the obesity epidemic sweeping the world, and especially America, in the late twentieth century. In her book *What to Eat*, 2006, Marion Nestle points out that 'the [US] food supply now provides an average of 200 calories a day from the high fructose corn syrup in soft drinks alone'.

Huge amounts of processed corn are used in the manufacture of 'industrial'

Zea mays (maize/corn)

food in the modern American diet—in everything from colourings to food glues to preservatives to the glucose used to brew beer and in the manufacture of margarine and mayonnaise. As Michael Pollan writes in *The Omnivore's Dilemma*, 2006, 'there are some 45,000 items in the American supermarket and more than a quarter of them now contain corn'.

Were a blight to attack the corn crop in America (not a fanciful notion, with the prevalence of GE crops from a single strain), the effects would be as disastrous as was the potato blight to the Irish in 1845 (see page 72).

Pulses

From the Latin *puls*, meaning pottage (a semi-liquid soup), we get 'pulse', the edible seeds of legumes. The Roman word *legumen* was used to denote all edible seeds that form in pods, and from this came the verb *lego*, to collect or gather. But because the word 'legume' now means any vegetable in French, English needed a new word—hence pulse. In reality, the two words are interchangeable, although pulse usually means that the bean has been dried and must be soaked or cooked slowly to reconstitute it.

Legumes are always double in form and split easily when the skin rubs off: think of double-peeling fresh broad beans, or the two halves of a peanut. In India, a distinction is made between *gram* (the whole unpeeled pulse) and *dal* (skinned and split pulses).

The pulses include lentils, broad beans, peas, peanuts, chickpeas and many more; with 18,000 members, the Leguminosae, one of the largest families of flowering plants, is second only to the grasses, or cereals, in producing food crops for the world. In many countries, and especially in vegetarian societies, pulses are an important source of protein, complex carbohydrate, dietary fibre and minerals and vitamins.

The pulses have a long history, and were among the more important foods for the hunter-gatherers. While not having the sweetness of tree fruits, they were filling and made a good substitute for meat in times when game was in short supply.

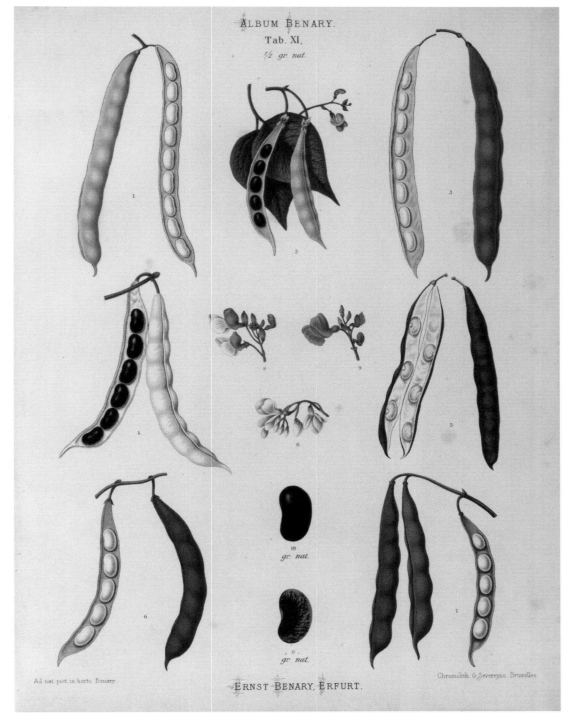

ALBUM BENARY.
Tab. XI.
½ gr. nat.

ERNST BENARY, ERFURT.

Phaseolus coccineus (runner bean)

SOY BEAN

'Tofu already has a place in the dietary panorama of Italy.'
Arnoldo Mondadori, The Magic Harvest, 1993

In its various forms, the soy bean, *Glycine max*, is the most widely eaten plant food in the world. It has long been consumed in China, Japan and Southeast Asia, where traditional diets contain little meat. More lately in the West, the soy bean in its various forms has been touted as a 'miracle food', and it is a major ingredient, along with corn, in a wide variety of industrial foods. In its natural form, soy contains in balance all the elements needed to sustain life.

The soy bean plant is an erect leguminous annual with a woody stem ranging from 30 centimetres to 2 metres (1–6 feet) in height. Its many branches carry heavy foliage and small mauve and white flowers. Its pods appear in groups of three or four and carry two or three seeds each. An important attribute of the plant is that its roots, more than those of any other leguminous plants, distribute nitrogen to the soil.

It is another plant whose origins are lost to time, and attended by legends of its discovery. In soy's case, this is the story of two Chinese bandits who, lost in the desert, survived on the beans of a then unknown plant. In any case, it was probably domesticated in China around 3000 BC. Chinese Buddhist priests are believed to have taken the soy bean to Japan in the sixth century, along with their faith.

Most of the crop in Asian countries is processed and transformed, sometimes with fermentation, into such products as tofu, miso, soy milk, soy sauce, salted black beans and, in Indonesia, tempe. The Japanese eat the immature bean boiled (*edamame*), and grow about sixty varieties for this purpose.

Soy sauce was the first soy product to cross over to the West, imported by Dutch traders in the seventeenth century (the name 'soy', now used in most European languages, originated at this time). But it certainly was not the last. Perhaps its slow acceptance in the West was, as Alan Davidson in *The Oxford Companion to Food* has pointed out, because soy beans cooked in the way beans are cooked in the West, are tough and bitter. But industry will find a way.

Before 1915, the soy bean was used in America solely as animal fodder. In that year, after boll weevils destroyed the cottonseeds then used to make oil, soy beans were called on to supply the deficit, and afterwards began to enter the diet. By 2003, American soy beans accounted for one third of the world's crop, with Brazil and Argentina rushing to catch up.

In America, some 11 billion kilograms (25 billion pounds) of soy bean meal and oil are used every year in margarine, salad and cooking oils and as ingredients in industrial food products—12,000-plus food and animal fodder products contain soy in some form or other.

The rise and rise of soy in the West is creating a number of environmental problems. Firstly, soy is another agricultural product that is increasingly being genetically engineered, and secondly, during 2005–06, Brazil produced more than 53.4 million tonnes of soy beans, creating additional pressure on the Amazon rainforests.

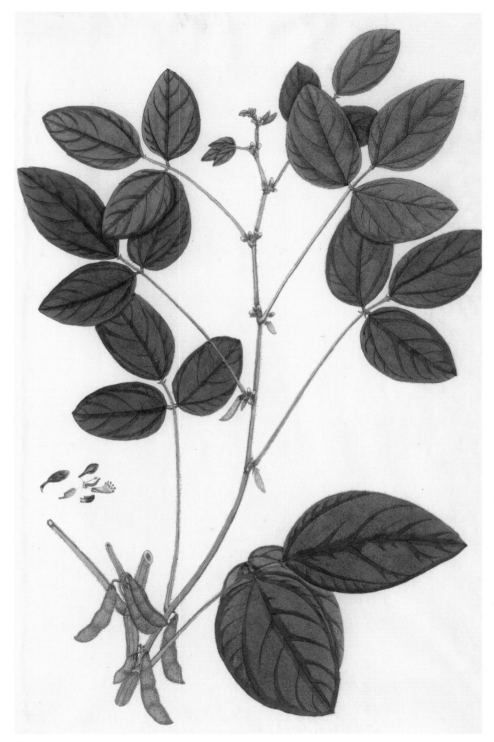

Glycine max (soy bean)

PEANUT

Not a nut, but actually a legume, the peanut (*Arachis hypogaea*)—also know as the groundnut, goober or earth nut—is a migrant from Peru. It is an important food for some, a snack food for others, the progenitor of a cartoon, and potentially deadly for the one in 50 children and one in 200 adults who have what is termed peanut allergy, a hypersensitivity to substances in peanuts which may lead to severe physical symptoms.

There are several varieties of peanuts, and they grow in two major patterns: an upright form, with nuts all growing near the main root, or a trailing form, with the nuts scattered along the creeper stems. The flowers are small, bright yellow and pea-like in appearance.

After the flowers are pollinated and fertilised, the stalk (peg) below the fertilised ovary elongates and curves downward towards the soil. It usually takes about ten days after fertilisation for this 'peg' to disappear into the soil, which is where it matures—hence the name groundnut.

After leaving Peru, the peanut spread to West and East Africa with the Portuguese and from there made its way to the Philippines and Southeast Asia. Today, India is the world's largest grower of peanuts, followed by China and North America.

Like many other American migrants, it quickly entered the foodways of its host countries, as, for example, satay sauce and gado gado in Indonesia and the Malay Peninsula and the 'groundnut chop' of West Africa. Peanut oil is the preferred cooking oil throughout Southeast Asia, although it is not, as Charmaine Solomon points out in her *Encyclopaedia of Asian Food*, 'the highly refined, flavourless oil we get in the west but an unrefined version of the same thing, full of peanuty flavour'. It is also, Solomon says, particularly suited to stir frying and deep frying as it can stand high temperatures without burning, and absorbs very little flavour so it may be strained and reused.

But it is probably peanut butter that is the Western world's favourite way to eat the peanut, either smooth or crunchy, and with lesser or greater amounts of sugar and salt.

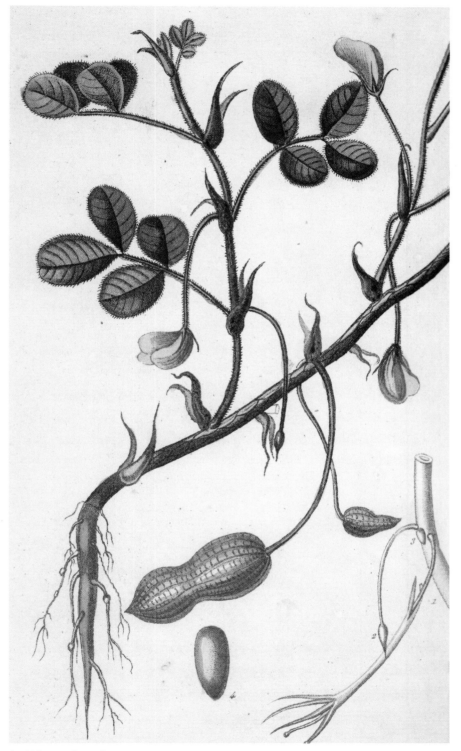

Arachis hypogaea (peanut)

BROAD BEAN

'Avoid the broad bean.'

Pythagoras, c. 580–490 BC (the reason for his injunction is not clear, but some think it is because he believed the beans to contain the souls of the dead)

With two names, *Vicia faba* or *Faba vulgaris*, the broad bean is the original European bean, and carries some heavy baggage from ancient times. It might also, according to Maguelonne Toussaint-Samat, 're-open the whole question of the origins of farming'.

Tens of thousands of years ago, the broad bean was picked and eaten in its wild state in what is today south-eastern Afghanistan, as well as Central Asia and the foothills of the Himalayas. That original bean has seeds the size of little fingernails, but cultivation in ancient times, perhaps first in Kashmir, improved it and it grew to the size we know today, the size of a thumbnail.

As for the origins of farming, the archaeologist Chester Gorman discovered evidence in 1972 that two types of broad beans were being cultivated in south-eastern Thailand as early as 7000 BC, at least one thousand years before plant domestication in the Middle East, until

now seen as the 'cradle of agriculture'. Perhaps all of those early cultivators were helped by the wild plant's efficient reproductive system: when the pod ripens, it rolls into a spiral and ejects its seeds onto the ground.

When young and green, broad beans can be eaten raw or lightly fried or boiled. Mature, they develop a tough skin that needs to be removed. And, like other pulses, they are also dried.

Although the Egyptians have used a brown variety of the broad bean in their national dish, *ful medames*, for centuries, in ancient Egypt they were considered an unclean food, and Herodotus claimed that their priests wouldn't even look at them. It was the general belief that the souls of the dead migrated into beans. Alan Davidson advances the theory that this was because the Greeks used the same word for both 'soul' and 'wind' (a consequence of eating beans), *anemos*. Perhaps for this reason, they were eaten

at funeral feasts. In Greece they were also used as ballot papers—you would cast a bean for the candidate of your choice.

Pythagoras, although a vegetarian, had a real aversion to the broad bean. One story has him facing death rather than escaping his pursuers through a bean field. As if these proscriptions were not enough to pile on the humble and delicious broad bean, there is also an ailment, called favism, which afflicts some people who eat them or even breathe their pollen. Luckily only a small percentage of people suffer from this problem, whose cause has now been identified and named as G6PD enzyme deficiency.

Vicia faba (broad bean)

Roots and rhizomes

Roots—tubers, bulbs and rhizomes—were the food staples of most farming cultures, and many of the world's most important civilisations. But they were, from the beginning, another of the food groups grubbed from the ground by the earliest human foragers.

The tubers, from the Latin for 'lump' or 'swelling', include potatoes, sweet potatoes, taro and yams.

Roots include turnips, carrots and beetroot. Of the bulbs, the most notable are garlic and the various forms of onion. The most important rhizome is ginger.

These dense, nutritionally rich and flavoursome foods were also, it has been argued, one of the first steps towards cultivation: digging the soil is the first action of the farmer. Indeed, some historians believe that roots were cultivated before grains.

Of all the underground foods, it is the potato that has the most remarkable story to tell, a story of success, tragedy and virtual takeover as the global vegetable.

Pl.317. A. Ail potager. Allium oleraceum L.
B. Ail jaune. Allium flavum L.

Allium oleraceum and *A. Flavum* (field garlic)

GARLIC

'Oh! wretched man! do not go near them; they have eaten garlic.'
Theorus, a character in Aristophanes' play The Acharnians, 425 BC

The subject of garlic, *Allium sativum*, divides the world. In the smelly corner, defending it to their last gasp, are the garlic people. A respectable distance away, recoiling in horror, are the pure of breath.

No other food—without exception—is the subject of so much folklore. The Egyptians used it for making mummies; the ancient Hebrews for making love; and the Greeks for girding the loins for battle. There was a section of the market in Athens called, simply, *ta skoroda*, garlic. Nero is reputed to have invented aioli (a sauce of garlic with olive oil), even though the priestesses of Cybele denied entrance to their temple to anyone who had been eating garlic. And then there are the vampires, who, it is well known, are repelled by garlic. The most likely source of this belief is that garlic is a mosquito repellent; because mosquitoes also 'suck blood', why not use it against the vampire as well?

Such a food, as we have noted, divides opinion violently, and it has had its detractors. The Indians believed that its smell meant the presence of evil spirits, a belief shared by Japan's Zen Buddhists, outside whose temples you will find an inscription forbidding garlic and wine. The Jains of India proscribe both garlic and onions in their diets, and King Alfonso of Castile issued a decree in 1330 forbidding knights to enter the court for four weeks if they had been eating garlic.

From ancient times, however, garlic has been prized for its medicinal qualities. Its presence in Gerard's *Herball*, 1597, with 'figge leaves and cumin ... against the biting of the mouse' only confirms modern science's view of it as a strong antimicrobial agent. Louis Pasteur examined garlic's use as an antibacterial in the nineteenth century and demonstrated its bactericidal properties under laboratory conditions.

Modern science has ascertained that the therapeutic efficacy of garlic and its remarkable odour are linked. In the 1940s it was discovered that a substance called alliin needed to be broken down before its anti-microbial properties and its odour became evident. In order to release this compound, it must be cut or crushed. Then, in a series of complex transformations, there arise the molecules that are responsible for garlic's antibacterial, antifungal and antithrombotic (preventing blood clotting) qualities.

Garlic can also be classified as a dietary anticarcinogen, with antioxidant properties that can reduce the incidence of certain human cancers. More specifically, other studies show that a compound in garlic—diallyl disulfide (DADS), an oil-soluble sulphur compound present in processed garlic— depresses the growth of the human cancer cells or kills them.

While most European names for garlic relate to its genus, *Allium* (Italian *aglio*, French *ail*, Spanish *ajo*), the English name arises from a curious hybrid: 'gar', from garfish, alluding to the shape of its leaves, and 'lic', or 'leac', meaning leek.

As a food, garlic can be mashed, pounded, pressed, diced, sliced, minced, powdered and granulated. It can be served as a vegetable in the form of baked whole bulbs, or added in such a way as to impart only a delicate flavour, as in the genteel 1950s women's-magazine directive: 'rub a salad bowl with a clove of garlic: discard the garlic'. But it's too delicious—and healthy—to be ignored.

GINGER

'Within the stomach, loins, and in the lung
Praise of hot ginger rightly may be sung
It quenches thirst, revives, excites the brain
And in old age, awakens young love again.'
Latin verse from the Regimen Sanitatis Salerno, *twelfth*
to thirteenth century

The rhizomes of the plant *Zingiber officinale*, which have both culinary and medicinal uses, are mainly eaten fresh in their countries of origin but are often powdered, preserved in syrup, or crystallised for export. Like cinnamon, ginger is a spice used as often in savoury dishes as sweet ones.

Ginger is yet another plant whose origins are obscure—wild plants are unknown—but it probably originated between northern India and east Asia, and has been cultivated since ancient times in both China and India.

The name 'ginger' has been through many linguistic incarnations. Firstly, the Sanskrit *srngaveram* ('of horned appearance', meaning its shape), from which came the Greek *dziggibris*, then the Latin *zingiber*, from which derived the French *gingibre*, the Spanish *gingembre* and the modern English ginger down a straight line from the Old English *gingiber*.

It was (and still is) used lavishly in Indian cuisine, but not so much by the Romans or the Greeks, although the Romans used it for medicinal purposes. Ginger really came into its own during medieval times, when, along with nutmeg, it appeared in a multitude of recipes. It can be found regularly in the dishes recorded

Zingiber sylvestre and *Z. angustifolium* (ginger)

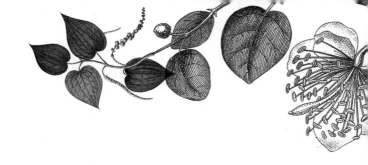

ONION

'It's hard to imagine civilisation without onions.'
Julia Child (1912–2004), American cook

by David Waines, selected from medieval Arabic culinary collections from the early ninth to the late thirteenth centuries and published in his book *In a Caliph's Kitchen* (1989). The three most mentioned spices in the cookbooks of the time—a period labelled by the French historian Fernand Braudel as 'a spice orgy'—were saffron, ginger and pepper. By 1547, over 1000 tonnes of ginger per annum was reputedly imported into Spain.

Ginger even makes an appearance in the Qur'an, where virtuous Muslims who die and go to Paradise will be served with 'cups brimful with ginger-flavoured water from the fount of Selsabil'.

Ginger has been used as a medicine in Asian, Indian and Arabic herbal traditions since ancient times. In China, for example, it has been used to aid digestion and treat stomach upsets, diarrhoea and nausea for more than 2000 years, and its beneficial properties were mentioned by Confucius (551–479 BC) and Dioscorides, Greek physician from the first century AD. Since ancient times, ginger has also been used to help treat arthritis, colic and heart conditions. Today, it is also used to provide relief from nausea following surgery and to relieve chemotherapy nausea.

The genus *Allium* includes many of those bulbs we call onions, as well as garlic, leek, eschalot and that bane of food and recipe writers in the English-speaking world, the long green vegetable variously called shallot, spring onion, green onion and, perhaps most correctly, scallion.

Here we will confine ourselves to *A. cepa*, the common onion, which is a native of Central Asia, where wild onions—although none directly linkable to *A. cepa*—still grow.

Since humans started scrabbling in the ground for food, the onion has been a staple. The ancient Middle Eastern civilisation of Ur (c. 2100 BC) grew onions; the Chaldeans (c. 600–500 BC) (in modern-day southern Iraq) used them to supplement their monotonous diet; the Pharaoh Cheops paid the builders of the pyramids in onions, garlic and parsley; and the Romans took them to Britain. Onions were eaten raw and cooked by all the common people of the ancient and classical world (the upper classes in Egypt did not care to eat them because of the smell on their breath). Columbus took both onions and garlic to the New World where they were greeted with enthusiasm (a few wild onions grow in the Americas, but were never a feature of indigenous diets there).

Many types of onion are grown in different parts of the world; the Vilmorin Andrieux catalogue lists over thirty varieties, and states: 'The strong odour and flavour of all parts of the plant caused it to be valued in very early times as a seasoning and, being easily grown, man has carried it with him into almost every climate in the world'.

Along with ubiquity goes suspicion. Egyptian priests were forbidden to eat them. In India, Brahmins and Jains likewise are denied the onion—it is said to inflame lust.

The onion's pungency, odour and ability to bring tears to the eyes when cut are all due to a complex of sulphur compounds. When the onion is cut or crushed, the admission of air allows enzymes to work on these compounds to increase the pungency and (aided by the release of the compound allicin) to bring tears to the eyes. In France there is, according to Maguelonne Toussaint-Samat, a north–south line dividing onion use, as there is for the use of butter (in the north) and olive oil (in the south). North of the Loire, she writes, 'butter and onions rule ... If Provençal cooks want to add a piquant ingredient ... they prefer the white part of leeks'.

Allium cepa (onion)

The Roots of Civilisation

POTATO

'Like an alien species introduced into an established ecosystem, the potato had trouble finding a foothold when it first arrived in Europe towards the end of the sixteenth century, probably as an afterthought in the hold of a Spanish ship.'
Michael Pollan, The Botany of Desire, 2001

If any plant deserved the label ubiquitous, it's the potato, *Solanum tuberosum*, now eaten in forms inconceivable in its native Peru and Bolivia. While wild potatoes can be found as far afield as Colorado, and other native peoples of the Americas ate them (the Navajos included), only the natives of the high Andes cultivated them.

The reason is relatively simple. In the lowlands, maize and manioc grew easily. On the tablelands, where those crops don't grow well, successive immigrant waves found the wild potato. Above 3600 metres (12,000 feet), neither maize nor manioc will grow at all. But on the Andean highlands, from Colombia in the north to Chile in the south, wild potatoes can be found growing at 4600 metres (15,000 feet), practically the snowline. As these highlands were populated, farmers began to cultivate several varieties of wild potato, choosing the hardiest hybrids.

Europeans first discovered the potato in Colombia, in 1537, when Spanish troops entered a village from which the inhabitants had fled and found maize, beans and what they called 'truffles'— potatoes. Potatoes arrived in Spain in the 1550s, and were subsequently grown in Italy as well, with little success. These first potatoes were small, watery and bitter.

Potatoes were first mentioned by John Gerard in his catalogue, *Gerard's Herball*, published in 1597, although he erroneously gave their origin as the American state of Virginia, naming them 'the potatoes of Virginia'. They were first described accurately by the French botanist Jules Charles de l'Écluse (Clusius) in 1601, who placed their origin, by guesswork, as Peru.

Clusius was also the first in a long line of botanists and writers to attribute aphrodisiac powers to the humble spud, writing, seemingly paradoxically, 'they are flatulent, and therefore some use them for exciting Venus'.

One Antoine Augustin Parmentier, a French army officer who was taken prisoner in Westphalia during the Seven Years' War, became familiar with potatoes there, and became convinced of their nutritional properties. After his release in 1763 he convinced Louis XVI of their worth. The French were still wary of the potato, believing it to be poisonous, so Louis and Parmentier conceived an ingenious method for their propagation. They had them planted and the crop guarded by the army, the insinuation being that they were only for the aristocracy. However, as the army only guarded the crops during the day, they were stolen by night and planted extensively. The potato became fashionable and, for his part in their popularity, a dish was named after Parmentier—*hachis Parmentier*, the forerunner of the American dish hash.

Later, when Napoleon's mistress Josephine became a fan of potatoes, they once again gained a reputation for aphrodisiac qualities, and the French courtesans of the time took to eating them.

Across the Channel, an English alchemist and writer on medical matters in the early eighteenth century claimed that they were 'good against barrenness in women and impotence in men'. At the same time, they were banned in Burgundy, because it was believed they caused leprosy.

No one knows how the potato got to Ireland, where it caused so much horror. According to historian William H McNeill, it arrived in the seventeenth century, not, as is generally written, with Sir Walter Raleigh, but via an unknown Spanish seaman.

But the Irish fell on the potato with enthusiasm for a variety of reasons.

Cereals did not grow well in Irish soil and, at the time potatoes arrived, Cromwell's Roundheads had seized all the best land, leaving only the poor land—where the potato flourished.

In the seventeenth century the potato was thriving across Ireland. A few acres of marginal land could feed a large family and their livestock, and give them control of their lives. And the potato gave them all the nutrition they needed—complex carbohydrates, vitamin C, fibre, and older potatoes some of the B complex vitamins.

In 1794, the wheat crop failed in England and the price of bread soared. The potato was suggested as a second food crop. The radical politician and agriculturalist William Cobbett opposed the idea, believing that the potato had impoverished the Irish by driving up the population—this was related to the tuber's lingering reputation as a sex aid. After noting the prevalence of large families in Ireland, another eighteenth-century agriculturalist wrote that it 'creates a vigorous population'.

There was a huge anti-potato feeling in England at the time for a variety of complex reasons. One was that it was inferior to wheat because there was no processing attached to its preparation—no threshing, grinding and bread making, just throwing in water and boiling. It was also seen as an economic threat: for Adam Smith, the price of bread was an economic regulator, and the price of wheat regulated economic behaviour. Potatoes, which were simply pulled out of the ground and could be neither stored nor traded, had no economic value. Indeed, their dependence on the potato had made the Irish vulnerable.

The appearance of the potato blight, *Phytophthora infestans*, in 1845, perhaps from America, spelt doom for the Irish potato crop—and the Irish. One contemporary account told of how,

Solanum tuberosum (potato)

between 27 July and 3 August, the crops went from blooming to putrefaction. A priest in Galway wrote: 'As to the potatoes they are all gone—clean gone. If travelling by night, you would know when a potato field was near by the smell. The fields present a space of withered black stalks'.

By 1851, the population of Ireland dropped to 6,575,000, a fall of 1,600,000 in a decade. In addition to deaths from the famine induced by the blight, there was at the time mass emigration, associated evictions from the land, and harsh living conditions; by 1854 the emigration represented between 1.5 and 2 million people. This diaspora swelled—and enriched—the populations of America, England, Scotland, Canada and Australia, with long-term cultural and political repercussions.

The blight visited all of Europe, but was only a disaster in Ireland because of potato monoculture. It was the country's worst catastrophe since the Black Death

of 1348. It has been estimated that the potato blight killed one million Irish in three years through starvation and disease, with thousands more going blind or insane.

According to Michael Pollan in *The Botany of Desire*, the potato crop in Ireland represented 'the biggest experiment in monoculture ever attempted, and surely the most convincing proof of its folly', and that 'monoculture is where the logic of nature collides with the logic of commerce; which logic will ultimately prevail can never be in doubt'.

Today, the arrival of the genetically engineered potato opens up the possibility of a repeat of the Irish experience. From hundreds of natural occurring species in the Andes, the bio-agricultural corporations would have us plant only a handful, the patents for which they would own. This would leave us vulnerable once more to the arrival of another devastating crop failure.

YAM

'I yam what I yam.'
Popeye

Yam is the name of the edible tubers of plants from the genus *Dioscorea*. The name is often but incorrectly used for other tubers such as taro and sweet potato.

The scientific name for this genus comes from Dioscorides, a classical Greek medical writer, and alludes to its remarkable uses in the realm of medicine—everything from the contraceptive pill to steroids (see Medicinal plants, page 156). The opposite is also true, as plants in the genus are the source of many poisons.

What yams lack in excitement as food, they make up for in carbohydrate and protein. In Fiji, some Pacific islands and some parts of West Africa, they are an important staple. Numerous species of yams grow in Southeast Asia, Africa and the Pacific Islands, and also in South America, and their history stretches back to the Jurassic period (from 206–44 million years ago).

Yams are not an inviting food. Firstly, they grow deep underground, as far as 2 metres (6 feet) down and must be laboriously dug up. Secondly, they must be cooked before they are eaten to destroy the bitter toxic substance dioscorine, which they contain when raw.

They can be rough or smooth, pale creamy brown or purple in colour,

Dioscorea decaisneana (yam)

and come in many shapes. Yams can be steamed, boiled, mashed, roasted or fried, or in African species made into the porridge, *foo foo*, as is done with cassava.

In Japan, the local species, *D. japonica*, produces tubers which are slim, brittle and grows up to 2 metres (6 feet) in length. It is sometimes called 'the eel of the mountains' and has a reputation as an aphrodisiac.

CASSAVA

'Of all the giant tropical roots, the one most frequently eaten in Western Europe is tapioca.'
Maguelonne Toussaint-Samat, History of Food, 1992

Manihot esculenta, cassava, sometimes called manioc, is a tropical root crop native to Central and South America and the Caribbean, and has been cultivated on the Amazon floodplain for several thousand years. It comes to the West. as tapioca.

The tubers are cigar shaped, with a pinkish-brown hairy rind and white flesh, and average about 25 centimetres (10 inches) long and 5 centimetres (2 inches) thick. There are two main groupings, classified as bitter and sweet. Because the skin of the bitter cassava contains a poison (a kind of cyanide, which indigenous people use in hunting and fishing), parasites don't touch it, and it needs very careful and elaborate preparation. It must be thoroughly peeled and then soaked at length in water before being crushed, grated and made into dough, a pottage or flat cakes. Christopher Columbus ate cassava at a feast in 1442. Curiously, in spite of the existence of sweet cassava, which is far more easily prepared, the bitter version is preferred in its homelands. The sweet variety, which contains none of the prussic acid that makes the other bitter, was taken to Africa and Madagascar at the time of the slave trade, and used as payment for slaves.

Manihot esculenta (cassava)

It is the flour from the bitter cassava that is treated to form flake, seed or pearl tapioca, which are (if less frequently in the modern era) used to make puddings and to thicken soup. In the Caribbean, a thick syrup called *cassareep* is made with it.

In Africa, it is boiled and pounded to make a porridge called *foo foo*, and in Indonesia, where it arrived in the eighteenth century, it is fermented to make *tapé*, a sweet and faintly alcoholic food eaten as a snack.

During World War I, cassava flour was introduced into European bread, although not as much as in South America, where it is still widely used. In Africa, cassava flour is used to make a cheap white bread, which, with the desire of Africans to eat foods like those of the 'developed' countries, is both popular and cheap.

TURNIP

'The turnip is a capricious vegetable, which seems reluctant to show itself at its best.'
Waverley Root, Food, 1980

The humble turnip, *Brassica rapa*, is a root with a distinguished past—although it's not really a root, just a swollen stem-base. But it is one of the earliest of cultivated vegetables, originating in Northern Europe about 2000 BC, and has graced the tables of kings and commoners alike.

The Romans took the turnip seriously. According to a story told by Alan Davidson in *The Oxford Companion to Food*, the consul Curius Dentatis was approached by his enemy while roasting turnips over the fire and offered a bribe to defect to the other side: he stuck to his turnips, the moral being that the turnip is an honest, rustic food.

Turnips turn up in Asia well before the medieval period in Europe; in China at this time they were also roasted. The turnip has methods of preparation peculiar to, and indicative of, the national traits of its devotees. The Japanese carve them often in chrysanthemum shapes; the French pick them very young and braise, fry or glaze them; in China they are dried and salted or preserved in soy sauce; and the luridly pink pickled turnip of the Middle East is a feature on all mezze tables.

Among the true swollen roots still in common use and of similar antiquity are the parsnip, the carrot, the beetroot and the swede, all of which have their adherents, their uses and their own tales to tell.

Brassica rapa (turnip)

SUGAR

'How and why sugar has risen to such prevailing importance among European peoples to whom it had at one time been hardly known is still not altogether clear.'
Sidney W Mintz, Sweetness and Power, *1986*

Humankind's obsession with the sweet has changed the world in profound ways. Sugar is most importantly produced from the sugar cane (*Saccharum officinarum*), but also from the sugar beet (*Beta vulgaris*) and a variety of sugar-producing palms. Honey, however, was the first sweetener, gathered wild from hives perhaps from the beginning of humankind. Pre *Homo sapiens*, hominids ate honey, just as present-day primate and non-primate mammals do. It is one half of the 'food of the gods' equation—the land of milk and honey. It is a curious food, a sort of vegetable product via the intervention of an insect. But as our obsession with sweetness grew, we turned to sugar from the cane.

Sugar cane is a giant grass native to the Ganges Delta of India, where it was most likely first milled. Although the Chinese later claim to have been the first to make sugar, there is a clear reference in a seventh-century book to the Emperor Tai-Hung sending workmen to learn how to make sugar in India and in Bengal.

The expedition sent to explore the Indus by Darius of Persia (549–486/85 BC) found a 'reed that gives honey without the aid of bees' and took it home. At first the Persians guarded the secret of its cultivation and the production of sugar, but eventually the plant and the methods of extraction spread throughout the Middle East.

Later, Dioscorides of Greece talks of a solid honey called *saccharon* (from the Sanskrit *sarkara*, meaning pebble or grit) 'found in the reeds of India and Arabia the fortunate'. It was around this time that Pliny wrote in his *Natural History* (c. 77 AD), 'It is used solely as medicine'.

For most of sugar's early European history, then, it was either a medicine, or an expensive food reserved for the tables of the privileged. But in 1000 AD the Arabs built a large sugar refinery on the island today known as Crete, whose Arabic name, Qandi, meant crystallised sugar—from which derives the word candy, meaning all sugar-based sweets.

The Arabs, by this time, were the masters of sugar and wherever they conquered, they built a mill. Along the way, at least one food historian believes, they invented a dark brown, sticky and highly fragrant product, caramel, *kurat al milh*, ball of sweet salt, one of whose first uses, according to Maguelonne Toussaint-Samat, was as a depilatory for harem ladies. Another derivation is *canna mella*, literally cane and honey, medieval Latin for the sugar cane plant, as proposed by Mark Morton in *Cupboard Love* (Insomniac Press, 2004).

Columbus took sugar cane to the New World on his second voyage in 1493, and it was first grown in Santo Domingo (the Dominican Republic) by enslaved Africans. It began to be exported back to Europe from 1516 from here, and from Brazil to Europe from 1526.

Sugar passed through Provence and the Languedoc on its way to northern Europe and reached England in modest quantities by the early thirteenth century as a spice. It remained far more expensive than honey up until the sixteenth century; then, for various reasons, honey production began to decline while the supply of sugar rose. By the seventeenth century, thanks to increased production—and slavery—in the Caribbean, it was the cheapest form of sweetening.

As the importation of sugar and wine rose in the last quarter of the seventeenth century in England, so did the consumption of sweetened and spiced wines. 'Gentlemen garrawse [carouse], only in wine, with which they mix sugar which I have never observed in any other place or kingdom to be used for that pleasure', wrote Fynes Morrison, a contemporary observer. 'The fondness of the English for sugar was so great', he continued, 'as to induce them to mix it with sweet wines'. It is interesting to note that by 1633, it was recognised that too much sugar would rot the teeth—but this had little effect on rising consumption.

The other great boost to sugar production was rum, which was taken up in a big way by the British Navy. In 1698, only 207 gallons of rum were imported to England. From 1771 to 1775, the annual average imports were 2 million gallons. An official ration of half a pint a day per sailor was increased to a pint a day by the end of the eighteenth century. The other boost to sugar was its addition to tea and coffee.

All this sugar was supported, from the early years of the sixteenth century, by the human misery of slavery. Between then and its abolition in 1886, an estimated 9.5 million slaves were taken to the Americas to work either in cotton or sugar production, and 2.6 million to the Caribbean, which was completely turned over to sugar. The first slaves, taken to Santo Domingo between 1503 and 1505, worked in sugar, and the last, smuggled into Cuba between the 1860s and 1870s, also worked cutting and milling cane. Along the way, the trade in slaves and sugar passed from Spanish to mainly English and French hands. After 1886, the complexion of the American and Caribbean population had been changed forever, a change that continues to have economic, social and political ramifications to this day.

At the time of abolition, sugar became embroiled in the politics of slavery. 'Every person who habitually consumes one article of West Indian produce raised by slaves is guilt of the crime of murder', thundered an editorial at the time. But it was impossible to give up sugar—it tasted too good. By 1900, it was supplying one-fifth of the calories in the English diet.

Given the right conditions, sugar cane may grow 2.5 centimetres (1 inch) a day. Once cut, the cane is chopped, ground, pressed, pounded or soaked in liquid. Heating the liquid containing the sucrose causes vaporisation and concentration of the super-saturated solution, which is cooled or crystallised to final or blackstrap molasses. That is the ancient method, and more or less how it is carried out today, though with more modern machinery. Supplementary processes lead to products that are less or more dark, pure white, crystalline or powdered, and a liquid that is called molasses in America, treacle in England, and in its more refined liquid version, golden syrup in Australia and Europe (but not America).

In the twentieth century, yet another sweetener arrived to feed our seemingly endless craving for the sweet: high-fructose corn syrup, which, being cheap to grow (corn farmers are heavily subsidised by the American Government) and produce, is a threat to the sugar-cane industry. Now moves have begun to use sugar cane to produce bio-fuel to replace dwindling supplies of petroleum.

What is the source of the allure of the sweet? Scholars theorise that sweetness is the marker of edibility for all mammals and pre-hominids; that we evolved from fruit-eating mammals; and that our first taste sensation is the sweetness of mother's milk. 'Sugar is pure sensation, crystallised pleasure', said American writer on the science of food, Harold McGee, in *McGee on Food and Cooking*, and it is also cheap—and everywhere. But the very availability and low cost of all manner of sweet things is blamed by the medical profession for the obesity problem and the rise of diabetes in the Western world. Pure sensation it might be—but our sugar cravings are not without consequence.

'Type 2 diabetes is at least 90 per cent about calories', nutritionist Marion Nestle has said, adding that although not every overweight person will get type 2 diabetes, 90–95 per cent of type-2 diabetes sufferers are overweight. Sweet foods and sweet drinks are extremely popular, and their calories are easy to consume in large quantities.

It appears that our overindulgence in this crystallised pleasure is a cause for concern. While, as the song says, a spoonful of sugar helps the medicine go down, twenty or thirty spoonfuls of sugar may well need their own medicine.

Vegetables

'Our best friends do not always get our best attention.' So begins the preface to the English edition of *The Vegetable Garden*, a remarkable book—actually a catalogue—written in 1885 by the Vilmorin family, proprietors of one of the oldest seed houses in the world. And it is true. Vegetables have been rather more often vilified and neglected than praised and protected.

A vegetable is an edible plant product, a definition that also and obviously includes salad plants—everything from cucumbers to cardoons are vegetables. They range from modified stems (the potato), to roots (cassava), to what are more properly defined as fruits (tomatoes). They are mostly savoury rather than sweet, with rhubarb (a leafy stalk) seeming to be an exception, although in reality rhubarb is sour and must be cooked with sugar to make it sweet.

They can appear on the plate dwarfed by enormous haunches of meat, or as side plates to be passed around the table. They are eaten raw, pickled, salted, preserved, boiled, baked, mashed, and in stews—curries in India—poured over sops of stale bread in southern Europe.

Despite the scarcity of ancient vegetables left to examine—time usually turns their remains to compost—we know they were not cultivated as long ago as the cereals and the pulses. Although most often a peasant food in ancient times (meat was for gods and heroes), they enjoyed a new prominence during the Renaissance, when asparagus and artichoke hearts were thrust into fashion. In the nineteenth century—and mainly in England, where, it must be said, vegetables (potatoes excepted) are neither respected nor treated well—there was real hatred of the vegetable. In 1888, James Salisbury, author of *The Relation* of *Alimentation and Disease*, stated that too many greens caused 'vegetable dyspepsia' and chronic diarrhoea. Humans, Mr Salisbury proclaimed, were 'two thirds carnivorous', a position also taken by Lord Byron in *Don Juan* when he wrote:

But man is a carnivorous production ...
Although his anatomical construction
Bears vegetables in a grumbling way,
Your labouring people think, beyond
    all question,
Beef, veal and mutton better for the
    digestion.

Across the Atlantic, and some years later, Henry David Thoreau replied:

Shall I not have intelligence with the earth?
Am I not partly leaves and vegetable
    mould myself?

Food historian Harvey Levenstein, author of *Paradox of Plenty: A Social History of Eating in Modern America*, reported that one of the first edicts of the new branch of science, Nutrition, at the turn of the twentieth century was to advise the poor to stop wasting their money on expensive vegetables (and fruit). That was immediately before the discovery of the importance of vitamins.

Vegetables certainly do supply vitamins, as well as minerals, carbohydrates and fibre, but little protein. They also supply colour, some of which is nutritionally useful: carotene is the orange in carrot, lycopene the red in tomato and chlorophyll the green in all the leaves.

At the other end of the spectrum, in the vegetable fan club are the vegetarians, the first of whom on record were Adam and Eve. Before the biblical Fall, all life was sacred, the beasts were tame and there was no killing.

Whole societies were, and are, captivated by vegetarianism—Hindus, Buddhists, Jains and the modern-day tribes of hippies. The poet Shelley was a vegetarian, holding the common sympathetic-magic view that meat was 'the root of all evil' and that vegetarians were kinder and gentler. This belief suffered something of a setback when Adolf Hitler's vegetarianism became widely known. Curiously, after he became Chancellor in 1933, all independent vegetarian societies in Germany were declared illegal unless they joined forces with the Nazi Living Reform Movement.

Different peoples have treated vegetables with varying degrees of reverence and indifference. The Chinese were and are pro-vegetable, devising ways to ensure fresh supplies even in the dead of winter, through such agricultural innovations as manure-based hot beds. The English, as already mentioned, are notoriously indifferent. The French are inclined to over-elaborate, smothering them with butter or cheese. The Italians love their vegetables—especially that late arrival the tomato—with a passion. When exiled to England by the inquisition, Giacomo Castelvetro so missed the beloved fruit and vegetables of his native land that in 1614 he wrote a book to their glory, *The Fruit, Herbs & Vegetables of Italy*,

Clockwise from bottom left: Round lettuce, Windsor's broad bean, green Windsor's broad bean, sweetcorn, early onion 'White Queen' and Strasbourg red beet

in which he recalled in loving detail the fresh produce of Italy, comparing their flavour and manners of preparation most often in an unflattering way with that of his new home.

They supply colour, texture, flavour and seasonal variety to our tables—we all should love our vegetables.

TOMATO

'Apples of love are very much used in Italy to putt when ripe in their Brooths and Soops giving it a pretty tart tast.'

Quaker merchant, Peter Collinson, 1742

Some foods seem to define nations, and the tomato, although more prevalent in the south than the north, could be said to define Italy. Many Italians would be shocked to discover that this vegetable (in reality a fruit), which many of them eat daily with pasta, arrived only 500 or so years ago.

The commonest form of tomato eaten around the world, *Lycopersicon esculentum*, originated in the lowlands of Peru, along the dry banks of the rivers that run between the Andes and the Pacific. Nine species of wild tomato have been discovered in Peru and Ecuador; all have yellow flowers, two have coloured fruit, and seven green fruit. But the early Peruvians appear to have ignored them—there is no word in their language for tomato and no evidence of their having been cultivated.

The variety responsible for our having adopted this fruit is *L. cerasiforme*, a self-pollinating plant producing flowers and small (2.5 centimetres/1 inch) fruit for five months of the year in tropical climates. The fruits are red or yellow, sometimes white, with a sharp, acidic but not unpleasant flavour. This variety slowly spread by natural means to the Gulf of Mexico, where it is believed the indigenous people began to cultivate and improve it from about 500 AD.

Cortez found them being eaten when he arrived in 1519. He (mistakenly) thought they were called *tomatl*, changed the name to *tomate*, and took seeds back to Spain. Like its nightshade family relative the potato, it was in for a rocky ride in its new home.

The tomato arrived in Seville, then a centre for international trade, early in the sixteenth century. Although it was definitely used in cooking in Spain—often in association with the chilli (see page 82); the Indians told the first Spanish colonists they belonged together), no recipes for the tomato appeared until 1745, in a book by Juan Altamiras, where thirteen of the 200 recipes use the tomato. One piece of evidence for its early adoption is its appearance in Murillo's 1646 painting, *The Angel's Kitchen*, in which it appears alongside eggplants and a pumpkin.

But it had appeared in an Italian cookbook before that, and the earliest printed recipe we know of was in a Neapolitan book, *Lo scalco alla moderna* (1692–24), which included a recipe for 'Tomato Sauce, Spanish Style'. It sounds very much like a modern recipe, using garlic, onions, parsley, oil and vinegar—but no chilli.

After Spain, the tomato arrived in Italy via Naples (which was under Spanish rule from 1503 to 1713), where Pier Andrea Mattioli mentioned it in his herbal in 1544 as 'another kind of mandrake'—the mandrake being a poisonous Mediterranean plant. In a later edition in 1554, Mattioli noted that it had a red as well as a yellow fruit and named it *mala aurea*—'golden apple' in Latin, and in Italian *pomodoro*, the name by which it still goes in Italy.

At first, the tomato was viewed with suspicion—it was poisonous; if it didn't kill you, it would make you sick; and, like the potato, it was accused of being an aphrodisiac—so when it entered Provence by way of Naples, it was given another name, *pomus amorus*, or *pomme d'amour*, the love apple. Once again, it was shunned at the table, and planted only as an insect repellent. It was not long before the Provençals were eating them with—and as—relish. Today, tomatoes, along with garlic, are at the heart of Provençal cuisine.

By the early nineteenth century, Brillat-Savarin, the philosopher in the kitchen, was writing that 'tomatoes are a great blessing to good cookery. They make excellent sauces which go with every kind of meat'. Today, more tomatoes are grown in France than any other vegetable—including the potato.

The English were somewhat slower to adopt the tomato. It arrived around 1750, and was taken up there by Jewish families of Spanish and Portuguese descent. In one of Flora Thompson's trilogy of novels, *Lark Rise to Candleford*, when a shipment of 'love apples', as they were known, arrived in a village around the end of the nineteenth century, the heroine is warned, 'Don't 'ee go trying to eat it, now, it'll only make 'ee sick'.

But it was in the nineteenth century that the large-scale industrial canning of tomatoes and the production of tomato paste began, especially in Italy, and America in the 1830s saw the first bottlings of tomato sauce. And in Spain, where no excuse is needed to have fun, the tomato is at the centre of the Tomatina festival at Buñol, near Valencia, where thousands of Spaniards and foreigners gather every year in August to throw 115,000 kilograms (254,000 pounds) of tomatoes at each other. The reason? No one remembers exactly, but it began in 1945, perhaps with a friendly tomato fight between two groups of locals.

Apart from being used as a missile, the tomato is one of the most common

Lycopersicon esculentum (tomato)

items of consumption in the world—as sauce, in salads, paste, and as a major ingredient in what might be the most commonly eaten item in global cuisine: spaghetti bolognaise.

CHILLI AND THE PEPPERS

*'It's a wonderfully perverse achievement for our mammal species
to have fallen in love with this anti-mammalian weapon and spread
the chilli much further than any bird ever did!'*
Harold McGee, McGee On Food and Cooking, *2004*

Is there any other vegetable that can inflict so much pain? There are around twenty-five species of chilli, most descended from the original *Capsicum annuum* found on the island of Hispaniola (later Haiti and the Dominican Republic) by Columbus.

The ingredient that supplies the 'hooo-eeee!' factor that either thrills or dismays is capsaicin, which protects the seeds of the fruit and seems, according to Harold McGee, to be aimed at repelling mammals. Birds are immune, so they swallow the fruit and disperse the seeds. This is the origin of at least one chilli, known in Thailand as the *prik ki neuw*, bird's eye (actually bird's shit) chilli—a tiny but extremely strong chilli that grows wild in the forests of Thailand.

There is much confusion in naming both the chilli (chile/chili in the United States) and the capsicum (bell pepper in the United States), a confusion that has its roots in Columbus' discovery of them. Even the use of the name 'pepper' needs some explaining.

The original purpose of Columbus' journeys was to find a sea route to Asia and thus to the spices of that region—especially India, and especially pepper, *Piper nigrum*, the most precious spice of the time. Instead, he 'stumbled across'

the Americas, whose islands he called the Indies, and their inhabitants Indians.

When Columbus recorded the chilli in his journal on 15 January 1493, he wrote that it was *mejor que nuestra pimienta*, 'a better spice than our (black) pepper'. The Spanish took to this idea, but changed the gender of the word by making it masculine, *pimiento*, to make it more powerful—as indeed it was. In time, just to confuse matters even more, the Spanish for 'chilli' changed to *pimentón picante*, hot red pepper, the word *pimentón* also standing for finely powdered (mostly) sweet red peppers—those called capsicum in the United Kingdom and Australia, from the Latin *capsa*, meaning box-like.

The word 'chilli' itself came from the Nahuatl people of Mexico, where the plant had been cultivated by the Aztecs and the Toltecs. The chilli was taken back to Europe, where it was little enjoyed, except by the Spanish (especially the Basques, who have their own chilli, the *guindilla*). But as soon as it arrived in Arabia, Africa and Asia, it was taken up immediately, especially in India, where it spread like forest fire through the lands and cuisines of the subcontinent, replacing black pepper as a heat transmitter. It is now as

hard to imagine India without the chilli as it is Italy without the tomato.

The heat of the chilli is measured in Scoville units, named after pharmaceutical chemist Wilbur Scoville, who invented the system around 1912. The system has since been updated with more rigorous modern chemical analyses, but retains the name. The 'coolest' chilli on this scale is the capsicum, or bell pepper, *C. annuum*, at 0–600 units; the hottest, the *naga jolokia* (*C. chinense* 'Naga Jolokia') from northern India, measuring up to 1,000,000 units.

The milder red and green capsicums found a ready home on the shores of the Mediterranean, and today there is a family of dishes employing the capsicum—almost always with tomato, and often with eggplant—in practically every country of that region. The Spanish *pisto manchego*, *tumbet* and *piperade*, the Italian *peperonata*, *ratatouille* from the south of France, *mechouia* from Tunisia are among them. In Hungary, the red peppers were ground into powder as *paprika*, just as they were in Spain as *pimentón*—perhaps the only similarity between two peoples who are in all other respects totally unlike.

But mention the word 'chilli' to anybody from the south of the United

Capsicum frutesceus and *C. caffree* (chilli and caffree chilli)

States, and you've mentioned a dish with a deep, often fanatical following: *chilli con carne*, literally chilli with meat. But once those two ingredients have been established, all others are subject to conjecture, even heated argument: the presence or absence of beans, especially, can cause grief among rival chilli lovers. The American frontiersman Kit Carson's last words were said to be: 'Wish I had time for one more bowl of chilli'.

For those who are concerned with the adverse health effects of eating the chilli pepper (there has been speculation that the chilli can cause cancer or stomach ulcers), Harold McGee reports, 'As I write in 2004, the scorecard is fairly positive'.

His reading of the literature convinces him that it is not implicated in increased risk of cancer, and that 'in sum it may encourage us to eat less of the meal it's in, and burn more of the calories we do eat'. There's a hot tip from one who knows.

Solanum melongena (eggplant/aubergine)

The Roots of Civilisation

EGGPLANT/AUBERGINE

'To dream of three aubergines is a sign of happiness.'
Middle Eastern proverb

Solanum melongena is another member of the nightshade family (with the potato, tomato, and pepper/capsicum/chilli), which received—as did most of them—a very bad press on arrival in Europe.

Unlike its South American vegetable cousins, the birthplace of the eggplant is believed to be India. Wild aubergines still grow on the dry hillsides of India as small, prickly perennial shrubs with bitter yellow fruit. Over the years, we have learnt to breed out most of the bitterness and prickles, although a collar of prickles surrounds the stem of the large purple variety most often seen in the West.

The first record of their cultivation dates from 500 BC in China, although they were probably farmed well before that in India. There are no mentions of the eggplant in classical Greek or Roman times, and no depiction of them in art—such a beautiful object appears for the first time in a German garden book in 1613, but it had to wait until the seventeenth century to begin its starring roles in still-life paintings. A rare and earlier instance was the use of a violet-and-white striped variety as the nose of the fruit and vegetable man painted by Giuseppe Arcimboldo in 1563.

For those interested in the origins of words, 'aubergine' is a fascinating study.

The work done by Ernest Klein in his *Comprehensive Etymological Dictionary of the English Language* (1966–1967) traces the word back to its ancient Indian name *vatin-ganah*, which emerges in Persia as *badin-gan*, and crosses to the Middle East and appears as *al-badinjan*. The Arabs who occupied Spain (Andalus) planted it under that name, but it later emerged in the Catalan language as *alberginia*, and into Spanish as *berenjena*. The Arabic name went to France and became *aubergine*, and this is the name adopted by the English. The Indian word *brinjal* can also be traced to *al-badinjan*. The descriptive name 'eggplant' was used for the first of the fruit to arrive in Europe, probably around the thirteenth century, via Spanish and Italian trade with the Arabs.

Another family of names—the Italian *melanzana* and the Greek *melitzana*—relates back to the Latin *mala insana*, mad apple, which tells much of the initial European reaction. The aubergine was originally considered inedible, and more, positively dangerous, responsible for leprosy, piles and bad breath if eaten without first being boiled in vinegar. As usual, it was the English who were the last to take to it (in the seventeenth century), and they continued to call it the mad apple right up until the fifteenth century.

It was embraced throughout the Mediterranean, from Baghdad to Andalus, and especially in Turkey, where a young bride was urged to bring, as her part of her dowry, one hundred recipes for cooking it. In Italy and Provence it quickly found its way to the heart of their cuisines.

In medieval Spain was found what is probably the antecedent of the Italian dish *melanzane parmigiano*, *berenjenas con queso*, a dish with roots back to the thirteenth century. A similar provenance can be traced for the Greek dish *moussaka* in the Turkish *patlikan musakka*. In Provence it features in *ratatouille*, whose relatives are the Greek *Briami*, the Turkish *turlu*, and, on the Spanish island of Mallorca, *tumbet*.

Perhaps the most famous aubergine dish is the Turkish *Imam Bayildi*, the Imam (Muslim prayer leader) fainted, the causes of which event are many and varied in the telling, two of them being that he fainted at the amount of (expensive) olive oil used in making the dish, or with delight at its flavour.

In India, Iran, Afghanistan and Pakistan it is pickled, and in Indonesia, the small fruits of a related plant, *S. torvum*, are eaten raw. It is extensively used in Thai cooking, most often the tiny pea-sized variety which clusters on a stem like grapes, or round white varieties.

SEAWEED

'The importance of this seaweed in Japanese food life can scarcely be overestimated.'
Richard Hosking, A Dictionary of Japanese Food, 1997

'Seaweed' is an unfortunate name for a useful—and delicious—series of plants also called hydrocolloids or macro algae. They are multicellular and come in three main colours—red, green and brown.

Seaweed is an important crop, with an estimated total annual value of US$5.5–6 billion, with five of those billions being for human consumption and the remainder for fertilisers, animal feed additives and various other uses. Industry uses 7–8 million tonnes of wet seaweed annually, either harvested or cultivated, with some thirty-five countries harvesting around their coastlines.

Their use as food goes back to the fourth century AD in Japan, and the sixth in China. The Japanese, especially, eat seaweed in many forms, and are especially fond of *konbu*, which is used in soup stock, and *nori*, which is used in sushi rolls.

Red and brown seaweeds are used to produce agar, which is used in microbiology as a culture medium and in the kitchen as a vegetarian gelatin, and also to make alginate and carrageenan, both of which are used to gel and thicken ice cream and to inhibit the production of large icicles. Alginates and carrageenan are used extensively in food products, dyes, gels, explosives and in paper sizing. The gelling quality of agar extracted with hot water from red weed was discovered in Japan in 1958.

Konbu is the Japanese name for a large group of brown seaweeds, most of them in the genus *Laminaria*, but also the inspirational source for the much maligned food additive and taste enhancer monosodium glutamate, not to mention the contentious fifth taste, umami.

Most of the konbu eaten in Japan grows in the cold waters off the coast of northern Japan, especially Hokkaido. Primarily, it is essential for making dashi, the most important stock in the Japanese cuisine. And it is with dashi that the story starts.

At the end of the nineteenth century, Professor Kidunae Ikeda, a biochemist at Tokyo Imperial University, was working on a taste map of the tongue, showing the location of the four primary tastes: sweet, sour, salty and bitter.

But he was pretty sure there was something missing, something he decided to call *umami*, Japanese for 'savoury' or even 'deliciousness', a taste he had isolated in cheese, meat broth and asparagus.

As is the case when solving a creative problem, the idea was constantly in the back of his mind, even when he was enjoying a bowl of his wife's dashi and tofu, in which he recognised umami in bucketloads. He asked her how she made it and she pointed out her store of dried konbu.

Intrigued, he began to examine the attributes and composition of konbu, emerging in 1909 with his discovery of the protein. glutamate, $C_5H_9O_4$, which emerged when he broke down glutamic acid. 'This study', he wrote in the paper he published at the time, 'has discovered two facts: one is that the broth of seaweed contains glutamate and the other that glutamate causes the taste sensation "umami"'.

Blessed with business acumen as well as scientific knowledge, Professor Ikeda's next move was to market a powdered flavour booster, the first monosodium glutamate (MSG) known as Ajinomoto ('the foundation of taste'). He had already patented MSG, which was made originally by mixing glutamate with salt and water. He died in 1936 a rich man, and is counted as one of Japan's Ten Great Inventors.

Since his death, further research has found that glutamate is present in almost all foods, but mostly in Parmesan cheese, with 1200 milligrams per 100 grams, although many manufactured foods have more—Marmite has 1750 milligrams per 100 grams. So vital is it to our bodies' functioning that we produce 40 grams of it a day; human milk contains ten times the glutamate levels of cow's milk.

Ajinomoto enveloped the world like a global snowstorm, taking off especially in Asia and hugely so in China. It came to America after World War II with returning soldiers raving about the Japanese army rations, when Ajinomoto (now owned by General Mills) allied itself to Kellogg— although it had long before stopped using konbu to make MSG. MSG is now made by the bacterial fermentation of sugar beet glucose or molasses.

Today, there is some dissent among scientists as to whether umami does constitute a fifth taste. In discussing this view, Richard Hosking writes in *A Dictionary of Japanese Food:* 'Opposing the concept of umami as a basic taste would mean opposing the Ajinomoto company, one of the world's largest and powerful food companies'. Hosking also points out that two other amino acids are identified with this flavour, sodium inositane and sodium guanylate:

Whether (those three amino acids) ... comprise the fifth flavour, or whether they should be considered primarily as flavour enhancers is a theoretical question. The fact is they do behave as very effective flavour enhancers when used in small amounts and correct proportions.

Before we leave the story, even though it has left konbu behind, we must mention Chinese Restaurant Syndrome, a 'malady' arising from a single letter by a Chinese–American doctor, Dr Ho Man Kwok, in the *New England Journal of Medicine*, musing over the possible causes of his experience of eating at Chinese restaurants which left him, for 15 or 20 minutes, with 'numbness ... general weakness and palpitations'.

This letter precipitated a witch-hunt for and the demonisation of MSG which proved, eventually, to be without any rational or scientific basis. The final nail in the coffin of the MSG scare should have been delivered by Dr Leonid Tarasoff, then head of the chemistry department at the University of Western Sydney, whose study published in the journal of *Food & Chemical Toxicology* in 1993 concluded that 'people who believed they reacted to monosodium glutamate were as likely to respond to the placebo (a substance containing no monosodium glutamate) as to monosodium glutamate, although the most common reaction was none at all'. Since then, although study after study showed that MSG is completely harmless, you will still find MSG scare stories on the net.

So you can happily eat dashi made with konbu with no fears for your health or sanity. MSG, on the other hand, should be looked at critically, not because it is dangerous, but because it is used by industrial food manufacturers to replace the flavour that processing has driven out. It has no place in a good cook's larder.

Fruit

Fresh fruit colours our plates, enlivens our palates and was, along with honey, the first source of sweetness in our diets. But research shows that fruit had a far more important role to play in human development. Some scientists believe it was the relationship between early primates and fruit that helped develop many of our important skills.

Humanity evolved in the forests and woodlands of equatorial and subequatorial Africa, where more than one hundred species of wild fruits and berries can be found growing. It was there that another of those symbiotic relationships between food and forager developed. In order to propagate, the fruit needed to spread its ripe seeds far and wide. As the fruit ripened, it changed colour and increased in aroma. When fully ripe, it was at its most enticing—and most fertile. It was then that it was eaten by the foraging primates, who dispersed the seeds, along with a healthy dose of fresh manure.

On the other side of the equation, it has been suggested that the development of colour receptors—uniquely, many primates, including humans, have three (the ability to distinguish between green, blue and red)—was brought about by their need for a richer visual spectrum

to recognise these changes in colour of fruit. Red became important in choosing a mate and led to some primates adopting red colouring themselves.

It has also been suggested that the ability to look for fruit, while sharpening sight and improving colour vision, also narrowed focus, making it more difficult to detect predators out of the corner of the eye. This caused primates to live together in protective groups, and encouraged group social behaviour. Thus the early honing of our sweet tooth to detect the choicest and ripest of fruits had wide implications for humanity.

Temperate fruits evolved over more than 5000 years ago in Central Asia and Asia Minor, the Caucasus and the Black Sea region (the Fertile Crescent), where there were large areas of woodland with wild pears, crab apples and cherry plums, which exist to this day. Further afield were the quinces of Azerbaijan, the apricots, cherry plums and medlars of Armenia and Syria. Nomadic movements along the Fertile Crescent brought the peach from China.

There is evidence of orchards and fruit markets around Pompeii and Herculaneum, and many European fruit-growing practices relate to Roman

occupation. When the Romans left England, agriculture generally subsided, and it was not until the arrival of the Normans that orchards were again planted or revived.

Today, all fruits grown are hybrids, mutations and descendants of ancient wild fruit. Sadly, much modern fruit is grown and picked for its ability to transport and keep rather than for its flavour. As orchards move further and further away from cities, much fruit is picked firm—that is, unripe—for transport, and hybrids are developed for their ability to handle long road journeys.

Most doctors and nutritionists would place the consumption of fresh fruits and vegetables at the head of the list of dietary disease prevention measures. Why? Not just because of the presence of nearly all our requirements of vitamins, minerals and dietary fibre, but because they are rich in phytochemicals, which nutritional science has discovered in the last twenty years to be of inestimable value in prevention of diseases like cancer and coronary heart disease. But why would anyone need to be persuaded to eat as much seasonal, fresh, ripe, luscious and locally grown fruit as they possibly can?

From the top: *Prunus persica* (peach), *Prunus armeniaca* (apricot) and *Prunus domestica* (plum)

APPLE

'All around the city one could see a vast expanse of wild apples covering the foothills, one could see with his own eyes that this beautiful site was the origin of the cultivated apple.'

Russian botanist Nikolai Vavilov, on discovering the original home of the apple at Alma-Ata in Kazakhstan, 1929

The sweet, innocent apple of every child's lunch box the world over carries a burden of mythological meaning. The golden apples of the Garden of the Hesperides (although, like the fruit of the Garden of Eden, not really apples) conferred immortality. The Egyptians of the time of Rameses II (1303–1213 BC) gave apples to the priests who were the guardians of knowledge. In search of the mythical 'water of life', Alexander the Great found apples, believed, by the priests who ate them, to prolong life. He obviously didn't eat them (he died at 33). As a feminine symbol, they are associated with Venus (an apple cut in half lengthways bears a slight resemblance to the female genital system). In fairytale, and still as a symbol of the feminine, there is the apple of the Brothers Grimm's *Snow White*, where the witch 'went into a quite secret, lonely room, where no one ever came, and there she made a very poisonous apple. Outside it looked pretty, white with a red cheek, so that everyone who saw it longed for it, but whoever ate a piece of it must surely die'.

The wild European crab apple, *Malus sylvestris*, is not a direct ancestor of the apple we know today, *Malus pumila*, but of the apples growing at Alma-Ata, which are most likely the result of natural hybridising and mutation.

The apple was in the second 'tranche' of domesticated fruits, after such ancients as the fig, the olive and the pomegranate. As nomadic tribes settled, they would select and retain the hardiest wild trees when the ground was cleared. If the tree couldn't be saved, it would be grafted on to seedling rootstock for later cultivation.

One reason for its late cultivation was that the apple will not grow true from seed. In other words, planting a seed will not necessarily result in a tree bearing the same fruit. To retain desirable characteristics, and to perpetuate a type, it is necessary for a cutting (scion) to be taken from the required tree and grafted onto suitable rootstock. This was first mentioned by the Greek philosopher and writer on botanical matters, Theophrastus, in 332 AD, indicating that the practice was known by the classical era.

Apples grow more abundantly in orchards with other apple trees, and the more apples growing in a district, the more each tree will produce.

The Romans loved their apples, classing them as luxury fruit, and by the end of the Empire grew thirty-two varieties, each bearing the name of their breeder. After the fall of the Empire, apple cultivation declined. The Arabs practised root grafting but, because they came from warmer climes unsuited to apple growing, they didn't include the apple in their horticultural portfolio.

But apple growing and cultivation continued in England and France in the thirteenth century and beyond, with the French developing many new varieties. The naming of apples began in England around 1200 AD, with Pearmain, Costard and Pippin being early named varieties. Across Europe, varieties were selected according to climatic conditions: in Scandinavia and Russia, for example, quick-ripening varieties were chosen.

The first apples were planted in America in the early 1600s by the governor of Massachusetts, John Endicott, and were quickly taken up by the Iroquois Indians. The spread of the apple was facilitated by the peregrinations of John Chapman, or Johnny Appleseed, whose seed-planting travels, between 1800 and 1845, down the Ohio River from Pennsylvania to Ohio to Indiana resulted in an enormous variety of trees springing up. His main aim, according to Michael Pollan in *The Botany of Desire*, was to spread the fruit for cider making.

Alan Davidson's *Oxford Companion to Food* lists thirty-four of the better known varieties out of the 7000-plus apple varieties grown today, and we end this section with the stories of two of them.

In 1872, farmer Jess Hiatt of Peru, Iowa, noticed a sucker growing from the rootstock of a tree and cultivated it. The resulting apples were bright red and very sweet. He sent them to the market as Hiatt's Hawkeye, but the variety was renamed Delicious and, since the 1940s, has been the biggest-selling American apple.

The most famous Australian variety, now known to the world, is the Granny Smith cooking apple which was, indeed, grown by a grandmother named Maria Smith, an orchardist along with her husband Thomas, near the Field of Mars common in Eastwood, now a suburb of Sydney. First recorded in 1868, and know then as Smiths Seedling, it took out the prize for cooking apples in the 1891 Castle Hill Show. Mrs Smith said at the time that it had developed from the remains of French crab apples grown in Tasmania. Sadly, she died in 1870, too early to see the widespread adoption of the apple named after her.

Malus domestica (Barcelona Pearmain, Scarlet Nonpareil, Margil, Cornish Aromatic and Cornish Gilliflower)

Prunus avium (sweet or wild cherry)

The Roots of Civilisation

CHERRY

'Loveliest of trees, the cherry now,
is hung with blooms along the bough …'
A E Housman, A Shropshire Lad, 1895

A fruit as valued for the beauty of its blossom—especially by the Japanese, who celebrate cherry blossom in poetry—as for its flavour, the cherry belongs to the genus *Prunus*, along with the plum, peach and almond.

There are two branches of the cultivated cherry tree. The sweet varieties derive from *P. avium*, a tree which can grow to 25 metres (around 80 feet) in height. It was native to western Asia but over the millennia migrated west and is now to be found wild in Europe, Turkey and North Africa and the lands either side of the Caucasus. It was gathered by primitive humans, and cherry stones have been found in Neolithic and Bronze Age sites (5000–1000 BC).

Like that of the apple, the cherry's cultivation occurred relatively late, in the first millennium BC, more than likely because it is unable to pollinate itself, and must be planted in groups to cross-pollinate and set fruit. And, as with the apple (and the pear and the plum), propagation is best done by grafting.

The sour cherry, sometimes known as the morello, *P. cerasus*, is a cross between *P. avium* and a shrub with bitter fruit, *P. fruticosa*, which grows wild in central and eastern Europe and in north-east Turkey. It can pollinate itself, and grows in the wild in much the same areas as the sweet cherry. The sour cherry is used for jams and liqueurs.

Cherries were known to both the Greeks and the Romans, and the sweet cherry was described by Theophrastus in his treatise on plants. There is an exchange in one of the books by the Greek writer Athenaeus, *Deipnosophista* (The Banquet of the Learned), supposedly a collection of table talk, in which a Roman claims the cherry tree was imported to the Mediterranean by a Roman general, Lucullus, and not the Greeks. Whoever did introduce them to the Mediterranean, it was the Romans whom introduced them to Britain.

In America, the cherry met its wild relatives, the American sand-cherries, *P. besseye* and *P. pumila*, and went into folklore as the tree that a young George Washington chopped down, but could not lie about.

In America, production centres on Oregon, Washington State and California. In England, Kent is cherry country, and in Australia, the cherries of Young, in New South Wales, are the best known.

Another distinctive cherry is the marasca or maraschino cherry (*P. cerasis marasca*). Originally from Dalmatia (now in Croatia), this is the variety used to make cherries in syrup as well as the liqueur of the same name. The distinctive almond flavour of this liqueur is due to the crushed stones, which release a strong almond flavour—in kirsch, the other cherry liqueur, they are left whole.

DURIAN

*'The durian is sometimes called the skunk of the orchard, and
its fruit are barred from aeroplanes and international hotels.'*
Suranant Subhadrabandhu and Saichol Ketsa, Durian: King of Tropical Fruit, 2001

Only one fruit could be described as infamous, and that is the durian. It inspires both revulsion and adoration, and is even suspected of being an object of rebellion in Singapore: the more the straitlaced government tries to ban it, the more Singaporeans stubbornly gobble up US$30 million worth a year.

Cultivated *Durio zibethinus* grows throughout the Malay peninsula and in southern Thailand, Borneo and New Guinea. Wild specimens nave been gathered in Sabah and it is generally believed to have originated in Borneo.

It belongs to the order Malvales, and the family Bombacaceae. There are about twenty-eight species, two being *D. graveolens* and *D. dulcis,* reputedly the smelliest.

It's a large, spiky, forbidding fruit, roughly the size of a soccer ball, weighing about 2 kilograms (5 pounds) and growing on trees that can reach 30 metres (100 feet) in height—be wary walking through a durian orchard, as death by falling durian is not uncommon.

But it's the smell that is loved, or hated. It has been compared to stale vomit, onions, pig droppings, cheese, civet cat, and sewage. Aficionados love the fruit's creamy texture and the flavour of ripe cream cheese and onion suffused with sweetness. Durianophobes run from the room when it appears.

It has been eaten in Southeast Asia since prehistoric times but was only introduced to the West about 600 years ago, being first mentioned by the Venetian merchant and traveller Niccolo Da Conti, who travelled to Southeast Asia in the fifteenth century. Botanist Georg Eberhard Rumphius (see Orchids, page 146) published a detailed account of the durian in his major work *Herbarium Amboinense* in 1741. It has been cultivated at a village level for hundreds of years, and commercially—mainly in Thailand— from the twentieth century.

The Javanese ascribe aphrodisiac qualities to the durian, and there are strict 'folklore rules' on what can be eaten before, after and with it. In some areas it is considered unwise or even unsafe to take sweet drinks or alcohol with it as the effects could, it is thought, be fatal.

Obviously, such a large and powerful fruit has built up a large and powerful legacy of folktales. At least one film has been made about it, *Durian Durian*, in Hong Kong. In Singapore there is a television comedy, *Durian King*, and the Esplanade Theatre, which is known locally as the Durian for its unusual shape.

An early Western supporter of the fruit was the English naturalist, anthropologist and evolutionary scientist Alfred Russel Wallace (1823–1913), whose book *Malay Archipelago* (1896) proclaimed that '... to eat durions [sic], is a new sensation, worth a voyage to the east to experience'. There are those who would disagree.

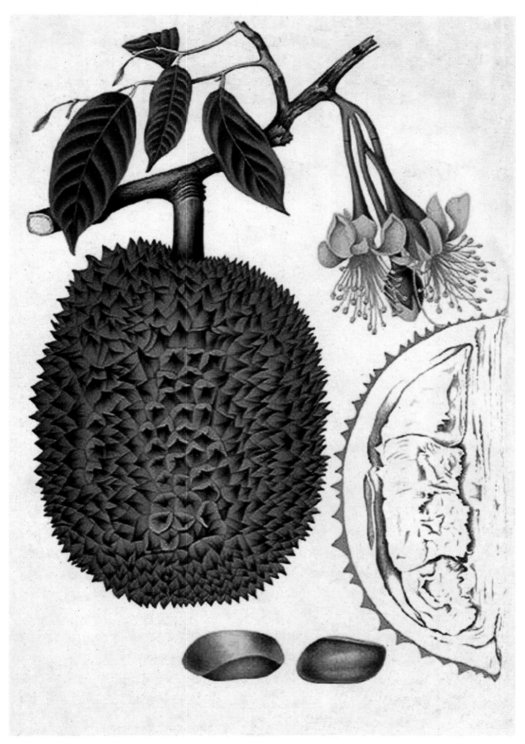

Durio Zibethinus (durian)

Ficus carica (fig)

The Roots of Civilisation

FIG

'Figs reproduce in a very odd way. For a start, they are not actually fruits at all, but flowers, and the most bizarre thing about them is that they are inside out ...'
Peter Blackburn-Maze, Fruit: An Illustrated History, *2002*

The fig tree presents us with two paradoxical images. First is the leaf, a biblical symbol of shame and modesty with which Adam and Eve covered themselves. Second is the fruit, often used as a visual metaphor for the female sexual organ, famously written about by D H Lawrence in his poem 'The Fig':

The Italians vulgarly say, it stands
*   for the female part; the fig-fruit*
The fissure, the yoni
The wonderful moist conductivity
*   in the centre.*

But the fig also had a political side. It was a fresh fig from Carthage held aloft by Cato the Elder in the Roman Senate that shocked his fellow senators into attacking and destroying Carthage: if it was that close ('It was still growing on a Carthaginian fig tree three days ago', he told them), then it presented a clear threat to the security of Rome.

The cultivated fig tree, *Ficus carica*, that which provides us with its beautiful and sexy fruit, is only one of 600 figs species (which include Australia's Moreton Bay fig and the Indian Banyan), and is a descendant of the wild caprifig, which spread from

western Asia into the Mediterranean in prehistoric times, then later travelled as far north as Germany and as far south as the Canary Islands. The wild fig is dry and unpalatable.

Wherever it grew, the fig—both tree and fruit—was used as symbol and metaphor. In India, it was sacred to Vishnu, the saviour of the world; to the Greeks, it was associated with Dionysus, god of renewal. Romulus and Remus slept under it at birth, and in North Africa it is a fertility symbol. African women use the white sap of the fig tree, which is associated with both milk and sperm, in ointments to encourage fertility and lactation.

Cultivation of the fig began in ancient times in either Egypt or Arabia, probably between 4000 and 2700 BC, and continued into the classical era (400 BC—1400 AD). The Romans knew of a dozen cultivated figs. But this process of cultivation created an even stranger reproductive system, the details of which are complicated, which relies on the wild caprifig and a tiny wasp, *Blastophaga grossorum*, It is extraordinary that the relationship involved in this intricate symbiosis between fig and wasp were known to Aristotle and Theophrastus in the fourth century BC.

During the Roman period, cultivars appeared that had little or no need for the fig wasp for reproduction, and these are known to us as 'common figs', while those that rely on the caprifig (or caprification) and the wasp are called Smyrna figs.

While the fresh fig is something of a luxury outside the Mediterranean, it has always been a staple there: every garden, every wall has its fig tree, and it is only a matter of beating the birds to the ripe fruit. Figs were a staple in Rome and southern Gaul, sometimes even replacing bread, and were used to fatten geese, whose swollen livers were called *ficatum*. Figs were introduced into Haiti and Mexico in the sixteenth century, and eventually found their American home in California, where they grew a black Spanish common fig called Mission or Franciscana.

Within the four main botanical categories of figs (Caprifig, Smyrna, Common and San Pedro) are hundreds of varieties, some eaten fresh—which is best done as close to the tree as possible—and others dried, tinned or used for jam.

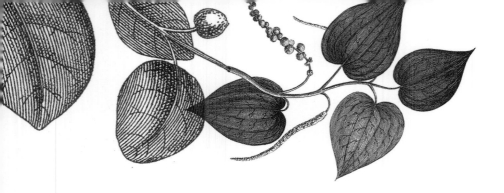

GRAPE

'Wine did not have to wait to be invented: it was there, wherever grapes were gathered and stored, even briefly, in a container that would hold their juice.'

Hugh Johnson, The History of Wine, 1989

The grape—and its inevitable and omnipresent product, wine—has been friend and foe to humankind for a very long time. As Hugh Johnson points out in *The History of Wine*, it is highly likely that Cro-Magnon man, who had the intelligence and organisation to paint the caves of Lascaux 16,500 years ago, would have discovered the not-very-well-kept secret of fermented grape juice.

The fruits of the genus *Vitis* grew in Western Europe and all over the temperate central part of the northern hemisphere. But that vine known as *V. vinifera*, the wine grape (because of its ability to accumulate sugar up to one-third of its volume), first grew on the south-east coast of the Black Sea, south to the Caspian Sea and east to Afghanistan, where it is still found. The wild form is known as *V. vinifera silvestra*, the cultivated as *V. vinifera sativa*.

The oldest evidence of the grape's cultivation—and of winemaking—to satisfy the experts were pips found in southern Georgia, belonging to the period 7000–5000 BC. Besides the evidence of the pips, there is, in the museum of Tbilisi, the capital of Georgia, a squat pot with a decoration at its mouth that has been interpreted as bunches of grapes. Believed to be an early wine vessel, it is similar in shape to those of the Greeks and Romans.

The grapevine is also a native of more southern regions, such as Persia, and is thought to have travelled down the Nile Valley, where it is identified as *V. vinifera occidentalis*, which could be the ancestor for many of our red-wine grapes. From Persia it eventually spread to northern India about 700 BC and China in 100 BC.

Clues to the growing of grapes and to winemaking abound in literature and archaeological finds. Egyptian tomb paintings from around 2240 BC show the cultivation of both large- and small-fruited grapes. In the Babylonian epic of Gilgamesh, from about 1800 BC, Gilgamesh finds an enchanted vineyard, presided over by the goddess Siduri, whose wine would have, had he been allowed to drink it, granted him the immortality he sought.

The first reference to wine in the Old Testament is in the ninth chapter of Genesis, which reveals Noah, more realistically than Gilgamesh, as the first drunk, a binge with curiously overblown consequences. After that there are well over a hundred mentions of vines and vineyards in both testaments.

It is curious that all the major legends about the invention of wine are linked to deluges—both the Gilgamesh and Noah stories, for example. Maguelonne Toussaint-Samat reflects that 'perhaps we are being told that wine should always be mixed with water', a practice certainly followed by the ancient Greeks, whose wines were so thick and sweet they would have been unpalatable neat.

The Romans and Greeks grew grapes not only for winemaking but for eating at the table and producing such things as verjuice and grape syrup. While the Greeks mythologised the spread of the vine by giving it a patron deity, Dionysus, the Romans spread the grape by planting the vine wherever their Empire spread, a process aided by its adaptability.

Other species of *Vitis* existed, in Asia, America and South Africa—the American species, the fox grape (*V. labrusca*), was seen and noted by a Viking expedition led by Leif Erikson in 1000 AD, probably in what today is Massachusetts, long before the arrival of Columbus. Indeed, it was American rootstock that saved the European *V. vinifera* from annihilation in 1860 by the aphid *Phylloxera vastatrix*. Phylloxera lives on American vines without hurting them, but when it was accidentally imported to Europe (and much later to

Australia), it threatened to wipe them out. The solution was to graft all vines onto American rootstock.

The rapid and wide spread of the grapevine and its ability to adapt to new locations has made ampelography, the science of identifying grape varieties by their appearance, a difficult one. As soon as wine grapes acclimatise, they are given local names and their origins are lost in time. Even so, more than 8000 have been named and identified, but only forty or fifty are table grapes, or used for drying as raisins and sultanas. Some grapes such as Muscat, Gamay and Zinfandel are used for both winemaking and eating.

There is much divergence of opinion among the religious as to whether or not wine should be drunk. And, as the grape is the medium for wine (and brandy and other strong liquor), we might end on a biblical quote which could be seen as giving us permission to enjoy wine, unlike Noah, in moderation, Ecclesiastes 9:7:

Go, eat your bread in joy, and drink your wine with a merry heart, for God has already approved what you do.

Vitis vinifera (grape vine)

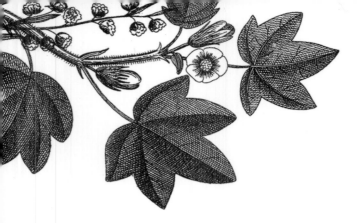

MANGO

'mangoes are not cigarettes
  mangoes are fleshy skinful passionate fruits
    mangoes are hungry to be sucked
      mangoes are glad to be stuck in the teeth
        mangoes like slush & kissing'
          Richard Tipping, 'Mangoes', 1994

If the durian is the king of tropical fruit, the mango is the queen. Luscious, sensuous, best eaten in a bath, many would say the mango is the best reason of all to have summer.

Mangifera indica, the Indian mango, a member of the Anarcadiacea family, is the descendant of the wild tree that still grows today in north-east India and Burma, where it originated. It has been cultivated for more than 4000 years, and grows best where the seasons are defined. Besides *M. indica*, there are between forty and sixty cultivars, with many having evolved to thrive in local conditions, such as the warmer climes of Indonesia and Malaysia. It also now grows in Africa, America, Australia, Mexico and Brazil. The evergreen tree on which this much-loved fruit grows can reach 40 metres (130 feet) and will thrive up to 1200 metres (3900 feet) above sea level.

References to the mango as 'the food of the gods' can be found in the Hindu *Vedas*, where the Lord of Creatures, Prajapati, is transformed into a mango tree. Alexander the Great is said to have relished the mangoes growing in the orchard at Sarnath, associated with the Buddha.

Indian photojournalist TS Satyan tells the story of former Indian prime minister, Indira Ghandi, taking mangoes to Moscow, and having them served to the Soviet leaders at a banquet. 'They created a sensation', he wrote. 'Many of the top leaders asked whether they could take them home to show their grandchildren. It was a sight to see cabinet ministers and bemedalled generals slipping mangoes into their pockets like school boys taking away chocolates.'

The Oxford Companion to Food claims the mango was first introduced outside India by the Chinese traveller Hwen T'sang in the first century AD, after which it spread eastwards, reaching Persia in the tenth century.

The Mogul Emperor Akbar, who reputedly ate up to twenty-five mangoes in a single sitting, is also said to have planted 100,000 trees and ordered milk and honey to be poured over them to sweeten them.

Although the mango grows around the world, India is still the largest producer, and the Alphonso the most popular variety. It is eaten ripe and out of hand, and green in Vietnam and Thailand as a vegetable. In India the green mango is made into a fiery hot pickle and also dried and powdered as *amchur*, which is sprinkled over snacks.

The bark of the tree is used to treat dysentery, and the dried leaves to cure diarrhoea. The fruit contains large quantities of vitamins A and C, thus making it a health food and proving, once more, that that which tastes good, is good.

Mangifera indica (mango)

Stimulants

The story of the three plants in this section is the story of caffeine, the most widely consumed behaviour-altering drug in the world. It is indeed an addictive psychoactive substance, yet coffee, tea and chocolate in which it is found are never (or hardly ever) cited by those who would ban all such drugs from public consumption and sale.

Caffeine is taken for breakfast, in one form or another, by most of the world's population, and, especially in America, is consumed in the form of hundreds of millions of bottles of cola soft drinks drunk daily by people of all ages. And if any substance can lay claim to have changed the course of human civilisation, it is caffeine.

Coffee, tea and chocolate arrived in the modern world by vastly different routes: chocolate via the rituals of a lost civilisation that practised human sacrifice; tea from China, steeped in tradition and superstition; and coffee, relatively late in time from the Yemen, but with slightly mysterious origins—why, for example, was such a powerful and useful drug unknown to the ancients?

All three in one form or another, have so insinuated themselves into our daily lives that many of us could not imagine a day without one or other or all of them. How many of us feel, as does the character in Bach's 'The Coffee Cantata', that 'Without my morning coffee I'm just like a dried up piece of roast goat'? Or like the Reverend Sydney Smith, who wailed, 'Thank God for tea! What would the world be without tea? How did it exist? I'm glad I was not born before tea'.

And as for chocolate, it has been said, 'There is good sex and bad sex, but chocolate is always chocolate'. Unless it is dark chocolate, when it is better than good sex.

Theobroma cacao (cacao)

CHOCOLATE

'Carefully prepared chocolate is as healthful a food as it is pleasant; that it is nourishing and easily digested; that it does not cause the same harmful effects to feminine beauty which are blamed on coffee, but is on the contrary a remedy for them.'
Jean-Anthelme Brillat-Savarin, **The Physiology of Taste, 1825**

No arrival from the New World has given so much happiness and pleasure as that pod which today we call *Theobroma cacao*—*Theobroma* being a new botanical genus created and named by Carl Linnaeus, meaning 'food of the gods'.

It was precisely that to the people who lived in the shadow of the tree on which the pod grows. First were the Mayans, whose elaborate civilisation flowered around 400 AD and then mysteriously vanished around 900 AD in Yucatan, a large peninsula between Mexico and Guatemala. Later were the Aztecs, who came from the north to fill in the gap, and drank a liquid made by whisking the roasted crushed beans with boiling water, chilli and other spices. The Mayans called this concoction *tchacahoua*, the Aztecs *tchocoatl*, from which we get the word 'chocolate'.

The tree was called by the Mayas *cacahuaquchtl*, which meant, simply, 'the tree'—the tree of the gods. It is an evergreen reaching a height of 6–12 metres (20–40 feet), indigenous to the forests of Yucatan; the insect-resistant variety in this region, then and now, is the Forastero.

The flowers grow directly from the trunk and older branches and are pollinated by a midge, but only a few flowers develop into pods, usually about 30 to a tree. They are large and oval, saffron or red in colour and harvested twice a year, when ripe pods are collected, split and the contents—the beans—scraped out. To maximise the flavour, the beans are left to ferment in the sun with their surrounding pulp, then dried and sent to be made into chocolate.

Cacao beans didn't return to Europe with Columbus—he did capture a canoe laden with beans on his third voyage in 1502, but knew nothing of them, except perhaps that they were used as currency. It was the conquistador Cortez and his soldiers, who invaded Yucatan in 1517, who learnt about the drink that was such an important feature of the Aztec culture, and which the Spaniards soon learnt to love—especially when they witnessed the ceremonial harvesting of the cacao, which was accompanied by human sacrifice to the god Quetzalcoatl, and orgiastic erotic games on the day of the harvest.

The drink was served, eventually, to the Emperor Moctezuma and the court in golden cups by naked virgins. The clincher for the Spaniards was when Moctezuma explained that he would never enter his harem without first drinking chocolate. They were convinced.

Aside from its reputed aphrodisiac qualities, chocolate was a profoundly important part of all Maya and Aztec ritual and ceremonial feasting, not only offered to the gods but also used to anoint newborn children.

It was the missionary nuns at Guajaca in Mexico who first introduced sugar and vanilla to chocolate, believing that the spices and flavourings added by the indigenous people made it a drink of the devil: the sugar turned it into a sweet Christian drink. These nuns also invented the savoury chocolate sauce known as *mole*, still used today in Spain.

The notoriety of chocolate reached Europe before the bean itself, and it was mentioned in many works on botany. It was not until 1544 that Dominican friars led a party of Maya Indians from Guatemala to meet the future Phillip II of Spain with gifts of chocolate and other New World products. Later in the sixteenth century, the beans began to arrive as a commodity.

It was soon introduced to the rest of Europe as an exotic—and expensive—spice, but also as a medicine. It also. became embroiled in a controversy over whether the drinking of chocolate constituted a breach of the Lenten fast.

In 1585, Pope Clement VIII drank a cup, and it fell upon him to decide the vexed question. But so popular was the drink by now, especially in Spain, that many priests felt that their churches would be empty if it was banned. They turned to the adage *liquidum non frangit jejunum* (liquid does not break the fast) and in spite of demurrals, that is where the matter rested.

Eventually chocolate was embraced by the clergy, so much so that it became the favoured breakfast of the Grand Inquisitor, prepared for him in silver cups by the nuns in his service, an ironic reminder of Moctezuma's chocolate virgins.

As demand outstripped supplies from Mexico and Guatemala, cacao trees were cultivated in Venezuela and the West Indies, primarily Jamaica and Trinidad. The variety here was known as Criollo, and supplied most of the chocolate for Europe in the seventeenth and eighteenth centuries.

But by the end of the nineteenth and early twentieth centuries, Forastero, taken as seedlings by the Portuguese, was being cultivated in West Africa, Sri Lanka, Malaya, Java, Sumatra and further east into Melanesia. Today West Africa is the major source of the world's chocolate.

One further variety is Trinitario, a hybrid of Forastero and Criollo, originating in Trinidad.

By the late seventeenth century, Italian cooks were using chocolate in both sweet and savoury dishes, and by the late eighteenth century it was also being used in an unsavoury fashion: Pope Clement XIV is widely believed to have been poisoned by a bowl of chocolate in 1774, perhaps the first recorded case of death by chocolate.

In London, drinking chocolate became fashionable from the seventeenth century, and chocolate houses (which were banned for a short time in 1675 as rallying points for radical politicians) sprang up all over: two of today's clubs, the Garrick and White's, began life as chocolate houses. Right to the end of the eighteenth century, it remained a drink for the rich.

The next big moment for chocolate came in Holland in 1828, when Conrad van Houten developed a press to squeeze out the fat—cocoa butter—from the chocolate, leaving as residue what we know today as cocoa. The cocoa butter was ground to a smooth paste, which became solid when cold. This was the first chocolate bar.

In 1842, the Cadbury brothers in England began selling a chocolate bar. Subsequent advances were by the Swiss Rodolphe Lindt, who developed the process of conching (finely grinding the cocoa butter to produce a smoother and richer block), and Daniel Peter, also Swiss, who produced the first milk chocolate.

Today, chocolate is mainly eaten as blocks of chocolate, used to enrobe various centres, moulded, used extensively by pastry chefs and to a lesser extent in savoury dishes. In Spain, it is still drunk much the same way as it way as it was by the Mayas and Aztecs, though without the chilli, accompanied by a fried doughnut called a *churro*.

And the latest chapter in the long history of the cocoa bean is that chocolate—good dark chocolate, which contains less sugar than industrial chocolate—may even be useful in keeping blood pressure down, blood flowing and the heart healthy: another case of good flavour being good for you. We knew it all along.

COFFEE

'Mm! how sweet the coffee tastes, more delicious than a thousand kisses, mellower than muscatel wine. Coffee, coffee I must have, and if someone wishes to give me a treat, ah, then pour me out some coffee'
Johann Sebastian Bach, 'The Coffee Cantata', libretto by Christian Freidrich Henrici, composed between 1732 and 1734

The drink that gets us going has been praised and blamed more, perhaps, than any other non-alcoholic drink used by humankind. The drinking of coffee has been linked to political subversion wherever and whenever it has appeared; literary supremacy in seventeenth century England; the success of the industrial revolution (it replaced beer for breakfast); and vice and disease at various times and places since it arrived in Europe from the Yemen, where it was first extensively cultivated.

The coffee plant is mainly grown for consumption as two species: *Coffea arabica*, the original plant from the Ethiopian highlands, and *C. robusta* (recently reclassified as *C. canephora*), indigenous to West and Central Africa. Both are small shrubs with bright green leaves and red berries (known as cherries), which hold the coffee bean.

There are numerous legendary stories surrounding the discovery of the use of coffee as a drink, the most persistent being that of the Yemeni goatherder Kaldi, who noticed that his charges didn't sleep and instead cavorted through the night. They had, it turned out, eaten the leaves and berries from a shrub that had been imported from Abyssinia.

What is known is that at first the berries were eaten whole, mixed with fat, and that later the pulp was fermented to make an alcoholic drink. The roasting of the beans began around the thirteenth century in the Yemen, although the first reference to the drink was found in the work of the tenth century Arabian physician Rhazes: he calls it *bunca* or *bunchum*. The discrepancy between these two dates is typical of the early history of coffee.

There are two theories as to the name 'coffee'. The first is that it comes from the Arabic *qahwah*, which *The Oxford Companion to Food* cites as a poetic name for wine, and that it was welcomed by Muslim mystics, the Sufis, as a substitute for wine and a means of extending the hours they could pray. The other is the ancient name for the area in which it originally grew, Kaffa in Abyssinia. It was named *kawah* when roasted, ground and brewed into a drink by the imam in a remote monastery in south Yemen, who first tried the drink, and noted it kept him awake and made his brain active.

Without realising it, the imam was experiencing what we now know to be the effects of caffeine: stimulation of the central nervous system and a relief of drowsiness and fatigue, quickening of reaction times and improvement of mood and mental performance. And, rather than being a dangerous drug, as has been suspected at various times during its history, it is now believed that caffeine is a major source of antioxidants—indeed, it is their most important source in the American diet.

Although tea leaves contain more caffeine that coffee beans (2–3 per cent as opposed to 1–2 per cent), brewed coffee carries more caffeine because a larger weight of beans (8–10 grams) is used per cup compared to tea leaves (2–5 grams).

Whether or not the first coffee shop, called Kiva Han, opened in Constantinople in 1475 (it may just be a corruption of the Turkish word for coffee, *kahvehane*), coffee first ran into political trouble in the Islamic world, where coffee houses opened in their multitudes from Constantinople to Cairo, and filled with coffee drinkers talking—as coffee drinkers are wont to do—nineteen to the dozen. A lot of that talk was political and, in totalitarian regimes, as all them were, such talk is dangerous. In the sixteenth century, Sultan Amurat III, a particularly despotic Turkish ruler (he assassinated his five elder brothers to gain succession and

Next page: *Coffea arabica* (coffee) and *Camellia sinensis* (tea)

cut off the penises as well as the testicles of his harem eunuchs—just in case), closed the coffee shops of Constantinople and had their proprietors tortured—just in case. Mahomet Kolpipi, the vizier of a later ruler, Mahomet IV (1648–1687), ordered all coffee shops burnt down and many of their customers thrown into the Bosphorus sewn up in leather sacks.

But coffee proved more powerful than despots, and marched on, gaining strength down the years and around the globe. The first reference in English to coffee comes in 1599, and the first English coffee house was opened in Oxford in 1650. Two years later, the first London coffee house opened.

Another important advance in the history of coffee was the defeat of the Turkish forces in the siege of Vienna. When the Turks fled, they left behind a huge number of sacks of coffee. One Franz Kolschitsky, who had, as a Turkish prisoner of war, learnt the art of making coffee, took some of these sacks and opened an oriental-style coffee house in Vienna, and eventually a chain of them across central Europe. His coffee was made first with whipped cream and later with ice, which became all the rage in Vienna, then Paris.

By the time of the French Revolution, there were 2000 cafes in Paris and, as suspicious as the king's police were, there was little that could be done: they became the hotbeds of the Revolution, with each of the heroes of that momentous uprising having their favourite—Robespierre frequented La Régence, Danton and Marat, Procope's.

Across the Channel, Charles II was also convinced that the coffee houses of London were breeding grounds for revolutionaries and dissidents. But they thrived and many became private clubs more famous for alcohol than coffee.

It was also in London that coffee became associated with literature; in

History of Food, Maguelonne Toussaint-Samat claims that 'without the coffee houses seventeenth-century English might not have flourished so well'. One must remember she is French, but the rollcall of English writers who were habitués of coffee houses is impressive: and includes Pope, Addison, Steele, Phillips, Johnson, Defoe and Dryden. By 1730, tea had replaced coffee as the English hot beverage of choice.

Alongside the history of coffee must be read the history of the machinery for roasting, grinding the beans and making coffee. Perhaps the oldest coffee pot still in use is the Ethiopian *jebena*, a round pot with a long spout which features prominently in Ethiopian cultural life: when a girl marries, for example, she makes coffee for her family and her groom's family and is judged by how well she does so.

The number of machines used, down the ages, to make coffee is truly bewildering, but many would agree that the art reached its height with the invention of the espresso machine, which forces heated water under pressure through compressed coffee. The first true espresso machine was patented in 1903 by an Italian named Bezzera, who failed to launch it onto the market and sold his patent in 1905 to Desiderio Pavoni, who did succeed in commercialising the machine. The rest is coffee history. From giddy goats in the Yemen to the skinny latte and espresso doppio—it was only a matter of time.

Finally, the effort required to extract coffee flavour from the coffee bean is an impressive measure of humanity's persistence in the pursuit of flavour and stimulation. When picked, the ripe bean is cleaned of its covering of fruit pulp by either wet or dry processing, both of which incorporate some fermentation. The next stage is washing, then the removal of the inner 'parchment' cell, which leaves the raw green bean.

The green beans are sorted, and then carefully roasted to varying degrees depending on the required result. The bean, itself a blend of 800 chemical components, doubles in size under heat, and changes from green to various shades of brown due to a series of chemical reactions that develop aroma and flavour. In general, the longer it roasts, the less acidity will be in the coffee, and the more bitterness.

The next stage is the making of coffee, a task best handled by those experts known as baristas, whose skills at the top end approach those of the winemaker: they must have knowledge of the origins of beans, the roasting process, how finely to grind them (which depends on both the required result and, often, the degree of humidity), the workings of their machine and the chemistry of milk.

There is no longer any controversy over the use of coffee in society. In the first years of the twenty-first century, coffee has won, hands down. But tea is fighting back.

TEA

*'If Christianity is wine, and Islam coffee,
Buddhism is most certainly tea.'*
Alan Watts, The Way of Zen, 1957

If coffee is the drug of discussion and action, tea is the drug of contemplation and silence. Coffee agitates, tea calms, and although both contain caffeine, as we have seen, tea delivers less.

But in some curious way, the methods of making these two drinks can be seen as metaphors for their effect on us. Coffee arrives best in a hiss of steam, a welter of pressure, from a hard machine. Tea, best served as in the Japanese tea ceremony, is prepared amid tranquillity, from a vessel admired for its age and handmade asymmetry (exhibiting what the Japanese call *wabi-sabi*, a beauty that is imperfect and incomplete). Coffee is out there, tea is in there.

Although tea is mentioned in first century BC Chinese texts, and is associated with Lao Tze, the founder of Taoism, it did not become a popular drink in China until the sixth century AD (during the Tang Dynasty), and probably arrived, according to *The World of Caffeine*, from either northern India or aboriginal tribesmen of Southeast Asia, who boiled the green leaves of the wild *Camellia sinensis* bush over smoky campfires.

But the Chinese literature of tea is vast, and begins, perhaps, with Shen Nung, 'Divine Healer', who listed the medical attributes of tea (accurately) in a book dated to 2737 BC. Lao Tze (c. 604– c. 521 BC) began the tradition, surviving to the present day, of offering tea to visitors when he stopped on the way out of China, disillusioned with his failure to spread the precepts of Taoism, and was persuaded by a guard at the western gate of the kingdom, over a cup of tea, to write the book that eventually became the *Tao De Ching*, the *Book of Tao*.

But perhaps the most Buddhist of stories concerning tea, and confirming Alan Watts' assertion at the start of this section, comes from the Tang Dynasty (618–906 AD). It is a story about the introduction of tea to China. The monk Bodhidharma, the founder of the *Ch'an* (later Zen) school of Buddhism, and who brought Buddhism to China, was given a cave near Nanging by the Emperor, where he sat unmoving for years, meditating. After nine years of this *za-zen*, or sitting meditation, he fell asleep. When he awoke, he was so disgusted with himself that he tore off his eyelids and flung them to the ground, where they took root and grew into tea bushes. The tea, with its caffeine, would enable him and others to meditate at great length.

The word 'tea' comes to English from the Mandarin *ch'a*, and this word is used, in one form or another, throughout the world, including *chai* in India, *thé* in French, and *tee* in German.

At first, tea was chewed as cakes of pressed leaves, then a powder of dried leaves was whisked with boiling water. During the Ming Dynasty (1368–1644 AD) the method of infusion still used today was the most common, and the tea ceremony, in which every gesture has significance, began to take root and was codified. This ceremony was deeply influenced by the Taoist poet Lu Yu's book *Ch'a Ching*, commissioned by Chinese tea merchants in 780 AD to sing the praises of tea; this it did in mind-numbing detail, describing poetically and at great length every aspect of tea making, devoting pages to the types of waters to be used (mountain was considered best) and descriptions of the different natures of boiling waters.

Tea arrived in Japan around the ninth century, and there evolved its own set of aesthetics and rules for the ceremony: in Japan, for example, only five can join in the tea ceremony at once, five being the symbol of union, and the number of fingers on a hand.

It did not arrive in the West until the beginning of the seventeenth century, when a Dutch or Portuguese ship embarked from Macao with a bale of tea leaves. It had been written about before this; the Dutch traveller Jan Hugo van Linschoten, in his *Linschoten's Travels* (1595), described in detail tea being taken in Japan: 'the aforesaid warme water is made with the powder of a certaine herb called *Chaa*'.

When tea did arrive in Europe, it created a north–south hot drink divide. Coffee was and remained the popular drink for France, Italy, Greece and Spain, while in England and Holland, tea was the tipple for rich and poor, aristocrat and commoner alike, taken, it must be admitted, in different manner according to station: giant pots of stewed tea for the poor, and dainty, almost transparent china cups and saucers for the rich. The English even developed rituals around the taking of tea. Milk first (to stop the delicate china from cracking), then sugar, followed by genteel sipping.

In France, inspired by tea aficionado King Louis XIV, tea had the reputation of being a drink for the idle rich, and was associated with dainty habits: little fingers crooked, tiny slices of cake. Louis himself took tea from a golden teapot, a gift from the Siamese ambassador.

To get the tea from China to England and Holland as quickly (and freshly) as possible, faster and faster boats were built; the tea clippers were designed to skim across the waves carrying large suits of sails. Bets were made on who would win, and the winners were rewarded with a handsome prize. After 1834, when India and Ceylon were planted extensively with tea, the trip was even shorter. The Chinese were not happy, and transferred their attentions to the Russian and Arab markets.

Tea also became famously embroiled in the politics of the American colony. As a consequence of an unpopular tax on tea, a cargo of tea to the port of Boston, designed to break the ban on tea imposed by the colonials, was thrown into the sea by a group of eminent Bostonians, an event known forever after as the Boston Tea Party. The prime minister, Lord North, placed an embargo on any other ships entering Boston Harbor, all the other ports stood in solidarity with Boston, and thus was precipitated the American War of Independence.

Around the world, tea has its rituals. The Russian samovar, a large water boiler, is used to dilute strong black Chinese tea made in a pot and drunk in glasses. In Morocco and other North African countries, tea is also taken in glasses, often with added leaves of mint. In China, the tea is most often infused directly in a large mug with a lid but without a handle. In Tibet, pressed blocks of tea leaves are brewed with rancid butter. In England, some black tea, most famously Earl Grey, is scented with oil of bergamot (a kind of citrus). Today, most tea is made using tea bags, and in America, much of the tea drunk is iced.

However it is drunk, in whatever receptacle, and however brewed, it has been calculated that around the world, every second of every hour, fourteen thousand cups are drunk.

Tea, like coffee, is grown in the shade of larger trees and is better the higher the altitude. The shrub is kept pruned to 1 metre (3 feet) in height. The fresh picked leaves are generally crushed and bruised to release their aroma, then fermented for some hours in a hot and humid place. The exceptions are white tea, which is made from unfermented buds; green tea, from unfermented leaves; and oolong, from semi-fermented leaves. To stop the fermentation, they are sent to a drying room, then sifted, graded, selected and blended before going to market, most often to London.

In recent years, claims have been made for the health benefits of green tea. Its proponents hold that the high level of anti-oxidants in the tea reduces the risk of coronary heart disease, a claim that has been rejected by the American Food and Drug Administration, but not by other bodies. The argument continues, but perhaps the best thing for the onlooker is simply to drink more delicious and refreshing green tea.

Fungi & mushrooms

They can kill you or cure you, give you intense hallucinations or mere intoxication, make you happy, or even, according to some sources, horny. They puff up bread, fizz up beer and make meat sublime. They are among the most remarkable things we eat, and yet most of us know little about them.

Today, did you eat salami, cheese or yoghurt, or drink wine or beer? Then you ate or drank a fermented product, and fermentation is carried out by fungi. The fruit of some fungi are mushrooms, but not all fungi produce mushrooms. Fungi and mushrooms are an integral part of the life system of the planet.

Green plants are the Earth's primary solar collectors—they use the sun's energy, rain and oxygen to make wood, flowers, leaves and roots. Chlorophyll is the molecule that absorbs the sunlight and uses its energy to synthesise carbohydrates from carbon dioxide and water in a process called photosynthesis.

Fungi are one of the groups of organisms that break down this complex organic matter—others are the bacteria and protozoans, but fungi are the most important. The enzymes they produce break down organic chemicals and eat cellulose, pectin and lignin (plant material), but also flesh, bones and other complex materials, recycling what they eat. And they have been doing this for at least four hundred million years. This is the process you see at work in your compost bin, and on the forest floor.

Their most visible presence is the mushroom, which springs up, often overnight, a mysterious object, appearing as it does after rain and thunderstorms, thought by the ancients to have been produced by lightning or thunder. 'They stand on the threshold between the living and the dead, breaking the dead down into food for the living', wrote Michael Pollan, while reminding us that the Mexicans still call them *carne de los muertos*, flesh of the dead. The alchemists of the Middle Ages decided that the mushroom was magic and somehow linked to creation, or life regenerated by death and decay.

Indeed they were mysterious, and their secrets would not be yielded until the invention of the microscope in 1665, when it became apparent that fungi were indeed very different from other living things. They were not plants because they did not contain chlorophyll, were unable to make their own food, and the food they used was digested outside the fungus body and absorbed through cell walls.

It was decided by the scientific community that they were sufficiently different to deserve their own kingdom, along with plants and animals—which they got in 1784. This three-kingdom classification system was used until 1969, when another system, Animalia and Funghi was devised by Cornell University ecologist RH Whittaker, who added two extra kingdoms: Monera, the single-celled organisms, which included bacteria, and Protista, simple, often multi-celled organisms with true nuclei and occasionally chlorophyll in their cells. This division continues to be debated, although it is still generally agreed that the fungi deserve their own kingdom.

What unites the funghi is a lack of chlorophyll; a relatively simple physical structure; and a reproductive system that relies on spores. With the addition of a little moisture, the spore swells like a germinating seed, the cell wall expands through a weak spot to create a thin protuberance which grows longer to become a hypha, and then branches to give rise to more hyphae—a large collection of which is called mycelium. The mycelium exudes enzymes, which begin to gobble up organic matter to feed its fungus.

The ways in which fungi and mushrooms enter the food chain are numerous. Some are: as mushrooms, the fruiting body of the fungus that we eat as field mushrooms, morels, porcini, truffles, and others; as yeast, the single-celled fungi grown and collected to make bread, beer and wine; as 'flor', another yeast used in making sherry; the fungi on the surface of cured meats (such as ham and salami), which 'cook' the meat; the mould that invades cheese, turning it blue, and which coats white-mould cheeses; and the cultures that turn milk into yoghurt.

Some members of the mushroom family are mycorrhizal (from *myco*, fungus, and *rhiza*, root), and grow in symbiotic association with the roots of trees. The roots are infected with the fungus, which sends nutrients back up to the plant and also feeds the fruit of the fungus, the mushroom, if there is a fruit. Although most species of plants have mycorrhizal relationships with fungi, those fungi with fruit are the most conspicuous, and include such renowned gastronomic treats as the Perigord truffle *Tuber melanosporum*, the chanterelle *Cantharellus cibarius*, the cep or porcini *Botulus edulis*, and the morels *Morchella elata* and *M. esculenta*.

Of course, not all fungi are benign. Ergot, the fungus on rye that causes madness, has already been noted (see page 53), and many mushrooms are either deadly or psychotropic. Fungal infections can be annoying (athlete's foot) or life threatening (histoplasmosis, a disease contracted from the fungus *Histoplasma capsulatum* which thrives in poultry litter, bird roosts and areas harbouring bats; it almost claimed the life of the singer Bob Dylan).

A genus of fungi worth mentioning as both damaging and beneficial is *Penicillium*. These fungi are among the most common causes of spoilage in fruit and vegetables—the mould that grows on your rotten orange is either *P. italicum* or *P. digitatum*. Yet another, *P. roquefortii*, is responsible for the blue in some blue cheeses, such as Roquefort, Gorgonzola, Stilton and, in wild form (not introduced to the cheese paste), the Spanish Cabrales. And it was, famously, the discovery of an infestation of *P. notatum*, which appeared to kill the staphylococcus bacterium in his laboratory in Scotland in 1928, which led to Alexander Fleming's discovery of penicillin, the first antibiotic, of inestimable value to humankind.

The word 'mushroom' dates from the ninth century, and derives from the French word *mousseron*, which today applies to a small class of edible mushrooms. As a wild food, they have been gathered from time immemorial. Residues of mushrooms and puffballs have been found in prehistoric caves in Switzerland, Germany and Austria. In favourable conditions (after rain, in the right season) the woodlands of Europe are full of mushroom collectors, silently scanning the forest floor for flushes of their favourite variety. It requires real skill to see them, as they are often coloured to recede into the background, or only visible as slight mounds in the bed of rotting leaves or needles on the ground. The lifesaving skills of selecting edible varieties have been handed down from generation to generation. Of the 120,000 recorded species, almost 200 are edible, and several delectable. Mushrooming is popular all over Europe, in Italy, Poland, Spain—but especially in Russia, where gathering is akin to a national religion.

The truffle (see page 117)—the underground mushroom of rarity, legendary flavour and expense—was as much valued in ancient Greece and Rome as it is today. Mushroom cultivation, now widely practised (especially of *Agaricus campestris*, the common field mushroom, in the West, and *Lentinula elodes*, the shiitake in the East) was also known to the Greeks and Romans. Their mushroom of choice was *Agrocype aegerite*, today especially esteemed in Spain as the *seta de chopo*.

The most highly prized mushroom in antiquity was *Amanita caesarea*, known as the royal agaric, or Caesar's mushroom. As the story goes, the empress Agrippina assassinated her husband, the Emperor Claudius, by feeding him *A. muscaria* instead of his favourite, its relative *A. caesarea*. The only problem with this story is that the toxicity of *A. muscaria* is in doubt, if not its psychotropic nature (see page 114).

Curiously, especially in the light of John M Allegro's book *The Sacred Mushroom and the Cross* (see page 114), the Bible, although packed with food references, does not mention the mushroom.

Modern European cultivation began in 1600, after the publication of a method by French agriculturalist Olivier Serres, and another in 1678 by a botanist named Marchant, who outlined a method for transporting mycelia. The most widely cultivated mushroom in France today is *A. bisporus*, the champignon.

Today, many mushrooms are cultivated for the table, among them the shiitake (see page 116) enoki, shimeji, wood blewitt, wood ear and, to a certain extent, the Perigord truffle (see page 117). But it is the wild mushrooms—the porcini, chanterelle, morel and saffron milk cap—that bring flavour and the memory and aroma of the forest to the table.

Edible mushrooms. Clockwise from top left: Calvatia gigantea (giant puffball), morella (morel), Agaricus bisporus (champignon), Boletus edulis (edible boletus)

AMANITA MUSCARIA

'Every aspect of the mushroom's existence was fraught with sexual allusions, and in its phallic form the ancients saw a replica of the fertility god himself. It was "the son of God", its drug was a purer form of the god's own spermatozoa than that discoverable in any other form of living matter.'
John Allegro, The Sacred Mushroom and the Cross, 1970

Why did Sir John Tenniel place the hookah-smoking caterpillar, the most famous depiction in *Alice's Adventures in Wonderland*, on this particular mushroom? Lewis Carroll's interaction between Alice and the Caterpillar could have come straight from a hippie-era novel: 'The Caterpillar and Alice looked at each other for some time in silence', and finally the Caterpillar tells her of eating the mushroom: 'one side will make you grow taller, and the other side will make you grow shorter'. Is there really any doubt that either Tenniel and Carroll, or perhaps both, had tried this legendarily hallucinatory mushroom?

A. muscaria, also known as fly agaric, possibly for its alleged ability to kill flies, is one member of the *Amanita* genus, two others being the seriously poisonous *A. phalloides*, the death cap, and *A. caesarea*, Caesar's mushroom, discussed in the introduction to this section.

A. muscaria is, like most members of the genus, a large mushroom, with a distinctively bright red cap with white flecks, white gills and a cup or volva at the base. It is to be found growing in fairy rings around the base of pine, fir and larch trees in Europe, but on its transportation to Australia formed an association with the eucalypt. Of its toxicity, authorities are divided, with the authoritative *Common British Fungi* offering: 'It is poisonous to man; in small quantities it has an intoxicating effect, but in large quantities it may prove fatal'. If so, fatalities are extremely rare, according to medical records (one North American journal reported two deaths in the nineteenth century), although the amount and ratio of chemical compounds in the mushroom vary widely from place to place. The two psychotropic ingredients are ibotenic acid and muscimol.

More folklore, rumours, myths and religious claims swirl around the red and white cap of this mushroom than any other. Most recently, it has been suggested by the ethnomycologist (ethnomycology is the study of the historical uses and sociological impact of fungi) R Gordon Wasson that it was the source of Soma, the mysterious god, narcotic of hymns in the Hindu *Rig-Veda*. In the introduction to his definitive collection and translation, *The Greek Myths*, the poet and mythologist Robert Graves wrote, 'I now believe that "ambrosia" and "nectar" were intoxicant mushrooms, certainly the *Amanita muscaria*; but perhaps others too'.

But most controversial of all claims for this mysterious mushroom were made by British philologist, etymologist and translator of the Dead Sea Scrolls, John Marco Allegro. He claimed that the biblical stories were a series of mushroom myths, and that Christianity itself was a mushroom cult—the mushroom being *A. muscaria*—involving 'frenzied god-possessed orgies' with political overtones which ran foul of the authorities at the time. His theories were a result of a painstaking examination of the languages of the Bible, tracing words and phrases back to their Sumerian roots, and how these relayed into Semitic Indo-European languages to show a picture that is not immediately evident from a surface reading of the received text. He outlined these theories in a book, *The Sacred Mushroom and the Cross*, which—due to furious condemnation by the Church and orthodox biblical scholars—ruined his career and, to a great extent, his credibility, although there is a renewed interest in his theory, especially among ethnomycologists. As their science develops, surely there will be a branch devoted entirely to the fascinating history of *A. muscaria*, which we have only been able to touch on in this book.

Amanita muscaria

SHIITAKE

'The Chinese regard shiitake mushrooms as one of the most beneficial botanical medicines. Chinese legends refer to it as a plant that gives eternal youth and longevity.'

James Marti, The Alternative Health and Medicine Encyclopaedia, 1995

The next time you tuck into a hotpot of slowly braised shiitake mushrooms with belly pork at your favourite Chinese restaurant, consider this. An extract from the shiitake called lentinan, a high molecular weight polysaccharide, has been demonstrated to be a highly effective anti-tumour agent. Not only that, but according to George W Hudler in his book *Magical Mushrooms, Mischievous Moulds*, 'a patient testing positive for HIV but without AIDS showed significantly increased immune system function with a drip infusion of lentinan'. Another component of the shiitake, the mycelium extract, has also been shown to 'inhibit HIV infection of cultured human cells and enhance effects of AZT against viral replication'. All that, and they are delicious.

The shiitake, *Lentinula edodes*, is the Asian equivalent of the West's field mushroom—the default mushroom of gastronomy. It is known in the West by its Japanese name, which derives from *shii*, one of the Japanese trees on whose dead wood it grows, and *take*, mushroom. In Chinese it is called *xianngu*, 'fragrant mushroom'.

A smallish mushroom, with a brown cap about 10 centimetres (4 inches) wide when fully grown, its cap is usually—and preferably—covered with a network of white cracks. There are two grades in Japan: *donko*, with a thicker rounded cap, and *koshin*, which has a fully opened and thinner cap. The *donko*, known in China as the winter mushroom, is preferred, because it grows more slowly in cold weather, and has more chance to develop its powerful aroma and flavour which, although offensive to some, its devotees find delicious. Shiitake can be bought fresh or dried, with the dried form preferred as offering more flavour, with the best-quality mushrooms selling for very high prices.

Shiitake are native to China, and have been cultivated for more than 1000 years, and gathered wild for much longer. Large-scale cultivation in the West began when Gary F Leatham published a doctoral thesis in the late 1970s on research into cultivation. Subsequent papers, including one published in *Mycologia*, the journal of the Mycological Society of America, built on this work. Leatham had noted that Japan produced US$1 billion dollars worth of the mushroom annually, a good incentive for potential American growers to plant it for import substitution, while developing and American taste for the shiitake.

Cultivation of the mushroom in America has been banned for many years because it was wrongly thought to be a fungus that attacked railway ties. The ban was lifter in 1972, so Leatham's paper was timely.

Cultivation is carried out one of two ways: either in the open on natural hardwood logs or in climate-controlled environments on artificial logs made of hardwood sawdust and a mixture of nutrients. Shiitake mycelium is a natural wood decomposer, so when the mycelium is introduced to the wood, it gathers resources and reproduces itself by producing mushrooms which then release spores into the air. The shiitake feed on the wood, and we feed on the shiitake.

TRUFFLE

'Since, during storms, flames leap from the humid vapours and dark clouds emit deafening noises, is it surprising the lightning, when it strikes the ground, gives rise to truffles, which do not resemble plants?'
Plutarch (c. 46–120 AD), Moralia, VIII, 'Table-talk'

The truffle is the mysterious, hideously expensive, contentious fruiting body of a mycorrhizal fungus whose very name is problematic. Strictly speaking, a truffle is any member of the *Tuber* genus whose fruiting body grows underground. It forms symbiotic relationships with beech, hazel, poplar and oak trees—both *Quercus robur*, the common oak, and *Q. ilex*, the holm or holly oak.

In truth, underground mushrooms in several genera are known as truffles, and of these, not many are edible. Most interesting is the genus *Tuber*, with nine members, of which only three interest the gastronome: first among these is *T. melanosporum*, the Perigord truffle, called by Brillat-Savarin 'the diamond of the kitchen'; then there are *T. magnatum*, the white or Alba truffle; and *T. aestivum*, the much maligned and admittedly less magnificent summer truffle.

Truffles are famously hunted with the aid of a truffle dog or pig, the dog being more favoured as it easier to control and less inclined to eat what it finds. The pig, which would have roamed wild in the forests of Europe prior to humans, would have been an essential part of the truffle reproduction strategy, the powerful aroma signalling to it where the truffle was to be dug up, eaten, and spread around the forest. A similar triangular relationship exists between Australian underground mushrooms and the native marsupial bettong and potoroo.

In Europe, truffles are hunted from December to February and they are, according to eighteenth century French gastronomic writer Grimod de La Reynière, 'only really good after Christmas ... So let us allow ignorant fops, beardless gourmands, and inexperienced palates the petty triumph of eating the first truffles'. In Australia, the season runs from June to September. Another indicator of the whearabouts of truffles is the hovering *Helomyza tuberiperda*, the truffle fly, which deposits eggs in the ground near truffles. Experienced trufflers note their presence and dig.

The presence of these odd-looking mushroom deep in the soil gave rise to all sorts of speculation as to their provenance. Theophrastus wrote that they were borne of rain and thunder; Nicander, writing a century after Theophrastus, opined that they were silt modified by 'internal heat'. Plutarch, 150 years on, suggested mud cooked by lightning.

But although truffles were much loved, desired and seen as food for the wealthy in ancient times, they may not have been the truffles we know today. In one of his Epigrams, Martial writes of them 'bursting through the forest floor', which truffles decidedly do not. In *History of Food*, Maguelonne Toussaint-Samat theorises that perhaps the mushroom Lucullus, Apicius and others wrote about was most often the tubular-shaped *Terfezia bouder*, the 'desert truffle', which grew on Lesbos and in Carthage (Tunisia) and Libya, because thrust up from beneath the ground.

By the fourteenth century, however, *Tuber melanosporum* was well known, and was served at the wedding feast of Charles VI of France and Isabeau of Vienna in 1385.

The appellation 'Perigord', attached to *T. melanosporum*, is used much as we speak of a Dutch carrot or a French bean, as a botanical description. Perigord is a location where black truffles have traditionally been found, but they are also found in the Dordogne, Savoie, Vaucluse and the adjoining department of Lot.

However, due to a combination of factors—the loss of 20 per cent of the male workforce after World War I, the encroachment of human occupation in the forest, and the exodus of the forest-

Tuber magnatum (white truffle) and *T. melanosporum* (black truffle)

dwelling truffle gatherers—truffle production in France has dropped considerably. Jacques Peybère is a third generation truffle gatherer and exporter from Cahors in the department of Lot. His family has been following the decline of the truffle for 100 years. In 1998 he said, 'In the beginning of the twentieth century in France, in a good year ... there were about 300–500 tonnes of truffles, some say 1000. I don't believe this; in a bad year 100 tonnes. And now, in a good year in France, between 30 and 40 tonnes. In a bad year 10. Three years ago [in 1995] we had only eight tonnes'. In 2005, 10 tonnes were harvested in France.

However, trufficulture is expected to lift production worldwide, despite the process of fruiting remaining a mystery. 'We know the mycelium. We know the contact of the mycelium with the mycorrhizae is essential. But we don't know how the mycelium makes a truffle', says Peybère. In spite of this, trufficulturalists in France, Australia, the United States and other parts of the world are having increasing success in planting trees whose roots have been inoculated with truffle mycelium.

The other important truffle is the Alba or white truffle, *T. magnatum*, which grows around the city of Alba and the Langhe area, both in Piedmont in Italy. The Italians swear that their truffle is the most magnificent; the French, of course, swear by theirs.

Perhaps the most mysterious aspect of the truffle is the flavour. How do you describe it? According to Jacques Peybère, you don't, and can't. 'The flavour is unique. You compare other things to it. When you taste a wine, for example, you say it tastes of truffles.'

But many have tried. The English poet William Makepeace Thackeray (1811–1863) wrote, 'Presently, we were aware of an odour gradually coming towards us, something musky, fiery, savoury, mysterious—a hot drowsy smell, that lulls the senses, and yet enflames them—the truffles were coming'. While not exactly describing the taste, in *The Philosopher in the Kitchen*, Brillat-Savarin wrote that, 'The truffle is not exactly an aphrodisiac, but it tends to make women more tender and men more likeable'.

More recently comes this effusion from English food writer Elisabeth Luard in her book *Truffles* (2006): 'Erotic, earthy, astonishingly sexy, exquisite, smouldering, penetrating, intense, heavenly compound of hashish, essence of opium—it can't be all in the mind. Or can it?'

And finally, to understand the essence of this elusive mushroom, an historic recipe, gathered by Waverley Root, in *The Food of France*:

Large truffles are seasoned and spiced, each one sprinkled with cognac, wrapped in a thin slice of fat salt pork, and then in heavy fire resistant paper, and tucked under the ashes and glowing embers of an open hearth. This is the original way of preparing the dish as it is still made in the Perigord.

A final, sad but true gastronomic note on the truffle from the French writer and truffloholic Colette: 'If I can't have too many truffles, I'll do without truffles'. Looking at the price of truffles at the present time, that means that the vast majority of us will be doing without truffles. We must console ourselves with porcini.

YEAST

'The word 'yeast' … is as old as the language and first meant the froth or sediment of a fermenting liquid that could be used to leaven bread.'

Harold McGee, **McGee on Food and Cooking,** *2004*

This microscopic single-celled fungus—hundreds of millions would fit on a teaspoon, and species of which exist in the air you breathe—has, it could be argued, brought more joy and heartbreak to humanity than any other organism since we first began to explore our surroundings. Of the 1500 or so species of yeast, the most useful are the *Saccharomyces*, which are used to bake bread, brew beer and to make wine and sake.

Yeasts reproduce by fission, budding or sexually, and feed on carbohydrates. Temperature is important to them; extremes of heat and cold will kill them. If *Saccharomyces* yeasts are provided with an environment rich in sugar, oxygen, moisture and grain, they will breed, grow and, in bread-making parlance, rise. The yeast can be introduced as a product—either *S. cerevisiae* or *S. candida*—or gathered as a 'wild' yeast from the air, which is how sourdough is made. The baker takes some dough, adds sugar—in the form of honey, fruit juice or fruit—and waits for the 'magic' to happen: the bubbling, fizzing and rising that indicate the presence of yeast, the bubbles of carbon dioxide given off as the enzymes in the yeast react with the sugar. In this instance, the yeast, often *S. candida*, works in partnership with lactic acid-producing bacteria.

In much the same way, surfaced-ripened cheeses (sometimes called washed-rind) are worked on by a combination of yeast and bacteria. In their case the bacteria is *Brevibacterium linens*.

If the yeast is provided with an environment rich in sugars—but not too rich—and starved of oxygen, two products ensue: carbon dioxide and ethyl alcohol.

It is not known when humans first noted the action of wild yeast on grain which had, perhaps, been mixed with honey. It could have been as far back as 12,000 BC. In the British Museum there is a model of a combined brew house and bakery dated 2000 BC.

As for the brewing of beer and wine, as previously noted, residues from a vat found in Hierakonopolis in Upper Egypt tell us that beer was made there around 3500 BC from wheat, barley, dates and grape pips, and other archaeological evidence has revealed that brewed alcoholic drinks have been around for about 25,000 years. As Hugh Johnson writes in *The Story of Wine*, 'There have been grapes, and people to gather them, for more than two million years. It would be strange if the accident of wine never happened to primitive nomadic man'.

Although we have been benefiting from yeast for tens of thousands of years,

it was only in 1859 that French micro-biologist Louis Pasteur discovered how yeast worked. Yeasts, or yeast extracts, can also be foods in their own right. The branded products Oxo, Bovril, Marmite, Vegemite and Cenovis are all yeast extracts made by adding salt to a suspension of yeast and heating it to break down the cells.

Not all yeasts are friendly. Some yeasts are opportunistic pathogens, and can infect people with compromised immune systems; others, especially of the genus *Candida*, can cause oral and vaginal infections which can be mild or occasionally fatal. Others can cause spoilage in food—seen as growth on meats and the fermentation of sugars.

The tension caused by alcohol use—moderation versus excess—can hardly be blamed on yeast: as George W Hudler writes in *Magical Mushrooms, Mischievous Molds*, 'One can neither praise the yeast for the joy they've bought nor blame them for the misery they've wrought!'

But we must marvel at the remarkable relationship we have with these tiny single-celled fungi. Indeed, at the heart of Christian ritual are two products created with yeasts: bread and wine.

Herbs & spices

Seeds, leaves, dried flower buds, barks and ground roots have savoured and flavoured our foods since first we learnt to cook—and when that was has been lost in time. If, as James Joyce in *Ulysses* has Leopold Bloom say in Davy Byrne's pub in Dublin, 'God made food. The devil the cooks', then it was the devil who whispered in their ear about seasonings. It's hard to imagine a world without herbs and spices, harder to still to imagine a cuisine without them. The devil, thankfully, is everywhere.

But first, definitions. For culinary use, herbs are the leaves and occasionally the roots of plants; in a broader medicinal sense, they can be roots, flowers, leaves or barks. Spices, mainly used in cooking (although sometime as we have seen, with reputations as aphrodisiacs), can be roots, seeds, barks, flowers and other parts of the plant or tree. All herbs and spices used in the kitchen have pleasant, often powerful aromas and flavours. They can, as a class, be called the aromatics.

The word 'spice' came into the English language from *espesse* or *espice*, via the Normans. A direct descendant is the modern French word *épice*. The first appearance of 'spice' was in Chaucer's *The Romaunt of the Rose* (c. 1150 AD):

And many a spice delitable
To eten when me rise from table.

The history of herbs and spices begins with the hunter-gatherers. If, as is surmised, tasks were divided by gender, then it was women who gathered the plant foods, and discovered their uses in cooking, medicine, magic and religion. This knowledge has always come down the female line. In *Women's History of the World*, Rosalind Miles writes that 'of women's duties, food gathering, unquestionably, came top of the list and this work kept the tribe alive'. She quotes a figure of 80 per cent of the tribe's total food intake coming from this task.

In his 'chap' book, *The Plant Magic Man*, Lawrence Durrell tells the story of Ludo Chardenon, who he encountered in a market in Arles, France, one of whose herbal remedies cured 'a relapsing eczema' that, Durrell tells us, the top doctors of Geneva, Paris and London had failed to cure. Later, Chardenon told Durrell that he had learnt his knowledge of herbs through walking the hills and *garrigues* (Mediterranean scrubland) with his grandmother. 'I learnt many a curious thing from her which stood me in good stead.'

Spices are scattered throughout both testaments of the Bible, as in this, from the first book of Kings (10:2) describing the visit of the Queen of Sheba to Solomon: 'And she came to Jerusalem with a very great train, with camels that bare spices, and very much gold, and precious stones'. Even then, spices were on equal footing, for value, with precious stones.

Herbs were the basis of humankind's first attempts at medicine; records show them in use in Sumeria 2200 years ago. Hippocrates (460–370 BC), known as the Father of Medicine, listed 400 herbal plants during his time. And these same herbs would have been used in the preparation of food.

According to Colin Spencer in his book *The Heretic's Feast*, Pythagoras (580/572–500/490 BC) prepared a special dish for the Eleusinian Mysteries, the chief religious agricultural festival which celebrated the sowing, sprouting and reaping of grain, which he would probably have learnt in Babylon.

The recipe was recorded as: 'Poppy and sesame seeds ... crushed with the flower stalks of the asphodel, the skin of the squill [an onion-like plant], leaves of mallow, barley and chickpeas, chopped in equal quantities with Hymettus honey'.

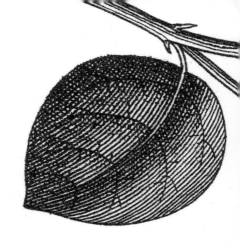

Another of Pythagoras's recipes, also quoted by Spencer, said to have been learnt from Hercules, who had learnt it from Demeter (although being gods, surely they only ever ate ambrosia?) includes: 'cucumber seeds and stoned raisins, coriander flowers, seeds from mallow and purslane, a little grated cheese, wheatmeal and cream'. Here, herbs were being used in both a culinary and ritual fashion: it makes sense, if you are to appease the gods, also to appease the appetite.

Later, the Romans perfumed their baths with lavender (the name derives from the Latin *lavare*, to wash) and devised many dishes that can be used to this day, like this for 'cumin sauce for shellfish' from Apicius: 'pepper, lovage, parsley, dry mint, plenty of cumin, honey, vinegar, broth'. Many other herbs used by the ancients have become extinct or otherwise disappeared. Silphium, called 'laser' in Apicius, and thought to have been a plant of the *Ferula* genus, was used by the Egyptians as a seasoning and a medicine—Pliny noted it as a herbal contraceptive (exactly what plant was labelled 'silphium' has been lost to time). However, one of its relatives, asafoetida— the sap from *F. asafoetida*, also known as 'devil's dung' for its powerful odour—is

used in Indian cooking today. The Romans also used nard, an Indian plant that Maguelonne Toussaint-Samat tells us they loved for its 'strong odour of decay'.

The first recorded mention of aromatic plants and products is from about 2000 BC. The Egyptians had a good knowledge of herbs and spices, using marjoram, juniper, frankincense, myrrh and mint. Cassia and cinnamon were brought from China and Southeast Asia to Egypt for use in embalming. From around 1000 BC, conventional history tells us, Arab traders began to dominate the spice trade and did so until the seventh century AD, with Mecca being one of the major stops along the spice route from the east.

An alternative and controversial theory, put forward by Patricia Crone in her book *Meccan Trade and the Rise of Islam*, holds that the classical accounts of trade between southern Arabia and the Mediterranean were erroneous, that the land route they described was short-lived. Crone says that none of the trade in exotic spices was mentioned in the Muslim sources that she examined. Mecca was off the beaten track. Her examination of the cinnamon and cassia described by Theophrastus and Pliny reveals that they were most likely different plants to

the plants that we call by those names today, and were probably shrubs that grew in the thorny woodlands around the Red Sea. Crone asserts that when spices did come from the east, they came by different routes.

However they got there, the Greeks and the Romans were heavy users of herbs and spices, and those not growing locally were imported. The Silk Road carved out by the advancing armies of Alexander the Great in the third century BC was also a spice road, and when he conquered Egypt, Alexandria became the major port for East–West trading.

An inventory of aromatics from a well-stocked Roman kitchen would garner about thirty-five items, everything from saffron to silphium, lemongrass to lovage, cardamom to catmint. Rue (*Ruta graveolens*) was a curious, exceedingly bitter herb, today used only as an additive to liqueurs—grappa with rue is popular in northern Italy.

Adding a hangover cure to a potent spirit might be seen by some as a pre-emptive strike. Pliny noted it could be used 'against headaches caused by a hangover' by taking 'an infusion of rue leaves' and it was also 'a healthy foodstuff, either raw or cooked'.

When the significance of the monsoons was discovered about 100 AD, and sailors learnt to use them, direct sea routes were established from Roman Egypt to the spice—especially pepper—markets on the Malabar Coast (the western coast of India, around the current state of Kerala). From India arrived ginger, cardamom and cinnamon. As they were expensive, exotic and supposedly erotic, spices came to symbolise luxury, sensuality and excess.

For whatever reason—the fall of the Roman Empire in 641 AD, the occupation of Spain by the Moors and the subsequent disruption of trade—the spice trade had practically died out in Europe by the seventh century, and did not revive again until medieval times.

Clifford Wright, in *A Mediterranean Feast*, posits three reasons for the medieval resurrection: the monotony of the European diet; the desire of the newly emerging bourgeoisie for luxury items; and an 'insatiable' desire for gold and silver among Europe's trading partners in the East, China and India.

Just as fervent was the European desire for spices. 'In the Mediterranean there was a demand for pepper spices and silk; a feverishly eager demand', wrote Fernand Braudel in *The Mediterranean and the Mediterranean World in the Age of Phillip II*. It was a demand that overcame many obstacles. As Braudel noted, 'One has only to think of how many times a sack of pepper from India, or a sack of cloves from the East Indies, must have been handled before it reached a shop, first in Aleppo, then in Venice, finally in Nuremberg'.

What caused this 'orgy' of spice use in medieval times is disputed, but more and more the evidence points to the influence of Arabic—and before that Persian—cuisine. Whether Mecca had been at the centre of the trade route or not, Arabic cuisine was aromatic with spices.

In his book *In a Caliph's Kitchen*, David Waines writes of the cuisine of Baghdad in the eighth century that: 'Balance and harmony among the herbs and spices in a dish was important', listing ingredients that fell into two categories, 'aromatic' or 'pungent', the former including rosewater, saffron and cinnamon, the latter pepper, cumin, asafoetida, thyme and caraway.

In *The Original Mediterranean Cuisine*, Barbara Santich rejects the commonly proposed reasons for medieval spicemania (spices were used to preserve; they were there to mask the flavour of spoiled or rotten food) by pointing to tradition—and profits. 'In its fascination with spices', writes Santich, 'mediaeval Europe is simply continuing a long established custom … in the ancient world, indigenous spices have always been a part of cuisine'.

Profit played its part with the returning Crusaders, who granted trading concessions to those coastal towns that had helped them financially. Santich cites the merchants of Genoa as having been granted commercial privileges in Antioch.

Only in recent years are we beginning to realise the importance to European culture—and that includes medicine and cuisine—of the time of the Arabic occupation of the Iberian peninsula and the correspondingly powerful Caliphate of Baghdad. This was reflected in the remaining recipe collections that date from around 100 years after the Moors were forced out of Spain, such books as two Catalan texts, *Libre de Sant Jovi* and *Libre del Coch*, both redolent with spice.

In the medieval garden, kitchen herbs were as important as they are today, but perhaps more important were herbs for the dispensary. Monasteries often had two herb gardens, one culinary, one medicinal. A sauce as popular then as it is now was green sauce, today's *salsa verde*, found on Italian and Spanish tables,

whose primary ingredient is parsley, often combined with marjoram, sage and mint.

The search for spices consumed the world from the Middle Ages on. Indeed, we owe the discovery of America to Christopher Columbus' mistaken belief that he was developing a new sea route to south and east Asia—then known as the Indies—where the spices came from. This was necessitated by the fall of Constantinople to the Ottoman Turks in 1453, and the subsequent difficulties in traversing what had been a well-worn and relatively easy land route to Asia under the accord known as the Pax Mongolica.

Columbus and his brothers formed a plan to travel to the Indies, the source of immeasurable wealth not just in spices but also silk and opiates, by sailing straight across the Atlantic. At the time, almost all Europeans (except perhaps the Portuguese and Basque whale fishermen) believed that there was no land between Europe and Asia. This misconception was made even worse by the fact that Columbus badly miscalculated the distance from the Canary Islands to Japan, even by the standards of the day. He died in 1506 still convinced that he had sailed along the east coast of Asia.

From this point we'll take up the story of spices and herbs by looking at individual portraits.

Common lavender, genuine Marjoram, garden balm,
peppermint, globe flower, oregano and mint

CINNAMON

'... then shall you be presented with a cup of claret hippocras,
which is right healthful and stomachal. Let us proceed.'
Panturge, in Rabelais' Gargantua and Pantagruel, 1532

The first spice mentioned by name (in the Bible and the Egyptian papyri), cinnamon is the dried inner bark of, principally and most importantly, the tree *Cinnamomum zeylandica*. It is often mistaken for (and deliberately by unscrupulous merchants) cassia, a less delicate aromatic from the bark of *C. cassia*, which grows principally in China.

The two can easily be distinguished both by aroma—cinnamon bark has a deeper, sweeter, more pervasive aroma—and by touch: cassia bark is thick and hard, while cinnamon quills are multilayered, soft and feathery. *Cinnamomum* is a genus in the laurel family (*Lauraceae*).

The hot, spicy notes of cinnamon—coarser in cassia—come from the phenolic compound cinnamaldehyde. The more subtle and seductive aroma of cinnamon comes from the floral and clove notes of linalool and eugenol respectively.

Today, as in ancient times, most cinnamon is grown in Sri Lanka (then Ceylan, later Ceylon), a fact well known by the members of the trading Polo family, even though Marco did not mention this in his book: he was, most likely, protecting his sources for reasons of trade.

While cinnamon was commonly used in great quantities in India, it was not used quite so much in Roman cuisine until the third and fourth centuries, although it was recognised as a medicine. The use of cassia in China is recorded from 2700 BC, and the Taoists revered it as the food of the immortals.

Much later, cinnamon became one of the most widely used spices of the Middle Ages (along with ginger and pepper), and was used extensively in casseroles, added to chocolate in Spain, and to mulled wine drinks. In North Africa it was used extensively, then as now, in dishes such as *tagine* and *pastille*.

By the sixteenth century, the secret of Sri Lankan cinnamon was out and the first to take advantage of it were the Portuguese, who protected their rights over the trade ferociously for fifty years: the Sinhalese were enslaved, and any encroaching boats were sunk.

In 1656, the Dutch, who had broken the Portuguese barricade some years earlier, obtained exclusive rights to the cinnamon trade by protecting the kingdom of Kandy in present-day Sri Lanka from the Portuguese. A hundred years later, the Dutch were sending 270 tonnes of cinnamon a year to Europe, but the natural resource was drying up; the cinnamon tree was disappearing from its natural habitats. It was at this point that one of their colonists, a certain De Coke, advanced the idea of cultivating the tree, a process that takes eight years. What followed was over-production, and then the collapse of the market as the English arrived in 1796 and added Sri Lanka to the Empire. Under their stewardship the market grew to 1000 tonnes a year, but by then, trees were being grown in many Indian Ocean countries, including Malaya, the East Indies, Mauritius and the Seychelles.

As Ian Hemphill writes in *Spice Notes*, 'The processing of cinnamon in Sri Lanka is possibly one of the most dexterous skills still demonstrated by traditional workers in the spice trade today'. The cinnamon 'peeler' takes a cut stem from the two-year-old shoots and scrapes off the outer layer of bark before discarding it. He then rubs the stem with a brass rod, to bruise and loosen the remaining paper-thin layer and prepare it for peeling. With great skill, he removes the fine bark, rolling one length into another, until he ends up with a metre-long 'quill' which is rolled tight and left aside to dry.

There are four qualities of cinnamon traded in Sri Lanka: whole, perfectly made, tightly rolled and evenly joined quills; damaged and broken quills, called quillings; featherings, or inner bark that is not large enough to make up whole quills; and finally, cinnamon chips made from shavings and trimmings.

The best way to use cinnamon in cooking is to buy the finest quills, and powder them as desired, or, in some recipes, to add a quill to the dish and remove before eating.

Essential oil of cinnamon is used for flavouring foods and in cosmetics, and as it is a powerful bactericide it is also used in food preservation. Today, it is particularly popular in America, where it is used in cereals and apple dishes, and is still one of the ingredients in Coca-Cola's not-so-secret formula.

Cinnamomum zeylanicum (cinnamon)

PEPPER

'Don't be too daring in the kitchen. For example, don't suddenly get involved with shallots. Later, when you are no longer a Lonely Guy, you can do shallots. Not now. If you know coriander, stay with coriander and don't fool around. Even with coriander you're on thin ice, but at least you've got a shot, because it's familiar. Stay with safe things, like pepper.'
Bruce Jay Friedman, **The Lonely Guy Cookbook, 1976**

Pepper is the one spice that everyone uses—so much so they may be surprised to hear it called a spice, and even more so to hear it called, as it often was, 'The King of Spices'.

We have to be clear exactly which pepper we are talking about here. One of the consequences of Christopher Columbus' poor navigational skills is that the chilli is called a pepper, and what is often called a capsicum is also a bell pepper (see page 82).

But in this instance we are discussing a number of members of the Piperaceae family, and specifically that staple of the table, *Piper nigrum*, black pepper, which also is the basic berry which gives us white pepper and red and green peppercorns.

P. nigrum, a climbing vine, is native to tropical coastal mountains of south-west India, but was transplanted around the seventh century to the Malay archipelago. It grows on a trellis, or intertwined around companion trees. Its large, thick, distinctively veined leaf is shaped like an ace of clubs, and its spray of small white spiky flowers produce bunches of tightly packed berries that begin life green and turn red as they ripen.

Pepper has been widely used for a very long time. Sanskrit texts show that the Indians were using pepper long before any other spice. Indeed, right throughout Asia, all those countries whose cuisines now use the chilli pepper to impart heat to their food used *P. nigrum* before the arrival of the chilli. Malaysian-born Australian food historian and chef Tony Tan has collected some of these pre-Columbian recipes, one in particular for duck, *itik golek*, from the state of Kedah on the north-western side of mainland Malaysia.

Pepper is one of those words whose roots, in many languages (*pfeffer* in German, *poivre* in French, *pepe* in Italian), lead back to a single origin: the Aryan word *pippeli*, originating in the valleys of the Ganges, the Aryans being the first exporters of pepper.

When introduced to Europe, pepper largely replaced myrtle berries, just as chilli had replaced pepper in Asia. Pepper is distinguished among introduced spices as being adopted almost immediately, and not just in the kitchen—it was awarded health-giving properties as a digestive and an aphrodisiac.

In the fourth century BC, in his *Inquiry into Plants*, the Greek writer Theophrastus described and distinguished between long pepper (*P. lungum* or *P. retrofractum*), a hot sweet pepper that grows in long catkins with tiny berries, and black pepper. The Romans loved long pepper because of its stronger flavour.

By the first century AD black and white pepper were known, Dioscorides, Galen and Pliny all having described the differences, although Pliny was a little confused, thinking they were different plants. Whether black or white, long or round, pepper was a very expensive spice in Roman times, and was used lavishly only by the very rich.

So expensive was it that it was given in tribute by foreign monarchs to show their allegiance to the Imperial city. Once the tables were turned and Rome fell, when Alaric, the king of the Visigoths entered, he demanded a handsome tribute paid in—pepper. More than a spice, it was a symbol of power.

In the Middle Ages, it was used as rent and presented to overlords, and included in dowries and parts of ransoms and fines. By some strange process of inversion, the term 'peppercorn rent' today means a symbolic, cheap rent.

Because of its many values, pepper was always an important item of trade. There were specialist pepper traders in France who called themselves *poivriers*.

In England, the Guild of Pepperers was first recorded in 1180. The ports of Alexandria, Genoa and Venice owed much of their wealth to the pepper trade. It was the quest for this 'black gold' that prompted some of the great voyages of discovery, particularly to the Malabar Coast. Vasco da Gama was one such explorer, who landed on the coast in 1498 and is today buried there. Since the time of Marco Polo (1254–1324), the Indians on that coast have been cultivating pepper for export to Europe.

At first, as was the case with cinnamon, the Portuguese dominated the trade. But once again, it was relinquished to the Dutch, this time in 1522, although the Portuguese were not entirely locked out, and a price war began which ended with pepper traded extensively by the Chinese, then the English. By the time the Dutch East India Company collapsed and the trade fell into the hands of entrepreneurs with fast schooners and ready markets for cheap product, pepper's reign as the King of Spices was over.

There is one other source of confusion emanating from poor old Christopher Columbus' delusions of Asiatic exploration. As well as calling the chilli a pepper, so keen was he to bring

P. nigrum back with him that he mistook the allspice berry (*Pimenta dioica*) for pepper, and called it *pimenta*, thus landing it with a misleading botanical name.

Black peppercorns are harvested six months after flowering and are either dried in the sun directly or plunged into boiling water and then sun dried, which accelerates the enzymatic action that turns them black and releases the volatile oil—piperine—that gives them their flavour.

Green peppercorns are picked when not quite full size or ripe and either stored in brine, or plunged in to boiling water for 15 minutes to inhibit the blackening enzyme, then dried to a dark green.

White peppercorns are made by removing the enzyme-containing pericarp (the wall of the fruit) before they are dried. This can be done by rubbing off the outer husk mechanically, but the favoured method is to pack the ripening fruits at yellow or pink stage tightly into a sack and immerse them in a clean flowing stream for a week or two, which loosens the outer core. Then they are washed to remove the pericarp and dried in the sun.

Pink peppercorns are made by putting ripe red fruits into brine, as is done for green peppercorns.

Each has their place in the kitchen. The white is preferred where black spots would mar the look of a dish, but also offers more heat than the black. The green was used extensively in nouvelle cuisine in sauces, but not so much since then.

Pepper may no longer be the King of Spices, but as long as we have salt on the table, there will be pepper, by its side.

ALL THE PEPPERS

In addition to chilli, capsicum and allspice, there are many other things with the name 'pepper', some from the genus *Piper*, some not.

Cubeb pepper *P. cubeba*

Sometimes called tailed pepper, and native to Indonesia. The red berries are littler larger than black pepper berries, and dried until black. Their flavour is variously described as pungent and bitter or peppery, piney and citrus like. The word 'cubeb' apparently enters English from the Arabic *al-kaababah*, of unknown origin but probably used by Arab traders along the Malay and Indonesian archipelagos.

Ashanti pepper *P. guineense*

Also known as false cubeb. The berries are smoother and redder in colour than cubeb. They are said to taste fresher and less bitter than cubeb pepper.

Guinea pepper *Amomum melegueta*

Also known as melegueta pepper, alligator pepper and, most commonly, grains of paradise. This pepper is the seeds of a perennial reed-like plant with large trumpet-shaped leaves native to the west coast of Africa. The reddish-brown seeds are about the size of a cardamom seed, and when powdered turn pale grey. It first appeared in Europe in ancient times, and was known to Pliny as African pepper. It was popular in the thirteenth century and again in the sixteenth, when the Europeans began to trade extensively along the west coast of Africa. Its popularity may well have been related to its name, coined, as Maguelonne Toussaint-Samat wrote, 'by some advertising genius before his time'. It was used by the Africans to give heat to dishes before the arrival of the chilli. Grains of paradise are hot, peppery and fruity.

Pink pepper *Schinus terebinthifolius* and *S. molle*

Also known as pepper rosé and pseudo or false pepper. In Australia, *S. molle* is widespread in rural areas, and known as the peppercorn tree; many Australians believe this is where true pepper comes from, although the version more often used for a spice comes from *S. terebinthifolius*. The red berries grow on graceful trees with either weeping, frond-like leaves (*S. molle*, native to Peru) or glossy oval leaves (*S. terebinthifolius*, native to Brazil). The berries are usually sold dried and are bright pink in colour. They taste sweet, warm and camphorous with a faint liquorice overtone (they are high in sugar), but have warmth rather than heat.

Szechwan pepper *Zanthoxylum piperitum, Z. simulans, Z. sancho* and *Z. schnifolium*

Also known as sansho, flower pepper, Japanese pepper and prickly ash, and most often the dried berries of *Z. piperitum*, the prickly ash, a small deciduous tree which grows, in its various forms, all over Asia but is native to Szechwan. There is even one native to America, *Z. americanum*, whose bark was employed by Native Americans as a stimulant and an antidote to toothache. The red berries turn reddish brown when dried and split open, when they need to be cleaned to remove seeds, sticks and some sharp thorns. It is used right across Asia, and particularly favoured by the Japanese, as sansho, and the Szechwanese, whose cuisine revels in heat. The berries of most species of *Zanthoxylum* are fragrant and woody, with citrus overtones and a curious numbing, tingling effect in the mouth. The leaves are also used, especially by the Japanese, and have a basil-like, minty flavour.

Mountain pepper

Tasmannia lanceolata and Dorrigo pepper, *T. insipida*. These Australian natives are similar, except that the Dorrigo variety, from a northern habitat, is milder in flavour. Mountain pepper is from a tree native to Tasmania. The deep purple to black fruits of the tree are dehydrated or preserved in brine. The leaves are also dried for culinary use. An initial sweet fruity taste is quickly followed by intense tongue-numbing heat, which builds without subsiding for some minutes. The dried leaves, which have peppery and cinnamon notes, are not quite as numbing but do build in the same way.

Schwarzer Pfeffer. — *Piper nigrum Lin.*

Piper nigrum (black pepper)

PIERRE POIVRE

'Peter Pepper piled his boat with the Dutchman's spices,
And Peter Pepper planted the spices that he had plundered, But the Dutchman plucked the
spices in Peter Pepper's plot, So, now, where are all the spices that Peter Pepper picked?'
Lewis A Maverick, 'Pierre Poivre: Eighteenth Century Explorer of Southeast Asia', Pacific Historical Review, June 1941

Although not strictly correct, the ditty above does serve to outline one side of Monsieur Poivre's many-faceted career. There is no doubt that he was a spice thief, even if, due to ineptitude and bad timing, not a successful one. But that is only part of his story. He is cited by Richard H Groves in his book *Green Imperialism* as one of the early environmentalists.

The presciently named Pierre Poivre was born in Lyons in 1719, and educated in Paris, first by the Missionaries of St Joseph and then the Jesuit Missions Etrangères, where he took initial training as a priest. Although at twenty too young to take orders, in 1740 he was sent by the Society for Foreign Missions of Bishop Lefebre to China and Cochinchina (Vietnam) as an 'ordinand', a promising lad who would eventually become a priest. On the way, he visited the island of Mauritius for the first time, the island that would become his second home and the base for his spice-pilfering adventures. Once in Canton, for reasons still unclear (or suppressed by Poivre himself), he was held under house arrest for two years. During this time he learnt Chinese and gained a considerable knowledge of Chinese natural history and garden design. Here began his lifelong and genuine interest in tree planting and water management.

It was here also that his vocation began to falter. And, perhaps. under the influence of Irish adventurer and entrepreneur Jack O'Friell, he began to turn his mind to some of the commercial opportunities offered in the East. Next—and depending upon who you believe—he was again in trouble with the authorities in Cochinchina and forced to leave, or he spent two years botanising before sailing in the *Dauphin* in 1745 en route to France. It was here that he lost his right arm. The *Dauphin* ran into an English man-of-war, the *Deptford*, and Poivre was shot in the wrist. The *Deptford*'s surgeon cut off his lower right arm while he was unconscious, and threw it to the sharks.

He was landed in Batavia (Jakarta) by the British and spent his time there profitably, studying the Dutch culture of spice trees. And so was born his life's grand plan: to break the Dutch monopoly on spices and to cut France in on the action by establishing spice plantations in Cochinchina—whether from patriotic or personal profit motives, it depends on whose account you read. Either way, he now left the priesthood and offered his services to the Compagnies des Indes (CoI), who ran Mauritius and other islands in the Indian Ocean. He sailed to Mauritius where he made a favourable impression on the governor, Pierre David, who gave him a letter of introduction to his father, a director of the CoI. But once again, his ship was attacked by the English and he was forced to spend time in Pondicherry in India. Finally reaching Paris in 1748, he presented the letter of introduction to Pierre David's father.

Now with official backing, he returned to Mauritius and began to plan and eventually execute three spectacularly unsuccessful attempts to steal nutmeg and clove trees from the Dutch-controlled Moluccas. The Dutch had ruthlessly and successfully maintained their monopoly over the nutmeg and clove trade since the final expulsion in 1605 of the Portuguese from the Moluccas—the only islands where these spices grew naturally. Rebellions were ruthlessly put down, smugglers blasted out of the seas, and plantations restricted to a handful of carefully guarded islands. The stakes were high. In the seventeenth century, the markup on cloves and nutmeg from point of origin to final sale was 2000 per cent, a price kept artificially high by the Dutch practice of spice bonfires to maintain scarcity.

It was against this backdrop of ruthless maintenance of their monopoly and quite justified paranoia concerning the possibility of smugglers that Poivre hove to off the Moluccan island of Meyo in 1755. His ship was in a poor state and the wind was in the wrong quarter. All he could do was squint through his telescope at the clove groves planted there. 'Nothing will console me', he wrote, 'for having been a stone's throw from this island, so fertile in cloves, and yet having been unable to set foot on land ...'

Later, he did succeed in getting hold of what he believed to be some nutmeg plants—although one botanist on Mauritius, when he returned with them, declared them to be false—but they didn't prosper. The infighting on the island and the opposition to his spice projects from the governor at the time, René de Magron, forced him to leave in 1757.

Back in Lyons, he went into semi-retirement with a state pension, but also joined the Royal Agricultural Society of Lyons, and the Royal Society of Paris, where he delivered lectures on his botanical and agricultural experiences. He also published his memoirs, *Voyages d'un Philosophe* (Travels of a Philosopher), which attracted some powerful and positive government attention. They approved of his plans to set up a French spice industry using plants purloined from the Dutch.

And so, in 1767, he headed back to Mauritius with the official government title of Intendant, and a budget to match. He was now able to employ two deputies to sail in search of nutmegs and cloves, Evrard de Trémignon and Sieur D'Etcheverry. They proved far more successful than had been Poivre, especially D'Etcheverry. His voyage on the *Vigilant*, amid intrigue, adventure and near capture by the Dutch, eventually returned to Mauritius where he handed over to Poivre four hundred rooted nutmeg trees, seventy rooted clove trees and thousands of nuts and seeds of both.

There followed years of bitter wrangling over the disposition of the spices. One faction wanted them to remain on Mauritius, another, led by Poivre, wanted them to be planted around France's tropical possessions. Eventually, and after Poivre's death (in 1786), his view prevailed, and Zanzibar, Madagascar and Martinique all had their spice gardens.

Sadly, the success of Poivre's spice quest coincided with the long, slow decline of the importance of spices in the markets and on the tables of the world. Others had also filched spice trees, and the end of rarity and isolation meant the end of fashion and desirability. Other crops were on the ascendant—rubber and tea for example. But there were other more complex reasons for this decline. As the world emerged from Medievalism into Modernity, heavily spiced foods, with some exceptions (panforte in Sienna, Christmas pudding in England and haggis in Scotland among them), were no longer eaten. It's hard to pinpoint one single cause of this decline.

Perhaps, for example, with the final expulsion of the Moors from Spain at the end of the fifteenth century, the clergy there decided that spices were a relic of the despised colonisers, and must be banished. It is curious that after 800 years of Arab occupation, Spanish cuisine today uses very little spice, pimentón from the New World and saffron from the Old being the two most prominent exceptions. Even black pepper appears less frequently on the Spanish table than it does in the rest of Europe.

Another reason could be the influence of the chilli—cheaper and more powerful than pepper—and the influx of other produce from the New World, the potato and the tomato for example, neither particularly spice-friendly foods.

If Pierre Poivre arrived at the end of the spice age, he was, at least according to Richard H Groves's *Green Imperialism*, one of the first conservationists. 'Under French rule between 1722 and 1790', wrote Groves, 'Mauritius became the location for the flowering of a complex and unprecedented environmental policy. This policy started to acquire a particularly innovative and deliberate character between 1767 and 1772 as a result of the personal intervention of Pierre Poivre'. In a speech made to the French Academy of Sciences in 1763, he had alerted members to the climate change occurring due to tropical forest clearance in the French colonies. Even if the aim was to protect crops, he worked to ensure that some forest was left intact.

Today you will hear Poivre's name praised in relation to the Pamplemousses Botanical Gardens in Mauritius, and it is true that he built on the collection of trees and other plantings in these magnificent gardens. But they were founded as a direct result of his original plans to open a spice market between Cochinchina and Mauritius by the governor at the time, Pierre David, to house the spice plants that Poivre planned to bring back.

Poivre returned to France in 1773, retiring to his home and garden at La Fréta, near Lyons, with his wife, Marie Françoise. He gardened, wrote and received a steady stream of visitors eager to hear tales of his adventures in the spice islands. He died there in 1786. Conservationist or thief, adventurer or patriot, if his only legacy is the magnificent gardens at Pamplemousses, then Pierre Poivre deserves our gratitude.

BASIL

'I pray your Highness mark this curious herb: Touch it but lightly,
stroke it softly, Sir, And it gives forth an odour sweet and rare;
But crush it harshly and you'll make a scent Most disagreeable.'
Nineteenth century American humorist and folklorist Charles Godfrey Leland

If ever there were a herb for a globalised world, it is basil. For there is, firstly for Europeans, the 'sweet' basil, *Ocimum basilicum*, alluded to above by Leland. But then there are at least—the very least— five others used by the Thais, Indians, Sri Lankans, Vietnamese and Indonesians. Without enumerating the botanical name of each there are also basils described as liquorice, cinnamon, clove, camphor, lettuce leaf and lemon. One of the joys of visiting Thai and Vietnamese groceries in summer is discovering new basil varieties.

In Europe, there were many rituals attached to the gathering of sweet basil: women were not allowed to do so, and the harvesting was accompanied by purification from a priest who had to be dressed in new clothing, with no metal anywhere on his body. Of course Pliny thought it to be aphrodisiac, and it was fed to horses during the mating season. In Italy and Romania, it was associated with love: an Italian girl leaving a pot of basil in the window was signalling her lover that he was welcome. In Spain, a pot of basil in the window means the residents don't want mosquitoes—it is an effective insect repellant.

Its English name comes from the Greek *basilikos*, meaning 'royal'. To the Indians, it was sacred. One species, *O. sanctum*, is known as holy basil. It is, then, a plant that is regal and revered wherever it grows. It is thus curious that a plant described as 'sweet', and which is so holy and regal, should also incite fear and loathing.

Although basil represented hatred and misfortune in ancient Greece, in the modern Greek Orthodox Church it is used to prepare holy water. In the seventeenth century, physician and author of *The Complete Herbal*, Nicolas Culpeper (1616–1656), quoted the French physician Hilarius, who believed that smelling it too much would breed scorpions in the brain. In ancient Greece and Egypt, it was also believed that basil would open the gates of heaven for the dead, and to this day, many Europeans place a sprig of basil in the hands of the dead. Indians place it in their mouths where, no doubt, it would sit side by side with rosemary.

Basil's use as a culinary herb in India is restricted by the reverence in which it is held in the Hindu religion. *Tulsi*, or holy basil, is regarded as an avatar Lakshmi, the goddess of wealth, and is the subject of many stories in Indian religion and folklore. According to one of those legends, Tulsi was the incarnation of a princess who fell in love with Lord Krishna, and so had a curse laid on her by his consort Radha. Tulsi is also mentioned in the stories of Meera and of Radha immortalised in Jayadev's *Gita Govinda*. The story has it that when Krishna was weighed in gold, not even all the ornaments of Satyabhama could outweigh him. But a single tulsi leaf placed on the pan by Rukmani tilted the scale.

A tulsi plant in the home reflects the religious fervour of its inhabitants, and it is important that they care for it. It is also an important plant in Ayurvedic treatments, regarded as an 'elixir of life' and used for everything from the common cold to heart disease. According to Alan Davidson, one exception to the culinary ban on the use of tulsi in the Indian home is a delicious 'brew of basil leaves, shredded ginger and honey, known as *Tulsi ki Chah* and served in winter'.

In Italy, especially, basil is the most important ingredient for such classic dishes as *pesto alla Genovese*, *insalata caprese*, and perhaps the most Italian of pizzas, *pizza margherita*, made with the colours of the Italian flag: red tomato, white cheese and green basil. It is best used fresh (when dried, it loses its intriguing and powerful aromas) and is best added late to dishes, as its flavour does not survive long cooking.

And at the end of this section on that high-spirited class of plants collectively known as the aromatics, let us quote from Patience Gray:

Pounding fragrant things—particularly garlic, basil, parsley—is a tremendous antidote to depression. But it applies also to juniper berries, coriander seeds and the grilled fruits of the chilli pepper. Pounding these things produces an alteration in one's being—from sighing with fatigue to inhaling with pleasure. The cheering effects of herbs and alliums cannot be too often reiterated. Virgil's appetite was probably improved equally by pounding garlic as by eating it.

Le Basilic

Ocymum Basilicum . L . S . P .

Gve de Rançis Regnault f.   Ital. Basilico , Angl. Basil . Allem . Citronen Basilicn .

Ocimum basilicum (basil)

ROSEMARY

'As for rosemary, I let it run all over my garden walls, not only because my bees love it but because it is the herb sacred to remembrance and to friendship, whence a sprig of it hath a dumb language.'
Sir Thomas More (1478–1535), Tudor writer, statesman and philosopher

Anyone who has wandered the coastlines of the Mediterranean in summer will remember the distinctive aroma of rosemary, *Rosmarinus officinalis*, the quintessential southern European herb.

It is a hardy, sun-loving perennial shrub with two main varieties and many cultivars. The two main types are a bushy upright plant and a low-growing prostrate variety, both with woody stems, leathery, deep green, needle-shaped leaves and delicate blue flowers.

The flowers, legend tells us, were white until the blue robe of Mary, mother of Christ, was thrown over a bush, and from then on it has been a blue flower, known as the rose of Mary. Perhaps more plausible etymology is that *ros* is from the Latin for 'dew', and *marinus* means 'belonging to the sea'. As it does grow on the coast, this seems likely, although the name may reflect the colour of the flowers. Most European languages follow along, with Spanish *romero*, German *rosmarin* and even Basque *erromero*, which may well be a loan from Spanish, as the original rosemary would not have survived the cold of the Basque countries.

Rosemary has long had an association with memory, remembrance, and the dead. *The Oxford Companion to Food* notes that a garland of rosemary, still green, was found in an Egyptian tomb by an eighteenth-century archaeologist. This appears to have been corroborated by a report, also from the eighteenth century, that when coffins were opened after several years, branches of rosemary which had been placed in the hands of the dead had grown to cover the corpse.

Greek scholars wore wreaths of rosemary in their hair to help them commit their studies to memory. Much later, John Gerard (1545–1611/12) wrote in his *Herball*, 'rosemary comforteth the weak, cold and feeble brain in a most wonderful manner'. Shakespeare has Ophelia say in *Hamlet*, 'There's rosemary, that's for remembrance'. And in Australia, sprigs of rosemary are worn on Anzac Day, a day of remembrance of those who died in war, specifically those who died at Gallipoli Cove in Turkey in World War I.

Today, science is investigating this long-held connection between rosemary and memory and is discovering, as it so often does when investigating folkloric beliefs, there may be something to it. Typical of many such studies is the mention of rosemary in a paper written by James Rouse MD, published in the *Journal of Applied Nutritional Science* in 1998, entitled '*Ginkgo biloba*: mind, mood and memory':

Rosemary leaves ... contain numerous antioxidant compounds, most notably carnosol and carnosic acid, which have been shown to be powerful inhibitors of lipid peroxidation [where lipid chains are oxidized into potentially harmful compounds]. Perhaps not coincidentally, rosemary has a long history of use as a memory enhancing herb and is known as the 'herb of remembrance'. In addition rosemary contains compounds such as carvacrol and limonene that inhibit acetylcholinesterase, an enzyme involved in the breakdown of acetylcholine ... a neuro-transmitter that plays a key role in cognition and reasoning, a deficit of which may play a role in memory loss associated with Alzheimer's.

Rosemary was most likely taken to Britain by the Romans, for by that time it was well established as both a culinary herb and a medicinal plant. Today, it is especially important as a culinary herb in Italy and Greece, where it is used to great effect in roasting meats, so much so that it is hard to imagine roasting a leg of lamb without the accompaniment of rosemary and that other great spice, garlic.

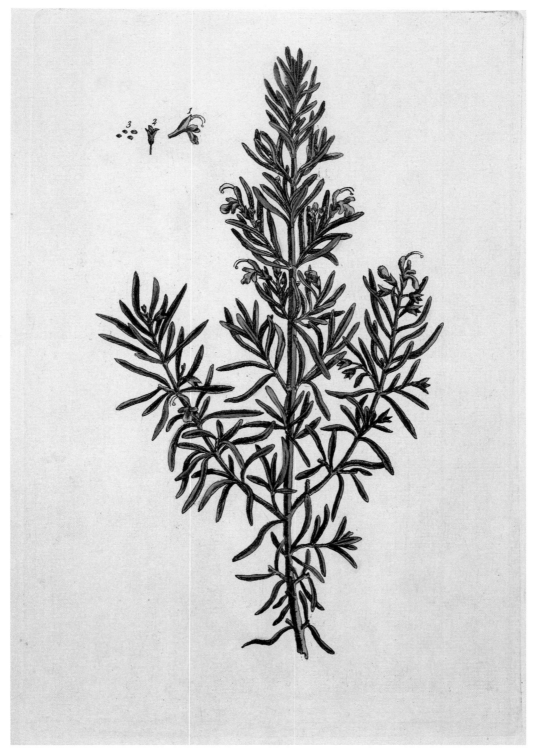

Rosmarinus officinalis (rosemary)

THE FIRST MODERN PERFUME

Rosemary was a key ingredient in the legendary Queen of Hungary's Water, which may have been a miracle cure, but was most certainly the first modern perfume.

The Queen Elizabeth of Hungary in question is difficult to pin down: one source gives her dates as 1305–1381, which accords with an important element in the creation of Queen of Hungary water. But first, the legend.

It was either a hermit monk or the court alchemist who formulated the water, either to cure Elizabeth of arthritis or paralysis or 'palsied and withered limbs'. She probably drank it, which was apparently what one did with perfumes at the time, and it would probably have been more pleasant to drink than the until then oil-based perfumes. It was the first alcohol-based perfume.

Although the distillation of alcohol had been known since at least the sixth century, it wasn't until 1250 that Arnaud de Villeneuve first distilled alcohol, what he called 'eau de vie', in France. And it is this eau de vie that is the basis of the water.

The following passage was published in 1656 (considerably later than the reign of Queen Elizabeth) in a small book by one John Prevot, whose two sons published it after his death in 1631. It purports to be her words:

I Elizabeth, Queen of Hungary, being very infirm and much troubled with the gout in the seventy-second year of my age, used for a year this receipt given to me by an ancient hermit who I never saw before nor since; and was not only cured, but recovered my strength, and appeared to all so remarkably beautiful that the king of Poland asked me in marriage, he being a widower and I a widow. I however refused him for the love of my Lord Jesus Christ, from one of whose angels I believe I received the remedy. The receipt is as follows:

Take of aqua vitae, four times distilled, three parts, and of the tops and flowers of rosemary two parts; put these together in a close vessel, let them stand in a gentle heat fifty hours, and then distil them. Take one dram of this in the morning once every week, either in your food or drink, and let your face and diseased limb be washed with it every morning.

It renovates the strength, brightens the spirits, purifies the marrow and nerves, restores and preserves the sight, and prolongs life.

Here endeth the legend, although it is said that the above, written in letters of gold, survives to this day in the Imperial Library in Vienna, although that has been challenged and perhaps could only be affirmed or otherwise by a trip to the Imperial Library.

As a perfume, it was 'launched' onto the market in 1370 by the French King Charles V, known as 'The Sage' and renowned for his love of fragrances. In his book *Perfume through the Ages*, Roy Genders suggests that it is more likely to have appeared in the 1600s, but in either case, it was the first alcoholic perfume—and it was rosemary based.

Flowers

Flowers

Flowers are nature's beauties with brains. An astonishing range of plants that are more than symbols of love and colourful objects in the poet's toolbox, they are essential to the reproductive cycle of the living world. In strictly scientific terminology, flowers are 'photosynthesising autotrophs'—they energise themselves by capturing the energy of sunlight. Animals are 'heterotrophs'—they use other organisms and organic matter to energise themselves.

Flowers employ an array of strategies to unite male and female sex cells to create new life and produce and maintain genetic variability within their populations—colour, scent, mimicry (of insects or of food sources)—all to keep going, keep growing. Flowers communicate closely with other species, such as bees and other insects, animals and, in ways not yet fully understood, with *Homo sapiens* as well as *Homo economicus*.

Flowers introduced vital resources into the Earth's biosphere—fragrance, nectar, fruits and seeds. Flowering trees, which produce fruit after the flowers, may even, it has been hypothesised, have aided in the development of primates. In the flowering fruit tree, ground-dwelling primates were provided with an alternative to their earthbound diet—but first they had to develop the agility to climb. And to recognise the colours of the flowers and fruits, advanced primates developed three sets of colour-sensitive cells in their eyes. To pick and peel the fruit, they developed flexible wrists and nimble fingers.

Even the negative was turned into a positive. While jumping from branch to branch helped develop three-dimensional vision, it also impaired peripheral vision, which is useful for spotting potential predators. The solution was for primates to live together in troops, and so develop complex social interactions.

But flowers are also among the most beautiful objects on Earth. Does this beauty have a purpose? Was our close attention to the colour, form and aroma of flowers rewarded by giving us first shot at the fruit that followed, and a memory of them so we'd know where to look next time we gathered that way? Or is there some deeper relationship with the beauty of flowers going on? A psychiatrist will tell you that an indifference to flowers is an indicator of clinical depression—unless that indifference comes from an adolescent male, who has his mind on the sorts of things the flowers themselves have their minds on: attracting sexual partners.

Flowers exist briefly, giving us pleasure, and then many of them die and provide us with food. We would do well to respect and revere them.

Pl. 15.

1. *Linum usitatissimum* ___ 2. *Linum Berendieri* ___ 3. *Malesherbia coronata.*
4. *Malesherbia linearifolia* ___ 5. *Cleome pentaphylla* ___ 6. *Cleome spinosa.*
7. *Helianthemum guttatum.*

Linum usitatissimum (common flax) and *L. berendieri* (yellow flax), *Malesherbia coronata* (crowned malesherbia) and
M. linearifolia (star of the mountains), *Cleome pentaphylla* (spider flower) and *Helianthemum guttatum* (rockrose)

ROSE

'... for the roses
Had the look of flowers that are looked at ...'
T S Eliot, Burnt Norton, 1935

Rosa, a genus of wild shrubs containing more than one hundred species, spread from China in the east to Japan in the northern hemisphere, along the Himalayan foothills into southern India, then west to Europe, south to North Africa and then to North America, from Canada to Mexico.

The original roses are difficult to trace—even the historic cultivars cherished in gardens for centuries are of uncertain origin. As Allan Paterson, author of *The History of the Rose*, noted, 'the subject of old roses is one of great complexity in which the non-specialist may be foolhardy to venture'. Or even the specialist.

Even the name of the rose is somewhat uncertain. It may come from the Greek *rhodon*, for rhododendron, meaning rose tree; or it could be related to *rhein*, flow, as the scent of the rose flows through the air; or *rota*, wheel, for the regular five-sided shape of the flower. Most German- or Latin-based languages use some variation on the word 'rose'.

What the rose represents is the history of humankind's search for perfection in its own image (the blowsy rose of Elizabethan times, the uptight buds of the Victorian rose). In Eden, according to the poet Milton, the rose was thornless.

The earliest recorded rose fossils were found in Austria in 1848, and later in Bulgaria, Colorado, Oregon, France, Germany, China and Japan. All are between three and 20 million years old. They are believed to have evolved after the separation of Laurasia from the southern landmass, Gondwanaland, as no wild rose has ever been discovered south of the equator.

The rose became the flower of a wide range of gods and powerful mortals, and the object of worship. Roses were identified with the living god Ahura-Mazdah in Persia; the earth goddess Cybele in Phrygia; and the sun god Helios in Rhodes. Vishnu thought so highly of the rose he fashioned his bride, Lakshmi, from rose petals. The Egyptians used roses as decorative motifs and one rose, identified as *R. richardii*, was preserved in the dry air of a tomb—the rose is a flower with a long association with death. In Knossos, the palace of the Minoan civilisation on the island of Crete, there are recognisable six-petalled roses on the palace walls and in jewellery motifs. Later, in the Classical era, the rose became the symbol of Venus and her other incarnation, Aphrodite.

'The rose is the perfume of the gods', runs a Classical era poem, 'the Joy of Men/ it adores the graces at the blossoming of Love/it is the favoured flower of Venus'. In one story Venus, hurrying to a tryst with Adonis, trod on a thorn, and from her drops of blood sprang the red rose, and from her tears, the white.

In ancient Greece, Dioscorides refers to two flowers we now know as *R. sempervirens* and *R. foetida*. Then, as now, 'doubling' (breeding roses with extra petals) was pursued—Herodotus and Theophrastus mentioned roses with one hundred petals. Up to fifty cultivars of roses were grown throughout the Roman Empire wherever there were gardens. It was a custom among wealthy Romans to release rose petals from the ceiling after a banquet—the famously decadent young Emperor Heliogabalus (203–222 AD) reportedly took this practice to excess and several of his guests were suffocated by them, the subject of a painting by Lawrence Alma-Tadema in 1888.

Curiously the Bible makes but one mention of the word rose as a flower, in the opening line of the Song of Solomon: 'I am the rose of Sharon'—although this is believed not to be a rose, but a crocus. The legend of Mary putting her veil to dry on a red rose bush, which then turned white, is German in origin.

The spread of the rose owes much to the spread of Islam. As the Arabs moved out of Persia, which they captured in the seventh century, they took with them many of the Middle Eastern flowers, including roses. They also took the concept of Paradise (a Persian word), whose gardens were heavily planted with roses. Their earthly gardens, from the beginnings of medieval Arab culture to the late-flowering gardens of the palace of the Alhambra in Granada, featured rose gardens as attempts to create heaven on earth. The Turks, after much deliberation, concluded that the rose was formed from the sweat of Mohammed (as was rice).

A rose with historical associations is *R. gallica officinalis*, a flower of many names (the apothecary's rose, the red rose of Lancaster, the Provins rose), which arrived in Provins, in the Île-de-France region of France, when the King of Navarre returned from his crusade in 1239–1240. It was, it is believed, an ancestor of the flower adopted by the Earl of Lancaster as the red rose of Lancaster. Two hundred years later, it had a starring role in the Wars of the Roses (1455–1487) fought between the houses of Lancaster and York (whose symbol was a white rose) over the succession to the English throne.

Henry Tudor's defeat of Richard II at the Battle of Bosworth in 1485 effectively ended the Wars of the Roses. Henry was crowned King Henry VII, married Elizabeth of York, and merged the rival symbols of the red (Lancaster) and white (York) roses into one, creating the Tudor Rose, under which symbol he further strengthened his claim on the throne by executing all possible claimants, the whole episode demonstrating humanity's ability to harness the most sublime and benign beauty to the cause of death, destruction and ruthless ambition.

The rose blossomed in Italy during the Renaissance, where the first two botanic gardens were set up in Pisa and Padua in the mid 1540s, initially to support schools of medicine (medicine was still grown in those days rather than produced in laboratories): from them developed the science of botany. They gathered firstly medicinal roses such as *R. gallica officinalis*, the apothecary rose, but then began to gather collections of local wild roses. The period from 1500 to 1800 was one of consolidation of plants from the Orient, the New World and the hedgerows of Europe.

Roses are also used in manufacturing perfume, as food, and still, especially in the form of red rose petals, in medicine. Although formerly employed for their mild astringency and tonic value, they are today used almost solely to impart their pleasant aroma to pharmaceutical preparations. As food, there is rose petal syrup, rose water (much used in Middle Eastern cuisine), rose petal jam and rose hip syrup which, during World War II, provided much-needed vitamin C to the British—rose hips contain twenty times the vitamin C of oranges. (The rose hip is the reddish-orange fruit of the flower, left in place when the petals have dropped.)

Bulgaria is the centre for the flowers grown for attar of roses, used in the perfume industry, the variety mainly grown being *R. alba*. This rose oil was reputedly discovered by the Persian noblewoman Nur Jehan, the wife of the Mogul Emperor Shah Jehangir, who observed the fragrant oil on the surface of a palace canal that had been filled with rose water.

It is somehow comforting to know, that to this day, if, like Nur Jehan, you inhale the deep and complex perfume of a rose, what you are experiencing is the real thing, and not a clever combination of chemicals from an aroma factory in California. So far, to paraphrase Gertrude Stein, a rose is a rose is still a rose.

Next page: *Rosa gallica officinalis* (the apothecary rose)

ORCHID

*'Orchids manufacture their intricate devices from the common components of
ordinary flowers, parts usually fitted for very different functions. If God had designed
a beautiful machine to reflect his wisdom and power, surely he would not have used
a collection of parts generally fashioned for other purposes.'*

Stephen Jay Gould, The Panda's Thumb, *1980*

Astounding, complex, bizarre—the orchid
family has astonished and captivated
botanist and collectors for thousands of
years. Those who believed the orchid to
be half bird or insect and half plant were
half right. Their aromas range from that
of rotting flesh to that of one of the most
seductive of natural spices. They are
among the most intriguing creations of
the natural world.

But firstly, what are they? In a
detailed analysis of that seemingly simple
question, Robert Dressler, in *The Orchid*,
concludes—and this is a simplified
version of the argument—that we can
treat orchids as 'an order, Orchidales,
with only one family, Orchidaceae'.

If that is the case, the Orchidaceae is
one of the largest and most diverse of the
families of plants, comprising between
a tenth and a fourteenth of all flowering
plant species, offering between 12,000
and 25,000 examples. And yet only three
physical features are common to all
orchids: the stamens are all on one side of
the flower; the stamen and the pistil are at
least partly united; and, finally, the seeds
are tiny and numerous.

Some orchids are epiphytic, growing
on another plant; others are lithophytes,
and live on rocks; some are saprophytes,
and use organic material manufactured
by other plants to grow on. Others live
in symbiosis with ants and are hosts
to ants' nests, with benefits to both ant
and orchid.

Most orchid species have spheroid
tuberoids, resembling mammalian
testicles, a curious feature which led to
their naming. In Greek legend, Orchis, the
lusty son of a nymph and a satyr, raped a
priestess during a celebratory feast for
Bacchus, thus outraging the Greek sense
of propriety and descending, in their view,
to the level of an animal. It was fitting,
then, that he was torn limb from limb
by wild beasts. The gods intervened and
metamorphosed his body into a slender
plant whose tubers were fashioned to
resemble the organs of his undoing. The
operation of castration is still called an
orchiectomy, and is performed mostly in
cases of testicular cancer.

The orchid is found on all continents
except Antarctica, growing in tropical
jungles and cold alpine climates alike.
Yet it's difficult to pinpoint their origin,
partly because they are so widely
distributed, and partly because of the
powder-like insubstantiality of their
seeds. Most information on the genesis
of the orchid comes from fossil finds.

The first to find these time-capsuled
specimens was the Italian palaeontologist
Abramo Bartolomeo Massalongo (1824–
1860), who found fossils with sufficiently
orchid-like characteristics to identify
them as such at Lake Bolca, in the north
of Italy. They dated back to the Eocene
period (54 to 34 million years ago).

Other findings followed in the later
nineteenth and early twentieth century,
but the discovery in Colombia of ancient
orchid pollen attached to a bee trapped in
amber has put the most recent common
ancestor of all modern-day orchids in
the Late Cretaceous period, pinpointed
by the researchers as between 76 and
84 million years ago, much earlier than
previously believed.

In China, there are no fewer than
1000 indigenous orchids. The flower is
first mentioned in Chinese literature
around 800 BC in the *Shih Ching*, or Book
of Poems. Confucius (552–479 BC)
prized orchids for their understated but
pervasive perfume which, for him,
symbolised those virtuous and wise people
'who make their presence and superiority
felt while never seeking to oppress others'.

The Greek philosopher and botanist
Theophrastus (372–286 BC) first
applied the name 'orchis' scientifically.

Rhyncholaelia glauca (formerly *Brassavola glauca*) (glaucous beaked laelia orchid)

The Romans liked the orchid because of its appearance and its links with satyrs, nymphs and randy gods, and it is mentioned by a number of Roman chroniclers, most notably Pliny the Elder. The fall of the Roman Empire had the effect of ending the prominence of the orchid in Italy at the time.

The orchid is the subject of many strange rumours and misconceptions, one of the oddest of which was perpetrated by the German botanist, physician and Lutheran minister Hieronymus Bock (or Tragus, 1498–1554). His hypothesis was that orchids sprang up in areas where birds had mated and spread their seed. This proved persistent, and was prevalent among German shepherds who noted that there were fields of orchids in places where animals of all types—not just birds—had copulated. This strange belief lasted well into the seventeenth century, in spite of strenuous scientific efforts to debunk it.

The orchid is one of those plants that inspires passion and obsession. The German amateur botanist Georg Eberhard Rumphius (1628–1702) completed his giant work, *Herbarium amboinense*—a catalogue of the natural history of the island of Ambon (previously Amboina) in Indonesia—in the face of disasters. He went blind while working on it, lost his wife and daughters to an earthquake, and then, when he sent the manuscript he had worked on for thirty years to Holland, the boat carrying it sank on the way. Rumphius set about rewriting it and it was finally published in 1741, nearly 40 years after his death. Orchids were one of his central passions, and he was the first to find pollen in the flower, to recognise the fruit and to realise that the white powder in the flower was, in fact, its seeds.

It is little known that Charles Darwin, another intrigued by the orchid, wrote a book entitled *On the Various Contrivances by Which British and Foreign Orchids are Fertilised by Insects*.

What are some of those contrivances? Perhaps the best known is that used by the *Ophrys* genus, whose flowers not only look like insects, but emit a mixture of aromatic chemicals identical to the pheromones of various female insects, with the intent of persuading male insects to attempt copulation with them to spread their pollen, a process called 'pseudocopulation'. The lady's slipper orchids (subfamily Cypripediaceae) attracts insects into a deep pocket with just one exit, where the insect is strewn with sticky pollen. Many of the *Bulbophyllum* species have a powerful aroma of rotting flesh, which attracts flies.

In the second half of the eighteenth century, exotic orchids began to arrive in Europe in great numbers, collected by pioneer orchidologists roaming the globe to track down rare species. The botanist who came to Australia with James Cook, Joseph Banks, was one of the fathers of modern orchidology.

Apart from their beauty, orchids also have a place in medicine and gastronomy. The genus *Vanilla* (from the Spanish *vainilla*, via the Latin *vagina* meaning sheath or pod) includes over 100 species. *V. planifolia* provides the magnificently scented seed pods from plantations in Mexico, Madagascar and Réunion which, when dried, provide the word's finest vanilla. Other varieties to produce vanilla pods are *V. tahitensis* and *V. pompona*.

In addition to flavouring food and adding scent to Cuban cigars, vanilla is used to flavour medicine, to control convulsions, for menstrual problems and as a diuretic. And of course someone had to have used it as an aphrodisiac: for this purpose it was greatly favoured by the Aztec ruler Montezuma (1466–1520).

And then there is *salep*, a natural gum made from the tubers of terrestrial orchids that was popular in Europe in Medieval times. It was made into a flour, which was used in soups and mixed in wine. Today, salep is used to make deliciously sticky ice cream in the Kahramanmaras region of Anatolia in Turkey.

There's no doubt that the orchid family will provide further surprises as we continue to study what has been called the supermodel of flowers.

TULIP

'Its background is full of more mysteries, dramas, dilemmas, disasters and triumphs than any besotted aficionado could possibly expect.'
Anna Pavord, **The Tulip,** *1999*

Even the first mention of this flower in Europe was clouded in controversy. In 1559, the Zurich physician and botanist Konrad von Gesner saw a prized Turkish flower in a garden in Bavaria, which he described in a book published two years later as *Lils rouge*, the red lily. He was, in a way, quite correct, because the bulbous flowering perennial genus *Tulipa* is a member of the family Liliaceae. But the name by which we know it in the West today is the result of a mistake.

More than practically any other flower, the tulip defies the botanist and taxonomist by being so varied and, even in one wild bed, appearing in so many different colours. And that is the source of its appeal to gardeners.

There are thought to be about 120 original species across the Old World, from their beginnings in the Tien Shan and Pamir-Alti mountain ranges in today's Uzbekistan, north to Prikalkhash in central Kazakhstan and the Altai mountains in eastern Siberia, where it's northward trek was stopped by the Arctic cold.

It moved south towards the Himalayas and Kashmir and then was carried by merchants along the trade routes to the Caucasus and the Balkans,

then to Italy France and Spain—a long march for a fragile flower.

Tulip species have been found in and around Shantung in China and there are about fourteen species growing in the mountains of Turkey, only four of which are indigenous, the rest having arrived with travellers, merchants and even diplomats. They finally reached the gardens of Europe by the mid sixteenth century.

The tulip was celebrated by the Persians as far back as the thirteenth century, was taken up by the Ottoman invaders in a big way, and eventually planted in the Topkapi Palace Gardens in Constantinople (now Istanbul).

Because the Turkish name for the flower, *lale*, a name they brought with the flower from Persia, had the same letters as the name of Allah, it was incorporated into religious ceremonies. And from the sixteenth century on, the tulip became the central motif of the empire, to the point it was embroidered in rows on the gowns of Suleyman the Magnificent (1495–1566). The tulip invaded all the Turkish decorative arts, and was the subject of exquisite miniature paintings and the motif in tiles, frescoes and rugs.

The period of the rule of Ahmed III (1703–30) is known by historians as

lale devri, the tulip era. By the 1630s, it is estimated there were 300 florists in and around Constantinople and many gardens planted with tulips along the Bosphorus. At this time the Turks adopted the system, adopted later in the West, of naming the most distinguished flowers.

And when both the Turks and Europeans began to breed the flower rather than select from the wild, the shape of the flower changed according to cultural preferences. In Europe, a round flower was preferred; Turkey preferred a tall thin flower with extravagantly long petals. These were given equally extravagant names: 'Pomegranate Lance', and 'Those that Burn the Heart'.

Even the first recorded arrival of the flower in Europe is in doubt. Ogier Ghiselin de Busbecq set off for Turkey in 1554 as Ambassador for Ferdinand I of Austria in Suleyman the Magnificent's court at Constantinople. It was originally thought that he wrote the letters in which he mentioned 'those flowers the Turks call "Tulipam"' around 1555, and brought bulbs back with him on his return from Constantinople in 1564. But afterwards, it was discovered that he didn't write the letters until twenty years later.

Tulipa lutea maculis rubens, Tulipa aurei coloris, Tulipa lutea prope calicem radis rubro,
Tulipa parte media viridibus signaturis, altera vero rubia and *Tulipa* cx *purpura rosea persica*

Busbecq was also wrong about the name. He confused his interpreter's description of the shape of the flower—like a *tulband*, turban—for the name. But the name stuck.

So it is also possible that the tulip first arrived in Europe with the French explorer Pierre Belon, who started a garden near Le Mans in 1540, in order to introduce new plants to France. In 1546, he went on a grand tour and in Turkey noted a flower that he called the Turkish lily (*Lils Turquois*) and pointed out that merchants had already built up an export trade in bulbs.

But the seminal figure in the propagation of the tulip in Holland is the peripatetic Flemish plant collector, botanical garden director and early tulipomane Carolus Clusius, or Charles de L'Ecluse. When he was transferred from the botanic gardens in Vienna to establish a new garden in Leiden, in Holland, he took tulips with him, and so zealously did he guard them, so possessive was he of them, they were stolen in the night (shades of the potato in Paris; see page 71) and seventeen provinces were stocked with tulips. This was the beginning of the strange phenomenon known as Dutch Tulipomania.

Between 1634 and 1637, the normally cautious and conservative Dutch went overboard for tulips. An exchange was set up where individual bulbs changed hands for the price of a house. At the height of the frenzy, one bulb changed hands for an amount equivalent to twenty-five years' wages for a bricklayer. And the reason for this is even more bizarre.

At the time, tulip flowers were prone to sudden and unpredictable bursts of extraordinary colour, known as 'breaks'—fine strokes of colour painted over the white and yellow ground of the petals as if by the surest hand in fine brushstrokes. No one knew how or why this happened, but many tried to find out, and weird and wonderful were some of the attempts to re-create the 'broken' flower.

The exact cause of this botanical phenomenon was not found until hundreds of years after the mania had died down. In the 1920s, it was discovered that a virus carried by the peach potato aphid caused the breaks as it progressed. Ironically, as it continued progressing, it also weakened the bulb, and flowers became smaller and smaller. And this was why the mania finally died out in the seventeenth century. Modern-day Dutch growers rid their flowers of this virus and the beauty of the breaks has receded into history, remembered only in the beautiful paintings of the time.

In the nineteenth century, the English loved the tulip for the very opposite reason: they admired massed tulipscapes of pure colour. The tulip is a clever flower, which can adapt its appearance to please whoever is looking at it—and ensure its thriving survival.

CROCUS

*'When released, saffron tints like nothing else; it is as if pure
sunshine had been magically infused to create the orange-yellow
of first light over a crocus-coloured sea.'*
Ian Hemphill, Spice Notes, 2000

Crocus is a genus comprising some eighty perennial flowering plants in the family Iridaceae, native to large subalpine and coastal areas of southern and central Europe, the Middle East, Africa and central Asia to western China, but here we are concerned with only one example, *Crocus sativus*.

In autumn *C. sativus* produces a mauve to purple flower whose three red-orange stigmas (that part of the pistil that receives the pollen) can be processed to render the product called saffron, which infuses dishes in which it is used with a warm yellow to golden-orange colour, a sweet, woody, slightly bitter flavour and a distinctive aroma.

Saffron has the distinction of being the most expensive food on the planet, more expensive, gram per gram or ounce per ounce (at time of writing) than caviar, truffles or foie gras. The reason is the laborious and labour-intensive method needed to harvest it. The stigmas can only be picked by hand soon after dawn, before the short-lived flower begins to wilt, and 200,000 flowers are required to produce one kilogram (2.2 pounds) of dried saffron.

Luckily, only a small amount—from 10 to 30 stigmas—is needed for one dish, as one part saffron can colour 100,000 parts of water. And it is whole stigmas (known as saffron threads when dried) that should be used rather than powder, as they have a better shelf life and cannot be adulterated with cheaper spices.

Traces of saffron as a pigment have been found in prehistoric cave paintings. Excavations dating from 2000 BC at the Minoan palace at Knossos, on the island of Crete, and at Akrotiri on Santorini, show saffron gathering. In her book *Women's Work: The First 20,000 Years*, Elizabeth Wayland Barber noted that saffron was used to dye the garments of women of high status in ancient times.

Throughout history saffron has been valued as a spice for its use in the method of 'endoring'—giving food a golden glow—and for its medicinal properties.

C. sativus is native to western Asia and Persia; its cultivation can be traced back to 2300 BC, and it was mentioned in the Egyptian medical papyrus the Ebers Papyrus, which dates from about 1550 BC.

The Greeks and Romans sprinkled saffron around their theatres, halls and public baths for its pervasive perfume, and it is said the streets of Rome were strewn with it when Nero entered the city, although in those times it was mainly used as a dye. But it is mentioned in Apicius as being used to infuse sauces for fish and poultry.

The Mogul Dynasty (1556–1707 AD) took it from Persia to India and it was extensively grown in Kashmir. Although used by the Chinese, it was never grown there, and came to them from Kashmir via Tibet, where it was known as the 'red flower of Tibet'. The Arabs took it to Spain around 960 AD, where it is still widely grown and used in cooking (especially with rice). It arrived in Europe with the returning Crusaders in the thirteenth century and in England around the fourteenth century. By the sixteenth century, it was being cultivated there on a fairly large scale.

The name 'saffron' comes via Spain, from the Arabic *sahafarn*, meaning thread, and/or *za'afaran*, meaning yellow. The Spanish word for it, *azafrán*, remains close to its Arabic roots.

In Spain it is most often used in rice dishes, most notably in paella; in the Middle East in pilaf dishes; and in the bouillabaisse of Provence. When buying saffron, care must be taken to ensure that it is the real thing. Safflower threads are often passed off, or dyed coconut fibre. These sorts of substitutions have been going on since saffron was first discovered. The general rule is: if it's cheap, it's not saffron.

Medicinal plants

Medicinal plants

The world of plants has interacted with the human world in the search for health, happiness and longevity since first we turned our gaze towards the plants that grew beneath our feet and the trees we lived among. And after a period when the practitioners of Western drug-based medicine turned their noses up at the use of herbs, barks, aromatic seaweeds and floral extracts in medicine, attitudes are changing.

In the last century, the sources of natural medicine were expanded to include higher and lower plants, marine plants, and animals. In less developed—that is to say, less Westernised—countries, herbal remedies may be prescribed by medical practitioners in 70 to 90 per cent of illnesses. And many non-Western disciplines, in particular Chinese medicine, are now finding support with practitioners of Western medicine. In America, according to the *San Francisco Chronicle*, 'UCSF, Kaiser Permanente and Stanford University Medical Center are among a growing number of medical institutions that offer traditional Chinese approaches'.

Hundreds of studies show clinically significant results with Chinese medicine treatments, a large number of which are herbally based.

The Western medical system's embrace of plant-based medicine—it is estimated that about 40 per cent of Western medicines are based on plants or plant extracts—has been accompanied by technological progress in the processes of purification, modification and synthesis; one of the barriers to acceptance was the wide variation in quantifiable results because of difficulties related to seasonality and varying strengths of different samples.

Another development stimulating research into plant medicines has been the emergence of drug-resistant bacteria, in the face of which ancient plant remedies have become a new source of hope for patients, drug companies and physicians.

Of the approximately 2000 acute and chronic diseases recognised by the medical profession, only 30 per cent are presently curable—the rest can only be treated symptomatically to a greater or lesser extent. The application of modern scientific methods to empirically proven plant remedies is stimulating interest in the science of phytotherapy, or healing through plants.

Chinese medicine has used herbal remedies for thousands of years. This was first recorded in a book from the Han Dynasty (206–200 AD), *Herbal Classics of the Divine Plowman*, which listed 239 plant-derived drugs. In the present day, some 500 items are used in traditional medicine.

It is estimated that 10,000 plant species have been exploited for medicine, and there are many thousands more yet to be considered in the light of their usefulness to medicine. Between 1941 and 1954, Richard Evans Schultes, the father of modern ethnobotany (the study of native cultures and their relationship with plants), collected more than 24,000 plant specimens from the Amazonia region for analysis in the laboratories at Harvard University. The collection is still being studied, and is far from complete.

In *The Healing Forest*, Schultes and his coauthor Robert F Raffauf raise an alarm:

... almost every primitive society has its own rich vegetal pharmacopoeia ... This wealth of ethnopharmacological information disappears often faster in many areas than the extinction of the plant species which rampant deforestation invariably entails.

Of course, the search for new medicines is, like much scientific investigation, a hit-and-miss affair, but no doubt there are still important breakthroughs waiting to be made. In the meantime, a major resource for future research into plant medicines, the tropical rainforest, is shrinking rapidly, vast tracts being cut down by logging companies and for cattle grazing. It has been estimated that nearly half of the world's species of plants, animals and micro-organisms will be destroyed or severely threatened over the next quarter-century due to rainforest deforestation.

Ethnobotanists, anthropologists and conservationists feel they are working against time, and plead with governments to recognise, in the words of science journalist Christopher Joyce, that the world's forests are 'more valuable standing than cut'.

Atropa belladonna (deadly nightshade)

ATROPINE

'It seems that the man has been changed into a fish; and flinging out his arms, would swim on the ground; sometimes he would seem to skip up and down and then dive down again.'
Sixteenth century observation of a man who had taken belladonna

Atropine is an alkaloid extracted from the deadly nightshade plant, *Atropa belladonna*, also known simply as belladonna, a member (along with the eggplant, tomato, potato, tobacco and capsicum) of the extensive Solanaceae family and a prime example of a plant that is at once a poison and a useful medicine.

The name belladonna, 'beautiful lady' in Italian, derives from the practice of Renaissance noblewomen using its mydriatic (pupil-dilating) properties to enhance their beauty. It was also said to have been used in this way by Cleopatra.

In a totally different vein, belladonna was an important ingredient in medieval witches' brews, and was equated with erotic female energy. It is said that witches would rub it on their bodies and engage in orgies, and that it was an aid to their flying on broomsticks. Others speculate that the drug enabled them to hallucinate that they were actually flying, as can be seen from the quotation at the head of this section.

In addition to helping witches to fly and noblewomen and queens to look more beautiful, belladonna is an effective poison whose use is documented throughout history. In his 1582 book *The History of Scotland*, George Buchanan relates that in the time of Duncan I of Scotland, Macbeth poisoned an army of invading Danes by offering them liquor mixed with belladonna, called at the time 'dwale', then overpowering and murdering them in their sleep.

More positively, it was also used from very early times as an anaesthetic, being recognised as such by Dioscorides. At that time, the atropine was derived from the mandragora, *Solanine glucoside*, another member of the Solanaceae family.

The toxins present in belladonna are atropine, scopalomine and hyoscyamine, atropine being the main component. The root is the most poisonous, then the leaves, then the berries. It is the leaves and roots that contain the atropine. Generally, atropine lowers the 'rest and digest' activity of all muscles regulated by the parasympathetic nervous system. It is a narcotic, diuretic, sedative, antispasmodic and mydriatic; this last quality makes it valuable in the treatment of eye diseases, being used to dilate the pupils for testing sight.

To this day atropine is used as a premedication for anaesthesia, and to treat a variety of stomach and intestinal tract disorders including peptic ulcers, diarrhoea, irritable bowel syndrome, diverticulitis, colitis and pancreatitis. Atropine is also used to control bed-wetting and frequent urination, prevent motion sickness, and to treat alcohol withdrawal symptoms, Parkinson's disease, asthma and poisonings due to certain insecticides or plants.

The increasing variety of uses of atropine has made *A. belladonna* a much sought-after plant, with breeders devoting time and energy to selecting for high atropine yielding specimens. In the world of medicine, it is believed that even more uses will be found for this versatile but dangerous plant.

GINSENG

*'I'm not sure ginseng is any better for you or me than a carrot, but just in case
the Chinese are right, I grow it in my garden. I stick a root in a jug of gin and
call it Old Duke's Gin and Ginseng.'*

James Duke, botanist, as quoted in The Wall Street Journal, *20 November 1992*

For more than 5000 years, the fleshy, man-shaped roots of plants in the *Panax* genus have captivated Eastern healers, especially in China and Korea. The botanical name of the most used species—*Panax* ('all healing' in Greek) *ginseng* (from the Chinese *renshen*, man-shaped)—tells the story.

Ancient legend underpins the use of ginseng in Chinese medicine. It was written that it was first used and noted by the mythological Yan Emperor, also known as Shennong (the divine farmer) who not only was said to have taught the Chinese farming, but to have started herbal medicine, 5500 years ago. The legend has it that he tested and tasted hundreds of plants to discover the original Chinese herbal pharmacopeia. His original work was lost, but passed down the centuries verbally, and finally published as *Shennong Bencao Jing* (Shennong's Herbal) during the Liang Dynasty (502–557 AD). In it, 365 herbs—including ginseng—are listed and divided into three classes depending on their toxicity.

It was also mentioned in *Jijuzhang* (Interpretation of Creatures) written by Shi You some time between 48 and 33 BC, and prescriptions including ginseng are to be found in *Shanghan Lun*

(Treatise on Fevers) written between 196 and 200 AD. In Korea, it is first mentioned in 2137 BC by Osagoo, the fourth emperor/ high priest (or 'Dan Gun'), of the ancient kingdom. There are numerous mythical stories concerning ginseng, one being that of the young man whose mother was suffering from an incurable disease. He found a miraculous remedy in a dream where the mountain spirit presented a ginseng plant to him.

Ginseng refers to all thirteen species of *Panax*, but mostly to those growing in China and Korea. The more recently discovered *P. vietnamensis* grows as far south as Vietnam. There is also a North American ginseng, *P. quinquefolius*, which was known to Native Americans.

So-called Siberian ginseng is not a true *Panax*, but another plant altogether, *Eleutherococcus senticosus*. This, like the *Panax* plants, is an adaptogen (a natural herb that increases the body's resistance to stresses), but it has nowhere near the potency, nor does it carry the mythological baggage, of true ginseng.

Prepared ginseng comes in two basic forms, red and white. White ginseng is young, from plants four to six years old; the root is peeled and sun-dried, which bleaches it to a yellowish-white colour.

Red ginseng is harvested from six years, is steam cured rather than peeled, and often marinated in various herbal mixtures. This is the ginseng most often associated with stimulating sexual prowess and increased energy. Once processed as red or white, ginseng may be taken as pills or tea, or simply ingested as dried root.

Although ginseng is now known to have beneficial effects on the central nervous and cardiovascular systems, and the gastrointestinal tract, and has been shown to be an anticarcinogen, its main use for thousands of years has been in the area of sexual prowess: as a charm, a love potion and to increase sexual potency. And recent studies have shown that it actually works.

A Korean study of forty-five patients with erectile dysfunction (ED) published in 2002 showed that ginseng increased erectile function. A study in Brazil of 60 ED patients showed that *P. ginseng*, as part of a vitamin supplement, made a significant improvement. The November 2002 edition of *Urology* carried details of an effective double-blind study, and the January 2003 *Journal of Family Practice* carried a report from a group of doctors in Virginia who noted it as a safe and effective alternative to Viagra. (For more

plants with reputed aphrodisiac qualities,
see pages 204–11.)

Once again, as with any plant-
based remedy efficacy in any clinical
use depends on variety, age of harvest,
extraction method and physical form.
As reports of positive clinical trials filter
through, Western medicine will begin to
standardise these variables, and no doubt
ginseng will enter into the mainstream.

Panax quinquefolium (American ginseng)

The Roots of Civilisation

MEXICAN YAM

'While the pill may not necessarily have triggered more sexual activity among the unmarried, it is important not to under rate the psychological impact it had on single women.'

Lara V Marks, Sexual Chemistry: A History of the Contraceptive Pill, *2001*

If vegetation could talk, one plant could proudly boast of having had a profound influence on the quality of life, the quantity of sexual intercourse, and divisions in the Roman Catholic Church in the late twentieth century. The plant is the Mexican yam (*Dioscorea mexicana*), whose Spanish name is *cabeza de negra* (black head). It was extracts of plant steroids from the Mexican yam that led to the production of the oral contraceptive.

Scientists working on this problem had realised, by the 1930s, that high doses of steroids, specifically androgens, estrogens or progesterone, inhibit ovulation, but the animal sources they were working with proved far too expensive. Turning to the plant world, work was carried out in 1949 with a Colorado wildflower (*Lithospermum ruderale*), which had been used as a contraceptive by the Navajo Indians. A pill was produced and trialled on four British housewives in 1952, but production didn't go ahead, mainly because the company that produced the medication feared the social and political consequences.

In 1953, testing began on women in Calcutta using a medication based on the Indian field pea, *Pisum sativa*. This failed because of a low rate of efficacy and a lack of funding. Scientists now realised what was needed was a plant that contained large quantities of these sex hormones, or steroids. Chemical companies in America had long been sponsoring research into finding such raw materials.

But the real breakthrough occurred in 1939, when Russell E. Marker, a professor of organic chemistry at Pennsylvania State University, discovered that steroidal plant compounds known as sapogenins could be used to synthesise progesterone. At the same time, the sapogenin Diosgenin was found in the plant *Dioscorea tokoro*, an east Asian perennial yam, as well as roots from sarsaparilla, agave and other true yams (also in the *Dioscorea* genus).

The pharmaceutical company Parke-Davis was supporting Marker, who had developed a five-stage process for the conversion of sapogenins into progesterone, with three further stages to produce testosterone. Realising he needed plants with larger quantities of sapogenins, he initiated plant-collecting expeditions to Texas and Mexico. This led to the discovery that the wild Mexican yam contained large quantities of Diosgenin, and that discovery led to the production of the oral contraceptive pill. But first Marker had to leave Penn State and set up a company, Syntex, in 1944, to synthesise progesterone—because Parke-Davis did not believe in its commercial viability, a decision they must surely have regretted soon after.

But it was not until 1960 that the first contraceptive pill was produced. And it was not until after a court case (*Griswold vs Connecticut*) in 1965 that the pill was made available to all American married women, and yet another (*Eisenstadt vs Baird*) in 1972 before it was made available to unmarried American women. Gradually, the rest of the world followed suit, although Japanese women had to wait until 1999 for legalisation.

After long deliberation, the Roman Catholic Church came out unequivocally against the use of the oral contraceptive pill in a 1968 papal encyclical, *Humanae Vitae*, which reaffirmed the Church's position that contraception was against God's will. Although it has never retreated from this position, many Catholics have simply ignored it.

By 1974, the oral contraceptive pill was being produced from synthetic hormones, a process developed by Mitsubishi Chemicals in Japan. But it was the inedible Mexican yam that made the whole thing possible, and changed our lives forever.

Dioscorea mexicana (Mexican yam)

The Roots of Civilisation

QUININE

'It is supremely ironic that the continent from which the natural treatment for malaria came was not afflicted with the disease until European settlers introduced it.'
Toby and Will Musgrave, An Empire of Plants, 2000

Malaria (from the Italian *mala*, 'bad' and *aria*, 'air') has plagued humanity for thousands of years, and there is still no cure for it. It is a potentially fatal disease, caused by parasites in the genus *Plasmodium* that live in both humans and in mosquitoes of the genus *Anopheles*. The disease is spread by the bite of an infected female mosquito.

Until the discovery of quinine, derived from the bark of the cinchona tree, there was no adequate treatment, and attempts to cure or relieve the symptoms included bleeding, herbal mixtures, and, in one case, a prescription that suggested reading Homer's *Iliad*—whether as cure or distraction is not recorded.

It was in Peru, around 1630, that Jesuit missionaries were told that the bark of what was subsequently named the cinchona tree was an effective febrifuge (fever-controlling substance). It is also possible that the Jesuits discovered it themselves, as they were in the habit of chewing the bark of trees looking for medicinal qualities, and would have recognised the bitterness of cinchona bark as signalling the possibility of it having some medicinal use.

The Peruvians, who knew it as *quinquina* (the bark of barks), had

impressed the Europeans with their knowledge of herbal medicine: they used different parts of the tree as treatment for skin diseases, to treat fevers, for intestinal problems and to combat swelling in the legs. It is said that the Quichau Indians of Ecuador learnt the properties of *quinquina* by watching jaguars cure themselves by gnawing at the bark.

There are forty species of evergreen trees in the *Cinchona* genus, all indigenous to the Andean highlands of South America. They reach a height of 15–20 metres (50–65 feet) and take three to four years to produce small, fragrant, yellow, white or pink flowers and small oblong fruit. The bark of these trees produce four alkaloids, the most important of which is quinine.

The trees are harvested of their bark today in much the same way they were 150 years ago. Strips are cut off with a knife, rolled, dried and sent to the processing plant. They are then wrapped in damp moss, which protects them from infection (the moss has an antibacterial action) and stops them dehydrating.

Today, nearly half the quinine produced enters the food industry, and some is used in tonic water, a hangover from the days of the Raj in India, to which

it was added to accustom the population to the bitter taste of quinine. So accustomed did many become that today, gin and tonic remains a popular drink around the world. The harvest is estimated currently to be 5000 to 10,000 tonnes per annum, yielding about 5 per cent quinine.

Malaria was unknown to the Mayan or Aztec civilisations, but was introduced to America by Europeans. And it was a high-caste European, the Countess of Chinchón, the wife of the Spanish viceroy to Peru, who, according to legend, was the agent for quinine's introduction to Europe.

In 1638, she fell seriously ill with malaria, and nothing her physician, Dr Juan de Vega, could prescribe eased her symptoms. In desperation he turned to the native remedy, the powdered bark of the *quinquina* tree, which he mixed with wine. She made a full recovery and returned to Spain in 1640 with a large supply of bark. Although this is not documented history, Linnaeus nonetheless named—and misspelt—the genus *Cinchona* in her honour.

Once in Europe, it became known as Jesuit bark, as the priests used their Native American contacts to harvest, export it—and reap the profits. In the 1650s, this did not appeal to the Protestant section of the population, especially in England. England's Lord Protector, Oliver Cromwell, the leading Protestant of his times, died from malaria in 1658 rather than take 'the powder of the devil'.

It was Robert Talbor, born in 1642 and trained as an apothecary, who was responsible for the final acceptance of *cinchona* in Europe. In 1671, Talbor had settled in Essex, a low-lying coastal district where malaria (known then as the ague) was endemic, and gained a reputation for curing patients from this affliction. He did not widely advertise the fact that his effective concoction had, as its most effective ingredient, Jesuit bark.

At that time, King Charles II came to Sheerness, near where Talbor was practising. Prior to this, a French nobleman of unknown identity had been cured by Talbor, and it was he who passed Talbor's name on to the king's physician—the king was also suffering from malaria. He was cured—or rather had his symptoms relieved—and in gratitude knighted Talbor, who was then sent to France to cure the king's niece. After that, he went to Madrid, relieving malaria symptoms there, then returned to England and died a rich man in 1681.

The Jesuits retained their control over the cinchona bark market, sending it to Spain, Portugal, France and Italy as well as to northern European countries, the Netherlands and Germany. This demonstrates just how widespread malaria was at the time, a situation that persisted until the twentieth century, when the low-lying swamps were drained, thus removing the mosquito breeding grounds.

In 1820, French scientists isolated the active component in cinchona bark, naming it 'quinine' after the Native American name for the tree, *quina*.

Colonisation took malaria to North America, killing colonists and Native Americans alike, and infecting people up until the 1940s. And as Britain's colonisation expanded, so too did the demand for the cinchona bark. It was fear of the loss of supplies due to the number of trees being felled that prompted the British to attempt to plant cinchona plantations in the colonies.

A series of derring-do adventures by Spanish, Dutch and English explorers in search of the elusive cinchona seeds in the nineteenth century largely failed, and victory fell, eventually, to one Charles Ledger, an alpaca trader who lived on the shores of Lake Titicaca, in Peru. He smuggled out either two or six kilograms (4 or 13 pounds) of seeds (the amount changes in different accounts) with a servant, who offered them to the British, who refused them, and then to the Dutch, who bought them. From these seeds eventually grew the 12,000 trees in the Dutch plantations in Java.

The beginnings of the British collection of trees was due primarily to the efforts of Richard Spruce, a plant collector for Kew Gardens who, under questionable circumstances, collected 1000 seedlings and seed in 1860, and successfully sent 637 of the seedlings and almost 100,000 seeds addressed to the director of the gardens.

Following the isolation of the active ingredient of cinchona, in 1820, scientists around the world worked hard looking for a cure for malaria, for long to no avail. In 1934, a German pharmaceutical company developed the first synthetic antimalarial drug, resochin. In 1943, prompted by the capture of Java by the Japanese the year before—one of the side effects of which was to cut off quinine supplies to protect troops—American chemists Robert B Woodward and William E Doering worked out a way to make synthetic quinine—chloroquine—from coal tar. This prompted the World Health Organisation in the 1950s to attempt to wipe out malaria using a dual strategy of destroying *Anopheles* mosquitoes with DDT, and dosing vulnerable human populations with synthetic antimalarial drugs. Unfortunately, as documented by Rachel Carson in her 1962 book *Silent Spring*, DDT proved to have disastrous environmental side effects, and the only result in terms of malaria was to create pesticide-resistant mosquitos and choloroquine-resistant strains of *Plasmodium falciparum*. Sadly, a major result of the WHO program is that while in the 1940s only 10 per cent of the population was at risk of malaria, by the 1970s that figured had increased to 40 per cent. Today, that figure still stands. In sub-Saharan Africa alone, 3000 children under the age of five die of malaria every day.

But because of growing resistance to the synthetic quinines, the real thing is again being used a part of a strategy to control the disease and allay the symptoms of those unfortunate enough to be afflicted by it, although no longer used as a preventative.

So this remarkable drug, derived from the bark of a tree, which had a hand in shaping an empire and saving the lives of kings and commoners alike, continues to prove useful.

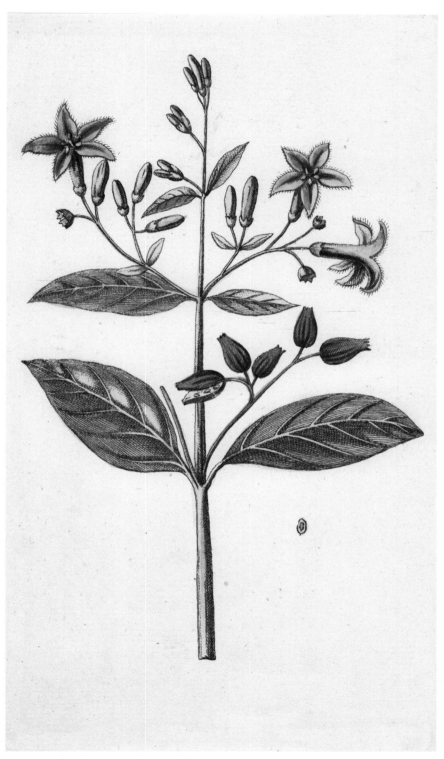

Cinchona officinalis (cinchona tree)

Poisonous plants

Poisonous plants

The story in the Bible of the prophet Elisha cooking gourds from a wild vine in a pottage (soup or stew) during a food shortage is the first mention of a poisonous plant in literature. The gourd in question was probably the bitter apple, *Citrullus colocynthis*, the same size and colour as an orange, but containing a deadly poison. It is easy to understand how the mistake was made, especially in a time of drought and food shortage.

The history of poisons and poisonous plants goes back some 5000 years, to Menes, the first pharaoh of Egypt, who studied and cultivated poisonous plants, a study that continued up to the last pharaoh, Cleopatra, who died probably of suicide by poisoning.

The Greek myths tell us of poisoners such as Medea, and by the fifth century BC, the Athenian law courts accepted poisoning as a cause of death.

The first books on poisons were written by the Greek botanist, doctor and pharmacologist Nicander of Colophon (197–130 BC). His *Theriaca* was actually a list of poisonous snakes, scorpions and spiders and their antidotes (*theriac* means antidote), but the second book, *Alexipharma*, also dealt with poisons from plants, including hemlock.

The word theriac was joined by *mithridatum*, based upon the tale of Mithridates VI, the king of Pontus in Northern Anatolia, whose mother was a rabid poisoner and who, it was said, constantly took minute quantities of poisons to render him immune. This method works for rats, but not for humans. But in the story, when Mithridates was finally defeated by Pompey, he took poison to kill himself, but it didn't work and he had to ask a guard to run him through with a sword. Mithridates' recipe for his personal mithridatum was found, after his death (during his life it was a closely held secret), to be a bland mixture of ingredients such as rue, salt nuts and figs.

Poisoning was rife in the ancient world and Mithridates' mother was only one of many who secured the lineage of their families or themselves by administering poisons. In Imperial Rome alone, Drusus the son of Tiberius (14–37 AD) was poisoned; Caligula (37–41 AD) poisoned gladiators, jockeys and horses to manipulate results; and Claudius (41–54 AD), who destroyed Caligula's collection of poisons, was himself poisoned by mushrooms supplied by his wife Agrippina (see page

112). But the most prolific poisoner was perhaps Nero, whose tally was at least seven deaths: hemlock and the sap of a yew tree were two of the most favoured agents used.

Today, although we have much more knowledge of poisons, it is still difficult to define what plant is poisonous and what is not. For example, one plant may be well documented to have killed, another may be poisonous only to a few, and yet another only poisonous at a certain stage in its life.

The peanut or ground nut *Arachis hypogaea* is a perfect example. For those with peanut allergy—a reaction to the anaphylatoxins in these nuts—even a single peanut can be fatal. The most common vegetable in the kitchen, the potato *Solanum tuberosum*, is poisonous under certain circumstances; after prolonged exposure to light, it may contain enough of the alkaloid solanine to be poisonous—watch for a green tinge and sprouting. The leaves in rhubarb, *Rheum rhaponticum*, contain high levels of poisonous oxalates, and even the stalks should never be eaten raw.

Privet, genus *Ligustrum*, several species of which are commonly used as hedges (classed as a noxious weed in

Australia) is also poisonous, especially its berries. Many attractive garden flowers—iris, foxglove, buttercup and lantana—are all classed as poisonous to a lesser or greater extent. So we can come across poisonous plants in gardens, parks and in the kitchen.

Symptoms of poisoning from ingestion usually start with the mouth, with bitterness, tingling or burning, then move to the stomach and on to the whole digestive system. Some poisons sensitise the skin to ultraviolet light; others damage the liver.

Paradoxically, it has been found that many of the plants that kill can also cure. The Madagascar periwinkle *Catharanthus roseus* has been used as an aphrodisiac, and an excess can cause brain damage. But a substance found in its leaves, vincristine, has been found to kill the cells in some brain tumours. And from the bark of yew trees (genus *Taxus*), whose sap is a poison, a substance named Taxol has been extracted, that is used to treat lung, ovarian and breast cancers, and Kaposi's sarcoma. Another plant substance which also kills and can help, is curare, discussed in the next story.

CURARE

'Any student who may be destined to become a mystery writer should learn about curare.'
Professor Arthur C Gibson, Professor of Economic Botany, UCLA

Curare is not one but a number of different preparations used to tip poison arrows in South America. It comes from a variety of sources, most often the bark scrapings from the vine *Strychnos toxifera* or *S. guianaensis* or *Chondrodendron tomentosum*, and is often mixed with snake venom or extracts from other poisonous plants.

The practice of dipping arrows into poison is ancient—the word toxin comes from *toxon*, meaning 'bow' or 'bow and arrow'. Homer refers to poison arrows in the *Odyssey* (Book 1, line 260):

Odysseus, you see, had gone there
*   also in his swift ship*
in search of a poison to kill men,
*   so he might have it*
to smear on his bronze-headed arrows ...

Claudius wrote of the poisonous arrows of the Ethiopians. The Celts and Gauls also dipped their arrows in various poisons—most often yew-tree sap—but this practice died out with the advent of gunpowder. So when the first Europeans who went to South America were met with poison arrows, they initially thought it was witchcraft.

And well might they have. Curare kills by asphyxiating its victims, whose skeletal (voluntary) muscles are first relaxed, and then paralysed.

The hideous thing about this way of dying is that the victim is fully conscious, is aware of what is happening, and the heart continues to beat, even when breathing stops. Later this characteristic of the drug became useful to medicine.

The earliest known account of curare production was written down by an Italian monk, Peter Martyr d'Anghera, who had gone to convert the heathen in the sixteenth century. He published his account to the Spanish Court in a book called *De Orbe Novo (From the New World)*. He described the mixture being concocted by a cabal of female elders sealed in a hut for a couple of days, and reported that they often died of the fumes. Indeed, he wrote that the mixture was not considered strong enough if they did not die. When he asked what was in the poison, he was told scorpion stings, deadly ants and the juices of special trees.

This was indeed the truth, although the story about the death of those who prepared it was not. There were rituals attached to its production, the major ones being that curare-makers had to operate in an isolated part of the forest, were often required to refrain from sexual intercourse while making a batch, and women were often kept at a distance.

Young bark scrapings of *S. toxifera* and *C. tomentosum* were boiled in water, often with the venom of snakes and ants, and evaporated to produce a dark, heavy paste with a bitter taste. The Indians who produced it were not particularly scared of it, and would taste a drop to check that it had reached the required level of bitterness (taken orally, it is not lethal; the compounds are too large and too highly charged to pass through the digestive tract).

The potency would also be tested by firing a dart from a blow gun at a frog, and seeing how many hops it took before it died. Death for a bird could take two minutes, for a large mammal twenty minutes. Tribes had their own recipes, and many specialised in its production for trade.

The first samples of curare were taken back to Leiden, in Holland, in 1740. An English doctor, Brockleberry, working with this same parcel of poison, injected the leg of a cat with it, and noted that while the cat appeared to stop breathing, its heart kept beating. This was what eventually led Western medicine to see curare as a useful tool in anaesthesia.

In 1811 and 1812, Sir Benjamin Collins Brody experimented with curare and was the first to show that an animal can survive curare poison if its respiration is artificially maintained. In 1825, the adventurer and explorer Charles Waterton described an experiment in which he kept an ass alive by artificial respiration. Waterton was probably the first to bring *S. toxifera* to Europe, where it was named by explorer and trained botanist Robert Hermann Schomburgk (1804–1865) while in Guiana (now Guyana) in 1835. In 1850, George Harley used it successfully in the treatment of tetanus and strychnine poisoning.

From the early twentieth century, curare was used in anaesthesia as a muscle relaxant. It was Richard Evans Schultes who, in 1941, first researched and identified the more than seventy species that were used to produce the drug, enabling more precisely measurable and predictable doses for use in anaesthesia. Today, however, it is no longer used— even the synthetic varieties—as there are much safer and more reliable drugs for the purpose.

Curare is often confused with strychnine (see page 174), a poison obtained from the powdered seeds of

Strychnos toxifera (curare)

another species of *Strychnos, S. nux-vomica.* Strychnine is a convulsant poison— it increases the reflex excitability of the spinal cord. And although, like curare, asphyxiation is the cause of death, the victim suffers convulsions, violent changes in blood pressure and spasmodic respiration.

Of some comfort to anyone considering exploring the jungles of the Amazon where hunting is still done with blowpipe and curare—you're very unlikely to be the target: it's considered too expensive and scarce for use against humans. An exception was made for the invading Spanish.

HEMLOCK

*'Only one marriage I regret. I remember after I got the marriage license
I went across from the license bureau to a bar for a drink. The bartender said,
"What will you have, sir?" And I said, "A glass of hemlock".'*
Ernest Hemingway (1899–1961), American writer

The legendary poison of legendary poisoners is derived from a pretty herbaceous perennial plant with white flowers, *Conium maculatum*, which is often mistaken for fennel, parsley or white carrot, found in damp areas of Europe and Africa. It flourishes in the spring when most other forage is gone. The plant contains a number of alkaloids, the most toxic of which is coniine. To extract it, the juice is pressed out of the bruised leaves and heated.

Hemlock was one of the most common poisons used in ancient Greece for judicial killings, its most famous victim being Socrates, in 399 BC, who was found guilty of 'refusing to do reverence to the gods' and 'corrupting the youth'. Plato described his death in the *Phaedo*, and wrote that his last words were 'Crito, we owe a cock to Asclepius. Please, don't forget to pay the debt'. Asclepius was the Greek god invoked to cure illness, so these cryptic last words are interpreted as meaning that death is the cure for illness.

Plato's description of Socrates' death has long been suspected of being untrue by scholars. Such a calm death—a slowly ascending paralysis, beginning in the feet and creeping up to the chest, with his mind remaining clear to the very

end—struck many medical and literary investigators as unlikely.

At first it was thought that it was the wrong hemlock; there are many others with this name in the Umbelliferae family and the translation could have been misleading. It was not an easy matter to resolve: there's not much experience of hemlock poisoning today, and it's not a matter of a telephone call to a doctor.

However, *The Trial and Execution of Socrates* contains an essay by Enid Bloch in which she navigates 'a veritable thicket of botanical, toxicological, neurological, linguistic and historical complexities' to arrive at a confirmation of Plato's account.

Of most use to Bloch were the writings of a number of nineteenth-century physicians and toxicologists who not only self-dosed with hemlock but prescribed it for such problems as 'unmanageable children': what we would today call hyperactivity. Resulting experiments and deaths were recorded with typical nineteenth-century efficiency.

As Bloch reports, in virtually every recorded case of experimental or accidental ingestion, the poison progressed through the body as described by Plato, consciousness was preserved, and death, if it arrived, did

so when paralysis reached the muscles of respiration. Bloch concludes, 'Plato not only told the truth, he did so with astounding medical accuracy'. As with curare, hemlock's effects can be survived by keeping the victim on artificial respiration until the drug wears off.

Herbalists still use hemlock. A preparation from the fresh leaves, called Succus conii, is used internally for sedative and antispasmodic properties, and an ointment called Unguentum conii is used as a soothing application for haemorrhoids and in pill form as a sedative. It is also used extensively by homeopathic doctors—another poison with many faces, some kind, some cruel.

Conium maculatum (hemlock)

STRYCHNINE

'Then he brightened a little. His life, he reflected, might be wrecked, but he still had two thirds of Strychnine in the Soup *to read.'*

P G Wodehouse, Strychnine in the Soup, *1932*

Strychnine is a poisonous alkaloid found in the plant *Strychnos nux-vomica*, which is native to Myanmar, China, eastern India, Thailand and northern Australia. The tree is medium sized, with greenish-white flowers and orange fruit. The strychnine is derived from the large, disc-shaped dried seeds (called nux vomica) of the fruit.

Nux vomica was almost certainly known to the Persians and Arabs (as *kuchila*) as early as the fifth century AD. It arrived in Europe in the early sixteenth century, probably as a rodent poison, and was mentioned by the German Valerius Cordus (born 1515) in his *Dispensatorium* as a powerful emetic.

It was proposed as a cure for the plague, but it was soon discovered that the effects of the drug are cumulative: small doses, given regularly, would go unnoticed and end in death. This intriguing quality soon drew the attention of professional poisoners and others intent on getting rid of unwanted wives and rivals.

Difficult to trace it might be, but the death it delivered was horrible and easily recognisable. Strychnine—or nux vomica as it originally was called—is rapidly absorbed into the intestines and exerts its characteristic effects on the central nervous system. Victims have a sense of impending suffocation, convulsions, clenched hands, limbs are thrown out, temperature soars and hearing and sight become more acute. The convulsions become even more acute until death comes, caused by asphyxiation and exhaustion.

Many legendary poisoners of the sixteenth century used nux vomica, among them Hieronyma Spara, known as La Spara, who ran a school for poisoners in Rome, and Catherine Deshayes Monvoisin, known as La Voisin ('The Neighbour') who was burned as a sorcerer and poisoness in 1680.

The alkaloid strychnine was isolated from nux vomica in 1818 by the French chemists Caeniou and Pelletier from another plant in the *Strychnos* genus, *S. ignatii*, a native of the Philippines that had been introduced into Cochin-China (Vietnam), where it was highly esteemed as a medicine. The beans have the same qualities as *S. nux-vomica*. It took its name from the Jesuits, who valued it highly and used it as a medicine.

In eighteenth-century England, strychnine acquired the name 'inheritance powder', most likely because of its use by the notorious Thomas Griffiths Wainewright, poet, painter, friend of Charles Dickens and, by all accounts—although he was never found guilty of the crime—the poisoner of his uncle, his wife's mother and sister and others: all, apparently, with the aim of financial enrichment through inheritance. The poisonings could not be proven, so he was transported to Hobart on a charge of forgery, where he painted much admired portraits of local dignitaries and their families, and died in 1847.

In the nineteenth century, strychnine was used in small doses as a stimulant, a laxative and for labour pains, but is no longer used medically, except in homeopathic preparations such as nux vom. In some parts of the world it is still used as rodent poison, although not in Australia or America, where it is illegal.

But one place where strychnine is used abundantly in the modern world is in fiction: in 1921, Agatha Christie employed it to kill the victims in her first novel, *The Mysterious Affair at Styles*; in *Psycho*, Norman Bates killed his mother and her lover with a dose.

According to a report in *The Guardian* newspaper (30 June 2008), it almost killed Rolling Stones guitarist Keith Richards. 'Someone put strychnine in my dope', he said. 'It was in Switzerland. I was totally comatose but I was totally awake. I could listen to everyone, and they were like, "he's dead, he's dead", waving their fingers and pushing me about, and I was thinking, "I'm not dead!"' Curiously, seeing how rare it is these days, this sounds more like hemlock (see page 172) than strychnine.

Finally, according to Laurence Boyden, the son of Phar Lap's float driver, strychnine was the cause of the controversial death of that champion horse. He claims it was the strychnine and not the arsenic in a tonic fed to Phar Lap by his trainer and strapper Tommy Woodcock that killed the horse, and not, as long suspected by Australian punters, American gangsters. 'Even though they found arsenic in the hair tests, it might be more reasonable to think the strychnine was the more likely killer because there was greater room for error in the making of the preparation', Boyden was quoted as saying in an article in *The Australian* in 2006.

Strychnos nux-vomica (strychnine)

Psychoactive plants

Psychoactive plants

Psychoactive plants are those that possess the ability to alter mood, anxiety, behaviour, cognitive processes or mental tension—in other words, drugs, substances that humankind has used since the beginning of time.

'The universal human need for liberation from restrictions of mundane existence', writes social anthropologist Richard Rudgley in *Essential Substances*, 'is satisfied by experiencing altered states of consciousness'. And it has been thus since first we stood, walked, ate, grunted—and dreamed. The dream was our clue that not everything need be as it appears.

There are many plants that provide us with these experiences. They were first categorised, along with mind-altering drugs from other sources, by the German toxicologist Louis Lewin (1854–1929), and the classifications revised by ethno-botanist William Emboden in his 1972 book *Narcotic Plants*:

Inebriants: *substances causing inebriation, drunkenness. Mainly alcohol, but also ether, benzine and other solvents including glue and petrol.*

Hallucinogens: *substances causing acute visual, auditory hallucinations and visions. Includes all the psychoactive fungi, cannabis, peyote and other cacti, LSD, belladonna and a group of rare Amazonian plants.*

Hypnotics: *substances causing states of sleep, stupor or calm. These are the narcotics, including opium, heroin, mandrake, kava.*

Stimulants: *substances causing an increase in mental and/or physical stimulation not usually impairing the user's performance of daily tasks. Include tea, coffee, cocaine, tobacco, and the amphetamines [although not in their more modern forms like ice, re-crystallised methamphetamine hydrochloride which, while still a stimulant, will most emphatically impair the user's performance].*

There are obviously overlaps in this list— for example, cannabis could be classified both as an hallucinogen and a hypnotic— but it is a useful way of looking at the psychoactive plants.

Some commentators—including Rudgley—believe that Stone Age cultures used mind-altering substances. And, if we accept this, as the hunter-gatherer tasks were divided by gender, it's probable that the women of the tribe held the key to their use, giving rise to the female-dominated witchcraft tradition (see Atropine, page 138).

Close analysis of the visual patterns of prehistoric art offers evidence that it may have been inspired by the use of psychoactive plants. In the early fourth millennium BC, a new artefact appeared across Neolithic southern France that has been interpreted as being an opium-burning stand. One scholar, archaeologist Andrew Sharratt, asked: 'Is it a coincidence that the apparatus of the southern culture should appear at the same time as the Breton megalithic art reached its climax in the complex forms of the Gavrinis drawings?' This is a series of drawings of remarkably complex geometrical forms completed either in darkness or with the minimal aid of torches in caves in Brittany.

The later use of opium in the ancient world is well documented in writings from Egypt, Assyria and Greece. Its medical use as a sedative was known to the Egyptians, and Pliny the Elder recommended it for everything from snakebite to carbuncles. One study has suggested it was used in the Minoan civilisation in religious ritual—it is known that both Phoenicians and Minoans grew opium poppies and traded opium.

Similarly, hemp (see page 40) may have been grown for fibre and oil, but its psychoactive qualities would not have gone unnoticed. A 'pip-cup' containing charred hemp seeds was discovered in a third-millennium burial site in Romania.

Alcohol enters the scene somewhat later, in the fourth millennium, in Mesopotamia rather than Europe. The earliest alcoholic drinks were most likely made from dates, honey and sprouting grain. Could this later introduction of alcohol have been as shocking to people of the time, when the dominant drugs were opium and cannabis, as the reverse is today?

Sanctioned drug use has more to do with societal mores than with one drug being safer than another. And attitudes change. We have seen that most recently and acutely with tobacco. Until relatively recent times, tobacco was not only socially acceptable, but a desirable, almost compulsory adjunct to the sophisticated life. Opium and its derivatives were in daily use in Victorian England. While the idea of a drug being used in religious ritual may seem offensive to some today, in India, cannabis is used in the devotions of Hindus. And we tend to forget that at the centre of the Christian ritual is alcohol.

Whether we like them or not, the psychoactive substances will not go away, as attested to by the fact that every decade or so, new ones enter into use: LSD, PCP, crack cocaine, ecstasy, ice.

Why do people take drugs? It feels good. When asked, in 2001, by *New York* magazine whether he had ever tried marijuana, businessman and future Mayor of New York Michael Bloomberg said, 'You bet I did. And I enjoyed it'. It feels good, until, as often happens, the drug moves from the sidelines of the user's life to the centre, and then becomes their reason for being. Then it feels bad.

Drug abuse is rife in poor communities, and rich ones. The essential difference between the ghetto dweller snorting crack cocaine and the wealthy executive drinking a bottle of expensive whisky every night has more to do with money than the superiority of one drug over another. As Frank Zappa said, 'They're just substances, Man'.

So far, the 'war on drugs' has done little but create entire economies dependent on the manufacture and sale of drugs, massive corruption of public officials, and massive hypocrisy globally. While admitting to his marijuana use, Mayor Bloomberg continued the hard line on cannabis use. The CIA deals in heroin to support its 'allies'. And, in Queensland in Australia, a blind eye is turned towards cannabis plantations because their closure would wreak havoc on the local economy. We have yet to come to terms with our ancient need for altered states of consciousness.

COCA

'Cocaine isn't habit forming. I should know—I've been using it for years.'
Tallulah Bankhead (1902–1968), American actress

Sigmund Freud hailed it as a wonder drug. In Spanish Harlem, young women prostitute themselves for it. In law offices in New York and Chicago, young lawyers take it to work harder and play harder. In Hollywood, parties were not seen as a success unless there was a big bowl of the stuff on the middle of the room. Yet, in Bolivia, where it originates, its effects are compared to those of a strong cup of coffee.

These are all examples of the effects of the active alkaloid found in the leaves of the plant *Erythroxylum coca*, a native of the Andean highlands of Peru, Bolivia and Ecuador. And while it may not be a wonder drug, it is certainly one whose wondrous—or hideous—effects depend very much on how it is processed.

E. coca is a woody shrub that grows up to 3 metres (10 feet) in height, with golden-green tapered leaves and a yellowish-white flower which fruits to a red berry. It requires little irrigation, is drought resistant and can be harvested three, even four times a year. For these reasons—and in modern times the high demand for its leaves—it is very attractive to peasant cultivators, notwithstanding efforts by the US government agencies to move them onto other crops, such as coffee.

In coca's homelands, the raw leaves are chewed, or rather placed in a wad between gums and cheek with a little lime (from the ashes of quinoa leaves) to help release the alkaloids. There, it is used to alleviate hunger and thirst and to battle fatigue—local truck drivers are big users, getting through about 56 grams (2 ounces) of leaves a day.

The leaves have been chewed in much the same way, and for much the same reasons, since at least the sixth century AD and during the following Inca period. Mummies dating from that time have been found with supplies of coca leaves for the afterlife. The Incas believed the plant to have been a gift of the gods, and its use was restricted to the ruling classes, its cultivation a state monopoly.

When the Spanish arrived, they made sure that the slaves who worked the gold mines had ample supplies to keep them hard at work. Phillip II of Spain issued a decree declaring it essential to the wellbeing of the natives, but attempted to suppress its use in indigenous religious rites.

The leaves contain only from 0.2 to 0.9 per cent of the active alkaloid and don't travel well, so when they first arrived in Europe, coca was seen merely as a curiosity—until chemists managed to isolate the alkaloid. This was achieved in 1855 by a German chemist, Friederich Gaedke, who gave the compound the totally unmarketable name erythroxyline. In 1859, an improved purification process was described by Albert Niemann who gave his creation the infinitely sexier name of cocaine.

Yet it had to wait until the mid 1880s to gain commercial success, when it was first used in eye surgery. Surgeons welcomed it because patients under cocaine were still able to move their eyes as instructed (although, cocaine being what it is, probably only if they felt like moving them).

In 1884 an army physician, Theodor Aschenbrandt, conducted an experiment with soldiers of the Bavarian army, in which it was noted that their endurance was improved substantially after using it. Aschenbrandt published a paper on the experiment in a German medical journal, where it caught the interest of the young Sigmund Freud (1856–1939), who ordered his first cocaine the same year, and immediately became a cocaine enthusiast, if not an addict. He wrote several papers on its use, most notably '*Über Coca*', in which he sang its praises unreservedly, noting it produced 'exhilaration and lasting euphoria, which in no way differs from the normal euphoria of the healthy person … Absolutely no craving for the further use of cocaine appears after the first, or even repeated taking of the drug'.

Cocaine soon joined opium as an over-the-counter commodity. It was prescribed to counter morphine addiction, but, sadly, one addiction often joined the other. Until 1916, it was sold at Harrods in a kit labelled 'A Welcome Present for Friends at The Front', along with morphine, syringes and spare needles.

By the 1920s, cocaine use was so popular among the smart set on both sides of the Atlantic that Cole Porter could write, in his song 'I Get a Kick Out of You':

Some get a kick from cocaine.
I'm sure that if I took even one sniff
That would bore me terrific'ly too.
Yet I get a kick out of you …

But the real problems with cocaine abuse did not emerge until the late twentieth century. It came to be seen as the ideal drug, first for a hedonistic, self-centred and sexually adventurous section of society, and then for a marginalised, poverty-stricken and unemployed one.

The former group, the Greed Generation, was exemplified by Michael Douglas playing Gordon Gekko in the 1987 film *Wall Street*. The main attraction of cocaine for these high achievers was the feeling of omnipotence and the intense sexual high it gives—at first. After repeated use, the high provided by the drug becomes more intense than any high provided by sex, and eventually replaces it. The fallout from cocaine addiction in this period was high, with many formerly wealthy addicts losing everything—including their septum, that fine wall between the nostrils, which is eroded by constant sniffing.

During this time, cocaine became—and continues to be—an integral part of the world economy, and became embroiled in global politics. According to now declassified CIA papers, profits from cocaine sold in Los Angeles and Miami were used by the CIA to fund arms purchases for the anti-communist contra rebels in Nicaragua. In 1994, US consumption of cocaine was 250 tonnes annually, Europe's 150–200 tonnes and Brazil's 50 tonnes. In 2005, the United Nations estimated the global cocaine market at $US70.45 billion.

But the real problems in cocaine abuse arose with the advent of freebase in also smokeable crack cocaine, a form of the drug made from cocaine hydrochloride chemically treated with ammonia or baking soda—and much simpler and cheaper to make than freebase, which is processed with ether. Crack is indissoluble in water and smoked from pipes, or mixed with either tobacco or marijuana and smoked in a joint—the name 'crack' comes from the sound it makes when it's heated.

The euphoric rush of crack comes within seconds, orgasm is intensified and a feeling of omnipotence and all-powerfulness is reported. But this lasts only 30 to 90 minutes, and so powerful is the feeling that another hit is desperately sought, with depression and acute anxiety the result if this can't be found.

The US 2006 National Survey on Drug Use and Health (NSDUH) reported that approximately 8.6 million Americans aged 12 or older—3.5 per cent of the population—said they had tried crack cocaine at least once during their lifetimes. Additional 2006 NSDUH data indicate that approximately 1.5 million (0.6 per cent) reported crack cocaine use in the preceding year, and 702,000 (0.3 per cent) reported use in the preceding month.

As crack is cheaper than 'regular' cocaine, it became known as 'the poor man's drug' and spread with resulting devastation through the poor African-American and Hispanic populations of large American cities.

Crack cocaine and its attendant global and local problems are a far cry from the Bolivian truck driver with a wad of coca leaves in his mouth keeping him awake and alert for the long haul. It is the classic example of a drug altering its nature when removed from its cultural context.

Following pages: *Erythroxylum coca* (coca)

DRINKING WINE AND COCA COLA

In 1863, the Corsican entrepreneur and chemist Angelo Mariani launched Vin Mariani, one of a number of coca wines that came on the market in the late nineteenth century. But Signor Mariani's concoction was a runaway success and left the rest of the pack behind. His first customer, a depressed actress, was so grateful she told all her friends. Then Mariani himself wrote a book, which was actually a hymn of praise to the glories of coca—he himself was a devotee of the plant and a collector of Inca coca artefacts.

Vin Mariani became a favourite of the artists, writers and intellectuals of the time: Jules Verne, Robert Louis Stephenson and Emile Zola loved it and praised it, as did the composers Massenet, Gounod and Fauré. And then there was royalty—the Shah of Persia, Queen Victoria and King George I of Greece.

But the highest praise for Vin Mariani came from His Holiness Pope Leo XIII, who carried a personal hip flask to fortify himself in time of need. He awarded a Vatican gold medal to the pharmacist and businessman. Mariani was one of the first entrepreneurs to see the benefits of celebrity endorsement—and His Holiness duly appeared in an advertisement for his beverage.

The success of Vin Mariani was the inspiration for John Pemberton, also a pharmacist and a keen connoisseur of coca. Atlanta-born Pemberton's goal was to combine medicine and a refreshing and delicious drink in one formula. In 1885 he launched Pemberton's French Wine Coca, improving on Mariani's drink by adding the kola nut, which provided the kick of caffeine. He claimed, with some truth, that it was 'a most wonderful invigorator of the sexual organs' and, moreover, 'an intellectual beverage'.

Unfortunately, Prohibition arrived in the state of Georgia in 1886, and Mr Pemberton had to re-jig his formula and remove the alcohol to satisfy the law. His French Wine Cola became 'Coca-Cola: the temperance drink'.

In 1887, Pemberton, now stricken with cancer, sold two thirds of the rights to the formula for Coca-Cola to Willis Venables and George Lowndes, keeping a third interest. 'The only thing I have is Coca-Cola', he wrote at the time, adding, 'Coca-Cola some day will be a national drink. I want to keep a third interest in it so that my son will always have a living'. Tragically, son Charley died from a morphine overdose only six years later.

In 1904, bowing to the moral panic at the time about drug abuse, the manufacturers removed the cocaine from Coca-Cola, but, after a protracted fight with the Government, retained the right to keep the 'Coca' in the name.

GRAPES

'The vine bears three kinds of grapes: the first of pleasure,
the second of intoxication, the third of disgust.'

Diogenes (c. 412–323 BC), Greek philosopher and founder of the philosophical school, the Cynics

If not humankind's oldest drug (that distinction probably remains with opium), alcohol, in its various forms, is certainly the most popular, at least in Western culture. And alcohol in the form of wine—the most pervasive of the alcoholic drinks (along with beer; see page 46)—is simply the by-product of the fermentation of grapes with a little help from yeast (see page 119).

Before we approach the story of wine itself, the word alcohol has an interesting etymology. Originally from the Arabic *al-kuhul*—meaning kohl, that fine metallic powder (still) used by both men and women in Arabic countries to darken the eyelids. *Al* is the definite article in Arabic. In English, alcohol originally meant 'powdered cosmetic'. In 1672 the definition broadened to 'the pure spirit of anything', which was one part of the phrase 'alcohol of wine'. The first use of the word in the modern sense of 'the intoxicating element in fermented liquors' is recorded in 1753. In 1850, it was extended to organic chemistry to include that class of compounds of that same sense. It was a short wait—1852—for 'alcoholism' and another thirty-nine years, 1891, before we got 'alcoholic'. There is an irony in the word's origin in a language whose speakers are proscribed from using it.

Here we are primarily interested in the cultivated wine grape, *Vitis vinifera*, although there are other members of the genus *Vitis*. The fruit of the vine grows in various colours from almost black through to purple, red, pink, brown and 'white' (in reality, green). There are at least 2000 grape varieties, but many of these are 'clones', or at least variations, of an original European variety. For example, it was thought for many years that the grape variety Zinfandel, grown extensively in America, was an indigenous American variety, but DNA testing confirmed that it is identical to the Italian grape Primitivo. Sorting through these conundrums is the work of ampelographers, experts in the study and classification of grapevines.

The existence of these clones and variants impresses upon the wine lover the truism that wine is grown in the vineyard: the soil and climatic conditions give each vine its individual character.

But the grape grew wild across the central part of the Northern Hemisphere long before the cultivation of *V. vinifera*, long before the continents split apart—the American grapevines are ancestors from that time.

It is impossible to pinpoint the 'invention' of wine, but archaeologists, by studying sites where an accumulation of pips has been found, are able to identify those where the vine was first cultivated. The earliest such remains confirmed as being from cultivated vines are in present-day Georgia, where carbon dating places the pips at 7000–5000 BC. Excavations in Turkey, Syria and Iran, while dated earlier (8000 BC), are not as conclusive.

Another piece of evidence for the early existence of wine in Georgia is a squat clay jar called a *kvevri* held in the museum at Tbilisi, which scientists have dated to between 6000 and 5000 BC. Aside from resembling the wine jars of the ancient Greeks (*pithos*), it has, on its sides, little knobs that could easily be interpreted as bunches of grapes.

Wine is one of the most important products of civilisation—some might say the most civilised of all of humankind's creations. As people began to settle, farm and congregate in villages and towns, from the end of the sixth millennium BC to the middle of the fourth, wine began its move south, from its origins around the Black Sea and the Persian Gulf through Asia Minor and into Egypt.

As trade contacts were being made between the peoples of the Mediterranean (first recorded in the third millenium BC), both vine and wine reached Crete, probably from Egypt or Phoenicia. The Greek word for wine, *oïnos*—and the root of the word 'wine' itself—is from the Cretan dialect. From Crete, wine moved to Greece, Sicily, southern Italy, Libya, into southern Europe and eventually to India through Persia. It then came back to Britain and eventually spread all the way north, although vines were not planted in Norway—in glass hothouses—until the eighteenth century.

'The Greeks did not actually invent wine', writes Maguelonne Toussaint-Samat in *History of Food*. 'They did even better, in making the god Dionysus its patron, they immortalized it.' Dionysus (Bacchus to the Romans) was also the god of agriculture and the theatre, and also known as 'the liberator', inducing madness and frenzy against order and discipline.

Wine's impact on the ancient and the Judaeo-Christian worlds was powerful. The ninth chapter of Genesis mentions that Noah disembarks from the ark, plants a vineyard and becomes drunk on the wine produced. The curiosity of this story is that there was no mention of wine or vines in the Bible before Noah and, as pointed out by Toussaint-Samat, all the legends of the invention of wine 'follow on from tales of great floods of water'.

In the Fertile Crescent the annual festival of the New Year, which was also a celebration of revival after the Flood, was accompanied by much toasting in honour of the Sailor of the New Wine.

The arrival of *V. vinifera* in China is well documented. The vines came via Persia in 128 BC, brought back by General Chang Chen from Fergana, a country east of Samarkand.

The Egyptians became enthusiastic wine drinkers—although beer preceded wine, as it did in most of the ancient world, as the preferred drink of intoxication. The

Festival of the New Moon and the Festival of the Full Moon were both occasions for unbridled drinking—indeed, the New Moon Festival was the one in which the common people were allowed to drink wine, it being reserved for the priests and the aristocracy at other times.

Drunkenness was not particularly frowned upon by the ancients; on the contrary, it was often seen as an essential part of religious worship. The Greek word for ritual intoxication is *enthousiasmos*, meaning divine possession. The cult of Dionysus forgave acts of folly committed in his name.

The Bible, unlike the Qur'an, does not proscribe wine. Indeed, there are many quotations that acknowledge and openly accept it. 'Go thy way, eat thy bread with joy and drink thy wine with a merry heart' says Ecclesiastes 9:7, and 'Drink no longer water, but use a little wine for thy stomach's sake and thine often infirmities', we are advised by Paul in the First Epistle to Timothy 5:24. Although Noah is not admonished for his inebriated state, Ham is severely punished for broadcasting his father's drunken nakedness to his brothers. And, as mentioned elsewhere, the transubstantiation of wine is at the heart of the mystery of the Communion: 'Drink, this is my blood'.

The vine arrived in southern Italy from Greece, and, although vines were grown by the Etruscans in present-day Tuscany, they, too, probably came from the east. The Etruscans were also probably in Burgundy, selling wine, before the Greeks. But after the defeat of Carthage in the Punic Wars (264–146 BC), the Romans turned seriously towards agriculture—and viticulture. In *The History of Wine*, Hugh Johnson points to 171 BC as an important date for the vinification of the empire: that was the year that the first commercial bakery opened in Rome. Before that, the Romans ate porridge (*puls*); from then

on, it was bread and wine. The Romans expanded their authority over the Greek vineyards in the south, and by the time of the Emperor Augustus (27 BC–14 AD) the wine industry was well established across Italy. There was even a well-established great vintage of a first-growth wine: the 121 BC Opimian Falernian, a white wine made from Amineum grapes. Opimius was the consul that year, and Falernum a vineyard on the borders of Latium and Campania.

Augustan wine was sweet and strong, often cooked and usually diluted—like most wine of the time—with water, even seawater. In spite of this, the Romans were discriminating drinkers and put much effort into making their wines. They and the Greeks traded wines with each other. The two Roman wine centres were Rome and Pompeii; Johnson calls the latter 'the Bordeaux of Roman Italy'.

By the last days of the Roman Empire, wine was plentiful and cheap—too much so. Owning vineyards became a gentleman's pursuit; there was no money in them. In 250 AD, a kind of a tax was imposed as a disincentive. Each grower was obliged to deliver a certain amount of wine for the army, and to supply the populace with subsidised drink, the only payment being the transport. Many wine growers ripped out their vines. To counter this, in 280 AD the Emperor Probus set the army to building new vineyards in Gaul and along the Danube. But by now the decline had set in; the barbarians were at the gate. The final irony of this story is that Probus was murdered in a vineyard on the Danube near his birthplace, Sirmium, in present-day Croatia.

The cradle of wine culture in the modern world is France, but how did the vine get there? Was it, as is generally believed, brought by the Romans, or did the Gauls have a pre-existing wine culture? It has been argued by some historians—though not convincingly—

Vitis vinifera (grape vine)

that the stone-age inhabitants of present-day France cultivated the grape. More likely, they fell upon the Roman wine with great gusto, as they had enjoyed Carthaginian wine before it.

But plantings on French soils had to wait until Julius Caesar won the Gallic Wars (58–51 BC). The sixty fractious Gallic tribes were more or less subdued and under Roman rule—and civilisation. Bordeaux, the site of the first plantings, had a wine trade with Britain and Ireland in the first century AD. Their own vines were most likely planted around 43 AD, when Claudius conquered Britain. Pliny recorded the vineyards of Bordeaux in 71 AD. Bordeaux was not a promising agricultural region, but it did offer a good river port, and a well-established market for wines. But with typical Roman thoroughness and a good application of manure, vines eventually flourished. And so the vine spread through France: north to Gaillac (the most northerly point, they thought, that vines would grow), the Rhône Valley, the Côte Rôtie, the Côte d'Or—and so on.

With the defeat of Carthage in 200 BC, the Romans gained the coastal parts of Spain, and inherited the Carthaginian plantings in what is today Tarragona and Andalusia. The wine was described as ordinary, except that from Ceret, called Ceretanum, which was a favourite of the first-century poet Martial. Today, we know Ceret as Jerez de la Frontera, the home of sherry.

While wine was, if not embraced, at least tolerated and at best incorporated into ritual by Christianity, it is proscribed by Islam. Its prophet, Mohammed (570–632), was born just as the Roman Empire was crumbling, in Mecca, where wine was a normal part of life. Within ten years of his death, it was totally banned for the followers of the religion he founded, although one of the earlier books of the Qur'an, dictated to him by the angel

Gabriel read in part: 'We give you the fruits of the palm and the vine, from which you derive intoxicants and wholesome food'. But a drunken incident in Medina involving his disciples turned him totally against wine—although he continued to drink an alcoholic drink made from dates, *nabidh*, and his favourite wife, Ayesha, quoted him as saying 'you may drink, but do not get drunk'. Today, the proscription of wine for Muslims is as powerful as it was in 642, in spite of such anomalies as the poetry of the Persian Omar Khayyam, whose *Rubaiyat* praises the vine and the wine, especially in this, the most famous verse (from Edward Fitzgerald's 1859 translation):

Here with a Loaf of Bread beneath
*   the Bough,*
A Flask of Wine, a Book of Verse—and thou
Beside me singing in the Wilderness—
And Wilderness is paradise enow.

But Omar Khayyam was not the only transgressor: the ruling classes loved their wine, as did the sybarites attached to the court of the Abassid caliphs (750–1258 AD) in Baghdad, where leisurely banquets followed by long discussions over copious cups were the norm.

At the fall of the Roman Empire, around 400 AD, the wine regions of France were fixed pretty much as they are today, and continued producing and exporting. In Bordeaux, then as now, they grew what was then called the Biturigia grape, today's Cabernet Sauvignon; in the north, the Allobrogrien, almost certainly today's Pinot Noir; and in the Midi, Muscat, among others. At this time, Italian wines were seen as superior to French.

The invasions of the Teutons, Visigoths, Vandals and Huns caused disruption to all western European agriculture, but with renewed peace, the monasteries took over the revival of viticulture and, later, under the Franks,

the Salic Law (from around 500 AD) forbade the digging up of vines.

Between the tenth and twelfth centuries, famines, peasant uprisings and banditry played havoc with European life in general and agriculture in particular—and the vineyards suffered. The returning Crusaders brought back new species from Corinth and Cyprus. The Hundred Years War (1337–1453) was devastating for all the provinces of France, but prosperity returned under Charles II. At the end of each period of fighting in Europe, the recovery improved the trade in wines, until it became one of the three pillars of medieval business, along with spices from the East and Flemish cloth.

In Spain, the Arab conquest in 711 AD cut trade for some time, but the prosperity in al-Andalus, as the Moors called their part of southern Spain, soon resulted in a civilisation easily the most advanced in Europe. In the matter of wine, these Spanish Muslims followed Omar Khayyam. The south was well furnished with vineyards. But as the Reconquista (the gradual resumption of lands by the Christian rulers) continued, vineyards were planted all across Spain. By the thirteenth century—still a good 200 years before the final expulsion of the Arabs from Granada in 1492—all the inhabited parts of Spain grew wine grapes, with the exception of the mountainous north. The town of Jerez in the south (formerly Ceret) became Jerez de la Frontera and eventually fell to the Christians under Alfonso X—there are sherry families to this day, such as the Valdespinos, who can trace their lineage back to the reconquistadors. Spain continues to this day to produce wines right across the peninsula.

The next major moves for wine culture were to the New World: North and South America, South Africa and Australia.

Vines were first planted in the Cape of Good Hope in South Africa in 1654.

Salt-damaged during the voyage, they didn't take. But next year's cuttings, from Germany, France, Spain and Bohemia, did. As the Dutch East India Company had no plans for vineyards in the Cape—rice for their slaves was the first priority—the further development of vineyards had to wait until later in the seventeenth century, and a new commander of the colony, Simon van der Stel. He brought a French winegrower with him and planted vines on his huge estate, Constantia, near the new settlement of Stellenbosch, in the 1680s. The red wine he grew there, Constantia, received lavish praise in Europe. That was the foundation of the now flourishing South African wine industry.

The first vines in Australia were planted by Captain Arthur Phillip, the first governor of the penal colony, within nine months of landing at Farm Cove in 1788, where Sydney's Royal Botanic Gardens are now situated. But the early days of the colony were chaotic and rum-soaked, and nothing came of these plantings. Success in winemaking was left to John Macarthur, formerly the paymaster of the Rum Corps and also a pioneer in Australia's lucrative wool industry. He planted his vines at Camden Park, west of Sydney, in 1815, having collected them from France, Madeira and the Cape. He subsequently won medals in Europe for his wines, as did the explorer Gregory Blaxland in the 1820s with wines he made at his farm on the Parramatta River 24 kilometres (14 miles) inland from Sydney.

By the 1830s, and beginning with the Hunter Valley north of Sydney, vines were planted in most of the winemaking regions still producing today. For many years, however, the majority of wines made in Australia were fortified, with the taste for good red and white table wines only developing in the latter part of the twentieth century.

Two distinct types of wine were produced in America: those made from the native grapes, *V. labrusca* and the curious scuppernong of Florida (*V. rotundifolia*, a type of muscadine), and those made using imported European stock. The first to plant European grapes in North America was one of America's founding fathers, William Penn (1644–1718). Planted sometime after 1683, his 200 acres (80 hectares) perished, proving that the north-east coast (in this instance Pennsylvania) was no place for vines.

In the 1770s, Thomas Jefferson experimented with European grapes, but eventually decided that the 'fox grape' (*V. labrusca*), despite its 'foxy' flavour, was the best for American wines. He also used the scuppernong grape, from which wine was usually made with the addition of brandy.

Although not much fancied as a wine grape, *V. labrusca* has been the saviour of wine industries around the world. When the phylloxera louse, which attacks the roots of the vine, appeared in Europe in the mid-nineteenth century, vine-growing regions were devastated. When growers discovered that *V. labrusca* was resistant to the louse, grafting scions of European vine varieties to its phylloxera-resistant *V. labrusca* root stock gradually became the norm. The irony was that the American vines were resistant to the louse because the louse came from America. As the Montpellier chemist and Darwinist Gaston Fouex argued, if the phylloxera were a European bug, it would have wiped out all the vines long before. It was the professor of pharmacy at Montpellier University, and one of the discoverers of the infestation in Europe in 1868, who, during tours of American vineyards in 1869 and 1873, confirmed that phylloxera was a native of eastern America. American rootstock has since proved the saviour of vines in Australia, New Zealand and California.

Long before the phylloxera disaster, California had proved to be the wine region of North America. Franciscan monks had made wine in their chain of 21 missions stretching from San Diego to San Francisco Bay since the early 1780s, using a grape they had brought from Europe, which they called Mission (called in South America Criolla), much of which was distilled as spirit for its keeping qualities.

In 1833, the Mexican government (then in control of California) secularised the missions, and the first secular wine was made in Los Angeles by an immigrant from Bordeaux, Jean Louis Vignes. From that beginning—where Union station now stands—grew the now prodigious Californian wine industry.

When the South American colonies declared themselves independent of Spain one after another in the 1820s, they began making their own wine, with that of Peru being, at first, the most favoured. In Chile, however, one Don Silvestre Ochagavia Errurariz, of a Basque family, was the pioneer in the nascent industry there in the 1850s, firstly by employing a French oenologist and secondly by introducing vines from Bordeaux including Cabernet, Merlot, Malbec and others. Argentina was not far behind, and Don Tiburcio Benegas is credited with the first modern vineyards dating from the 1880s. Today, Spanish winemakers like Torres have bought vineyards in South America and make wines there for the domestic and export markets.

We could just as easily have written histories of Cognac, Armagnac or any of the great liqueurs—indeed any of the distilled spirits that began to appear in Europe from around the end of the fifteenth century. But that would have required far more space than this book allows. And ultimately, it is the history of wine that is inextricably intertwined with human civilisation.

OPIUM

*'Everything one does in life, even love, occurs in an express train racing to death.
To smoke opium is to get out of the train while it is still moving. It is to concern
oneself with something other than death.'*

Jean Cocteau, The Diary of a Cure, 1958

Is there any drug so loved and reviled, so useful and dangerous as that made from the sap of the pretty poppy *Papaver somniferum*? In its various forms, it is used as an anaesthetic, a poison, an aphrodisiac, a deliverer of dreams, palliative relief for the terminally ill, to finance wars and revolutions, and as a reliable cash crop for peasant farmers. It is, according to historians, the first psychoactive substance used by humankind.

Its botanical name derives from the Greek word for poppy, *papaver*, and the Latin for sleep-inducing, *somniferum*. The plant is an annual with four-petalled white, pink, mauve through to deep red flowers that are short lived, dropping in a couple of days to reveal a round pod the size of a large pea. This grows rapidly to an egg shape with a diameter of 5–7 centimetres (2–3 inches), surmounted by a small crown.

The laborious harvest is carried out about two weeks after petal fall. A specialised knife is used to cut lightly into the pod (this is known as scoring, lancing, or tapping) in the late afternoon in the hope that opium sap will ooze out and coagulate on the pod. The cloudy white sap oxidises to a dark brown, sticky, viscous substance with a delicate perfume. It is then scraped from the pod with the knife, now moistened to stop the opium from sticking to its blade. Farmers who moisten the blade by licking it rather than dipping it in water soon become addicted.

The pod will continue to secrete opium for days, and may be tapped up to half a dozen times with an average of 80 milligrams (0.002 ounces) per pod, producing 8–5 kilograms (17–33 pounds) per hectare (2.5 acres). The sticky opium is processed, first by cooking it in boiling water, then straining it and boiling it again to produce a clean brown fluid that is left to simmer until it a thick paste forms. Once this is dried, the opium is ready for the addict, the trader or the laboratory.

Today, in most areas where the plant is commercially or legally grown, the opium-tapping stage is avoided and the pods are dried (in which form they are known as poppy straw) and processed to make morphine, codeine and thebaine. A by-product of this process is poppy seeds, used in the food industry and in salad oil.

Opium itself is a cocktail of sugars, proteins, latex, gums, acids and more than fifty alkaloids, including codeine, morphine, noscapine and the baine. Scientists are mystified by the large number of alkaloids in this flower, and several reasons are offered for their presence. Are they there to repel insects? To form the seeds? Or, most contentiously, to ensure continued cultivation by humans?

Opium can be swallowed, smoked, injected, sniffed, inhaled or absorbed through mucous membranes. It has been eaten in India for 1500 years, where it is said that the worse it tastes, the better it works. The Turks disguised the taste with spices such as cardamom and nutmeg.

As noted in the introduction to this section, there is a good case to be made for opium having been used since prehistoric times. More than a dozen Neolithic sites have been excavated containing *Papaver somniferum* remains in various forms, including poppy seeds at the entrance to a burial site in Spain dated to 4200 BC. In 3400 BC, poppies were being cultivated in lower Mesopotamia, and the Sumerians called it *hul gil*, joy plant. By the end of the second millennium BC it was known and cultivated across Europe, the Middle East and North Africa.

During that time doctors considered it a cure for practically every ailment. The earliest discovery of opium was in an Egyptian tomb dating to the fifteenth century BC. Thebes was famous for its

Papaver somniferum (opium poppy)

opium—indeed one of the alkaloids, thebaine, is named after it. Opium was commonplace in ancient Greece, where it was used both medicinally and spiritually. There are some who say it was used in Eleusis as part of the Eleusian Mysteries, ceremonies held every year for the cult of Demeter and Persephone. In a clay statuette from Gazi in Crete, the Minoan poppy goddess wears the seed capsules, sources of nourishment and narcosis, in her diadem. It is known that in that cult sphere, opium was prepared from poppies.

The Romans, inevitably, used it as a poison, and Agrippina, the Emperor Claudius' last wife, used it to kill her stepson, Britannicus, so that her own son Nero would inherit.

But it was the Arabs who spread the use of opium. They had been using it as a painkiller since Egyptian times, and over time, developed its production and trade. By the ninth century, scholars and doctors were writing extensively about it, especially the famous Persian polymath of his time, Abu Ali al-Hussein ibn Aboud Allah ibn Sina, know in the European world as Avicenna (908–1037 AD). In his book *The Canon of Medicine*, he described it as the most powerful of the stupefacients, described its value in treating dysentery, diarrhoea and eye disease, and in his poetry he sang its praises. It is said that he died of an overdose.

When the Arab Empire faded, opium was taken up by the Venetians, who imported it from the Middle East along with spices: Cabot, Magellan and Da Gama were all asked to bring opium back from their travels.

The Swiss-born physician, alchemist and astrologer Phillip von Hohenheim, better known in his time as Paracelsus (1493–1541), developed a secret remedy that included 25 per cent opium mixed with henbane, crushed pearls and coral. He wrote, 'I possess a secret remedy which I call laudanum and which is superior to all other heroic remedies'. In Europe and England it was used extensively for its anaesthetic qualities.

In the 1660s, an English physician, Thomas Sydenham (1624–1689), used the name laudanum for a tincture of opium and alcohol, which became the main form the drug was taken in the nineteenth century—usually mixed with red wine or port.

By the nineteenth century, there were scores of proprietary medicines containing opium, and almost every doctor had his own laudanum recipe. These included Mrs Winslow's Soothing Syrup and Atkinson's Infant Preservative, both containing around one gram of opium per fluid ounce. Poor mothers who were working long hours, left their children with minders, who would feed them the syrups. Then, when the mothers came home exhausted, they fed them the syrups again. A convenient side effect for the poor was that opium suppresses the appetite. During this time, one chemist in Long Sutton, Lincolnshire (population 6000) sold 85 litres (22½ gallons) of his tincture of opium a year. And he was not the only chemist in town.

In nineteenth century Europe, Britain and America, opium was used the way aspirin and paracetamol are used today. Between 1831 and 1859, imports of opium to England rose from 41,300 kilograms (91,000 pounds) to 127,000 kilograms (280,000 pounds). And, although the English grew poppies extensively in India, most of the imports came from Turkey.

It is important to keep the opiate use of the times in perspective with contemporary health problems. Mortality from cholera, malaria and dysentery was high, and opiates provided some relief from these illnesses (opiates remain one of the most effective treatments for dysentery). It has been suggested that the ready availability of the opium-based medicines saved more lives than it took. However, as the deleterious effects of chronic opiate use became increasingly recognised during the late nineteenth century, several factors helped ease the need for it: improvements in sanitation, drainage of swamp lands, and the introduction of acetylsalicylic acid (aspirin) in 1899 provided an alternative for moderate pain relief.

The first steps to control the availability of opium in England was the introduction of the Poisons and Pharmacy Act in 1868, which stated that only registered doctors could dispense the drug, and that chemists were only the purveyors—although patent medicines containing opium were not covered.

The first restriction in the Americas came in the form of the Californian Opium Den Ordinance of 1875, which was as much an anti-Chinese measure as anything. This was followed by an 1891 Californian law requiring narcotics carry a warning label, and an amendment in 1907 of the same state's Pharmacy and Poisons Act making it a crime to sell opiates without a prescription.

By the end of the nineteenth century, the rule of opium was clearly on the wane. But by then, chemists had begun work on isolating the active alkaloids. The first to succeed was Freidrich Wilhelm Adam Sertürner (1783–1841), then a chemist's assistant from Westphalia. In 1806 he published the results of his long research resulting in the isolation of an alkaloid from opium in the journal *Der Pharmacie*: he called it morphium, after Morpheus, the Greek god of dreams. We now know it as morphine. Others built on his discovery and by the 1820s, morphine was commercially available in Western Europe.

The next breakthrough was the ability to inject a solution containing an opiate. The first to do so was a Dr G V Lafargue of St Emilion in France who, in 1836, used a lancet dipped in morphine solution. The next step, the glass syringe, soon followed. In 1853, in Edinburgh, Dr Alexander Wood (1817–1884) published a paper outlining his method of injecting. A tragic footnote to this event is that his wife was the first recorded fatality from an injected overdose of morphine. Independently of Dr Wood, the French doctor Charles Pravaz (1791–1853) added a fine hollow needle to the syringe.

The widespread use of injections at this time was allied to the belief that morphine, unlike opium, was not addictive. This led to what was known as 'morphinism', and it became a pastime among the wealthy to have daily injections of morphine—even after its dangers were recognised. The other aspect of injection was that the dosage was higher: taking 20 ounces of laudanum a day delivered two grains of the opiate; injecting morphine meant some were taking the equivalent of 40 grains a day.

Injectable morphine proved a huge boon during wartime. Wounded soldiers could be treated without anaesthetic, and pain relief was more effective. It was also administered orally and in huge amounts daily to the troops against malaria and diarrhoea. It was used extensively in the American Civil War and the Crimean War. Many soldiers returned home addicted.

Recognising the problems that arose with the use of morphine, work began to find a more powerful non-addictive substitute. In 1874, C R Alder Wright, an English chemist, boiled morphine with acetic anhydride, naming the result diacetylmorphine.

But it wasn't until 1889 that a German chemist, Heinrich Dreser, working at Bayer Laboratories, began producing this compound. After clinical testing it proved to be a powerful painkiller. Bayer mass-marketed it under the name Heroin. Unfortunately for humanity, it was not only easy to make, but highly addictive. From 1898 through to 1910, Bayer marketed the drug as a non-addictive morphine substitute and a children's cough suppressant. It wasn't long before its highly addictive qualities were apparent. After World War I, Bayer lost some of their trademark rights to Heroin, and in 1924, the United States Congress banned the sale, importation or manufacture of the drug.

Starting in the 1970s, heroin became the predominant street drug of addiction in the West. Production centred on the Golden Triangle in Burma and, increasingly, Afghanistan, where it was reported in 2006 (by the UK's *The Financial Times*) that 92 per cent, or 6100 tonnes, of the world's heroin is made as a result of the Taliban-led insurgency in the southern part of the country.

According to the 2006 US National Survey on Drug Use and Health (NSDUH), approximately 3.8 million Americans aged 12 or older reported trying heroin at least once during their lifetimes, representing 1.5 per cent of that population group. Approximately 560,000 (0.2 per cent) reported past-year heroin use and 338,000 (0.1 per cent) reported past-month heroin use.

Today, Tasmania, in Australia, is the world's largest legal producer of opium alkaloids for the pharmaceutical market, producing 50 per cent of the world's concentrated poppy straw on 20,000 hectares (49,000 acres) of land.

It is unlikely that the problem will ever go away, heroin being the most profitable enterprise ever devised. Some figures from the American Drug Enforcement Agency:

- *Raw opium from the Shan States in Myanmar: $66–75 a kilogram*
- *Processed heroin in Bangkok: $6000–$10,000 a kilogram*
- *Same heroin in United States when cut and sold by the gram on the street: $940,000–$1,400,000 a kilogram.*

With such monstrous profits to be made, the trade will not stop, and governments will have to find alternatives to prohibition and police action to control the trade. The war on drugs engaged in by the United States now costs $50 billion each year, and some 450,000 Americans are in prison for drug offences. At the very least, the war on drugs is unsustainable, if not unwinnable.

THE OPIUM WARS

Cocaine may have transformed countries, been responsible for hundreds of deaths in skirmishes between rival cartels and drug law enforcement officers, but only one drug has ever precipitated not one, but two wars.

The Opium Wars, sometimes called the Anglo–Chinese Wars, were fought, whatever the official reasons, to maintain Britain's right to import and sell opium in China. According to Nathan Allen, author of the 1853 book *The Opium Wars*, 'China expends for the single article of opium, annually, nearly as much as the whole amount of the revenue of the United States'.

The English did not introduce the Chinese to opium. The first description of opium being used recreationally was recorded by Ming Dynasty writer Xu Boling in 1483. It was, he wrote 'mainly used to aid masculinity, strengthen sperm and regain vigour'. This association of opium with sexual prowess lasted until the twentieth century. A small amount was grown in Yunnan, but its use had been banned, for the first time, in 1729 by the Emperor Yeng Cheng. That year, only 200 chests were imported. By 1790, however, imports had grown to 4000 chests.

According to Allen, the plan to send opium from India to China was first suggested in 1767 to a council of representatives of the East India Company as a 'happy expedient towards raising the revenue for the supporting government'.

In 1799, the Emperor Kia King specifically prohibited the importation of opium. After that, opium-carrying ships were disguised and flew flags of convenience. The East India Company continued production and export, but refused to allow their own ships to carry it while encouraging others to do so. Soon, the trading company Jardine Mathieson (still trading in the East) became the largest dealers. Following the edict of 1799, the opium trade continued in China with the full knowledge and tacit approval of the British government. The Americans were also active in the trade, but not to the same extent, accounting for only ten per cent.

The precipitating event of the First Opium War was the appointment of Lin Tse-hsü as the Imperial Commissioner at Canton in 1839. His purpose was to root out the opium trade, and within two months of his appointment he had taken action against Chinese merchants and British traders, destroyed all stores of opium and had written an admonitory letter to Queen Victoria requesting the cessation of the opium trade. The English refused to back down. Lin threatened to cut off trade and expel the English from China.

In 1840, Chinese junks blockaded a British merchant fleet, one of which opened fire on a junk. This is how the war began, but it continued with a series of skirmishes which escalated when the British sent out a fleet of warships in 1840, which sailed up and down the coast shooting at forts and fighting on land. This lasted until 1842, when the British warships sailed up the Yangtze River to Nanking, followed by merchant ships carrying opium. Unable to withstand the full force of Her Majesty's Navy—and what almost certainly would have followed—the Chinese signed the Treaty of Nanking which opened China up to trade as never before. Five ports (Canton, Shanghai, Foochow, Amoy and Ningpo) were designated as treaty ports, and Hong Kong was ceded in perpetuity to Great Britain. Opium was hardly mentioned in this treaty, but the understanding was that the trade was to continue, unhindered, even though the British pressured the Chinese to legalise opium use, but failed. Both the French and the Americans forced a similar treaty on the Chinese in 1844.

Chinese attempts to control the trade were ignored by merchants, and the official British policy was to ignore the trade. By 1845, around 80 opium-running vessels were moored in Hong Kong harbour at any given time.

The spark for the Second Opium War was ignited when Chinese officers searching for a pirate boarded the *Arrow*, a ship flying a British flag but owned by a Chinese national from Hong Kong while it was moored at Guangzhou. In so doing, they hauled down the British flag.

The British sent a task force to seek redress for the incident and were joined by the French (a French missionary had been murdered in China). They took Guangzhou in 1857, then moved north and threatened the capital, Peking, in 1858. Another treaty was signed, the Treaty of Tianjin, which opened ten further ports to foreign trade and gave foreigners the right to permanent diplomatic residence in the capital.

When the British returned to ratify the treaty, they were attacked by Chinese forces who killed over 400 Englishmen and sank four ships. In 1860, a much larger Anglo-French force arrived, and invaded the capital, sending the Imperial court into flight and burning down the Summer Palace and 200 other imperial buildings. Missionaries were given the right to work in China and, finally, the opium trade was legalised. The reversal of that decision had to wait.

It wasn't until 1908 that a motion was put before the House of Commons to stop the licensing of opium dens in the colonies, including Hong Kong. It was carried unanimously. In spite of this, the Governor of Hong Kong, Sir Frederick Lugard, assured all concerned that there was not a problem, and there would be no loss of trade.

In 1909, the British government forced colonial authorities in Hong Kong to stop the trading of prepared opium into China, and in the same year, the Indian government stopped exporting. The official trade may have ended, but the trade went on, and expanded into heroin and morphine: it has been estimated that by the 1930s, ten per cent of the Chinese population was addicted to some form of opiate.

And the government of Hong Kong secured the concession to sell opium through licensed shops in the colony in 1914. By 1935, there were some 35 retail opium shops. The real end of government involvement in the trade had to wait until after World War II.

In 1945, the interim administration set up by the Commander-in-Chief abolished the opium monopoly. For the first time since the British took over Hong Kong 103 years earlier, opium was illegal, and the British government were out of the trade.

PEYOTE

'They eat a root which they call peyote, which they venerate as though it were a deity.'
Spanish visitor to Mexico, some time in the sixteenth century

The word peyote is derived from the Aztec *peyotl*, meaning caterpillar's cocoon and is a reference to the woolly centre of *Lophophora williamsii*, or its variant *L. diffusa*. This small cactus (also known as the mescal button) contains mescaline, and is one of a number of psychoactive cacti found in Central America.

Peyote grows in northern Mexico and south-western Texas. It is slow growing, flowers sporadically and produces small, pink, bittersweet fruit that some find delicious. The flower sits atop the button, which is sliced for its mescaline. The traditional method of harvesting is to slice off only the upper part of the plant, leaving the taproot intact, in the hope that the button re-grows. The buttons are chewed, or dried and boiled in water to make a tea, which, to some, is extremely bitter and may cause nausea.

The first European record of peyote and its use was made by Fray Bernadino de Sahagún (1499–1590), a Franciscan missionary who arrived in Mexico in 1529, and spent most of the rest of his life studying the Native Americans he found himself among. Sahagún estimated that two tribes, the Chimimeca and the Toltec, had been using it for about 2000 years. More recent archaeological diggings

have turned up specimens in a context suggesting ritual use which date to 3000 years ago.

The first complete description of the living cactus was offered by Dr Francisco Hernández, personal physician to King Philip II of Spain (1527–1598), who went to the New World to study Aztec medicine. He noted that, 'Ground up and applied to painful joints, it is said to give relief ... It causes those devouring it to be able to foresee and to predict things'.

It was used by the indigenous people both ritually and as a medicine (the plant contains two antibiotics). From the descriptions that have come down to us, it would appear that the ritual use by the Huichol tribe is the closest to pre-Columbian practice. They see their search for peyote—which they call *hikuri*—as a religious pilgrimage, and its ingestion as part religious, part healing.

The arrival of the Inquisition in 1571 saw attempts to suppress the use of the drug, claiming the hallucinations were the work of the devil. Some years later, the Cahuilla Indians outflanked the Inquisition by setting up a mission in 1692, *El Santo de Jesu Peyotes*—Saint Jesus of the Peyotes—where the cactus

was sanctified at the altar. Folklore surrounding this include a belief in the *Santo Niño de Peyotl*—the infant saint of the peyote—who could be seen among the plants and was their guardian.

The religious use of peyote was spread into North America by members of the Kiowa and Comanche tribes who, while visiting a group in Mexico, learnt of the sacred plant. They took it back with them and its ritual use spread, against the wishes of both local governments and the Church, but encouraged by tribal elders, who believed it would help stop the disintegration of their tribal customs. They organised themselves into a legally recognised religious group, the Native American Church, in the 1890s. Today, it has an estimated 250,000 members. Members of the church may quasi-legally purchase and use peyote buttons. In spite of a 1990 Supreme Court finding against two members claiming their right to take peyote under freedom of religion, most law-enforcement agencies turn a blind eye to it.

It's not just religious Native Americans who have been fascinated by the effects of peyote. In the late 1880s, German pharmacologist Louis Lewin was the first to analyse peyote, which

he regarded as extremely toxic, like strychnine; he was not much taken with its hallucinogenic properties. In the 1890s, German researcher Arthur Heffter isolated the mescaline alkaloid, and in 1919 it was synthesised by Ernst Späth.

Psychologist Havelock Ellis wrote of its effects in the article, 'Mescal: A New Artificial Paradise', published in *The Contemporary Review* in 1898. He took three buttons in his rooms in London, resulting in an experience that lasted 24 hours. He described inner lights, complex geometrical shapes and a clutter of kaleidoscopic effects.

So impressed was he by this that he gave mescaline to the poet W B Yeats, who was a member of the magical group, The Hermetic Order of the Golden Dawn. Another member was the notorious self-described warlock Aleister Crowley. He in turn gave the drug to the New Zealand-born poet and writer Katherine Mansfield, who felt only sick and remembered being annoyed by a modern painting.

Perhaps the best-known description of mescaline use was by Aldous Huxley in his book *The Doors of Perception* in 1954. This account inspired the Professor of Eastern Religions and Ethics at Oxford University, R C Zaehner, to try it. At first,

he enjoyed it, but then concluded that the use of intoxicants was artificial and anti-religious. He became vehemently opposed to their use, and clashed with psychologist and drug advocate Timothy Leary.

The widely differing views on the mescaline experience could, perhaps, be ascribed to culture. Medical anthropologist Marlene Dobkin de Rios described Anthony Wallace's 1959 work on the differing effects of peyote on European and Native American subjects. The Europeans tended to experience extreme shifts of mood from depression to anxiety, anxiety to euphoria. The Native Americans experienced a stability of mood and feelings of religious reverence. She concluded that it is not unusual for cultural expectations and backgrounds to colour the contents of altered states of consciousness.

TOBACCO

*'That lungs had a dual function—could be used for stimulation
in addition to respiration—is one of the American continent's most
significant contributions to civilization.'*
Iain Gately, Tobacco: The Story of How Tobacco Seduced the World, *2001*

Some 18,000 years ago, when Asiatic immigrants crossed the Bering Straits into what are now the two American continents, two of the many plants they came across were *Nicotiana rustica* and its close relation *N. tabacum* (from which most tobacco today is processed).

Archaeologists have established that tobacco was first cultivated in the Peruvian/Ecuadorian Andes between 7000 and 5000 years ago. There are Mayan drawings of tobacco being smoked and artefacts that may have been related to tobacco use from around 1400 BC. By the time Columbus arrived, the use of tobacco had spread throughout the Americas and the Carribean.

It is unclear how smoking began, but it probably grew naturally from the inhaling of snuff—finely powdered tobacco—through the nose. As tobacco moved north from the Andes, it was smoked, sniffed, chewed, drunk, eaten, used in eye drops, and smeared over bodies as insect repellant (for which is it still used today). The smoke was blown over brides, and tobacco was given as a gift, offered to the gods, used as a mild analgesic and packed around decayed teeth.

But the most common form of taking tobacco was smoking, in the form of cigars (tightly wrapped cured leaves) or a primitive form of cigarette (cured strips of leaf wrapped in other leaves or corn husks).

Tobacco also played a central role in shamanic training. In small amounts, tobacco has a mild effect on the central nervous system; in large amounts, it can be hallucinogenic. Many of the shamans would take enough to bring them to the edge of death.

The Mayans farmed tobacco and took it for pleasure. Their artwork reveals that human beings and gods alike smoked. The Aztecs continued to use tobacco after the Mayan collapse, and also continued to use it in the treatment of diseases: a recipe was uncovered for a cure for gout which include tobacco and 'the flesh and excrement of a fox'.

We know that tobacco use had reached North America by 2500 BC because of a pipe dated to that time. Subsequent research has shown that its use was almost universal on that continent, with the exception of Alaska and Canada. The tribes who occupied the major part of pre-Columbian North America all smoked, and used pipes, which themselves became objects of ritual and mythology. Although its use was restricted to men, tobacco itself was often portrayed as a female spirit.

Among many tribes, tobacco use and pipe smoking acquired a ritual function: before important decisions were made, the men would sit and hand around the pipe, smoke and discuss the issue in front of them. The Omaha Indians of Oklahoma had two sets of pipes, one for war and one for peace. The peace pipes were plain, the war pipes highly decorated. Sharing the peace pipe was a symbol of friendship, a ritual undertaken when sealing a treaty between two tribes and a prelude to many interactions.

Spain was first made aware of tobacco through the writings of Bartolome de las Casas (1484–1566; later Saint Bartolome) who rewrote Columbus' lost 'Land Ho' log, noting 'And the men always with a firebrand in their hands ... which are dried herbs, put in a certain leaf ... lit at one end and at the other they chew or suck and take in it with their breath which dulls the flesh and as it were intoxicates and so they say they do not feel weariness ... they call them tobaccos'.

The Spanish at first didn't recognise the commercial value of tobacco. But by the middle of the sixteenth century, they were cultivating tobacco in Santo

Domingo and Cuba and smoking cigars. Jean Nicot, the French Ambassador to Portugal, was introduced to tobacco by a friend in Lisbon, the botanist Damião de Goes. He convinced Nicot of its healing powers, and in 1559, Nicot took cuttings from de Goes' plants back to Paris, where he introduced Catherine de Medici, the Queen of France, to it. She too was convinced of its healing powers, and declared it 'the Queen of herbs'. Nicot was feted, and his name was eventually given to both the plant—at first *Nicotina*, then *Nicotiana*—and the active ingredient, nicotine.

It is generally agreed that if the adventurer and poet Walter Raleigh (1552–1618) wasn't the first to bring tobacco to England, he most certainly popularised its use, presenting it to the court of Queen Elizabeth I, and smoking it as he watched the execution of the Earl of Essex in 1601—and also, seventeen years later, before his own execution.

Being habit forming, tobacco had a ready, continuing and expanding market. It became a popular and lucrative crop in the American colonies—14 grams (half an ounce) of seeds could produce 20,000 plants. In its early days, the state of Virginia—with slave labour—produced the most significant crops. Virginia and Maryland increased their exports of tobacco sixfold from 1663 to 1699.

The Dutch also became enthusiastic smokers, and Holland became tobacco's gateway to Northern Europe. While Peter the Great of Holland (1689–1725) was an enthusiastic smoker and promoter of tobacco, James I of England (1566–1725) was vehemently opposed to the habit, writing presciently, in a 1604 treatise entitled *Counterblaste to Tobacco*, that smoking was 'a custom loathsome to the eye, hateful to the nose, harmful to the brain and damaging to the lungs'.

Notwithstanding regal disapproval, by 1614 tobacco was being sold across

Great Britain in taverns, inns, alehouses, apothecaries and specialist shops already known as tobacconists. About 227,000 kilograms (500,000 pounds) was being imported annually by the 1620s and anyone taking a seat in an alehouse was likely to be offered a puff from the communal pipe.

Although there were those in the seventeenth century who still believed tobacco was a cure for syphilis (the link being the belief that syphilis originated in the Americas), there was also an anti-tobacco lobby, based either on the ideas of James I, or around the notion (linked to a racist belief in the indecency and wanton behaviour of the Native American people) that it was a filthy habit.

At the beginning of the seventeenth century, tobacco began its spread to the Ottoman Empire, Persia and China. All succumbed to Lady Nicotine, especially Turkey, where a separate cultivar, Turkish tobacco, was grown, its cultivation being encouraged by the Ottoman rulers. There was some resistance from the Sultan Murad IV (1612–1640), who attempted to close the coffee houses where the *nargile*—water pipe—was extensively used to smoke tobacco, primarily because he believed them to be hothouses of sedition and plots against rule (see Coffee, page 105). But the worldwide spread was relentless, and all opposition useless.

As Europe headed into the eighteenth century, class divisions in the taking of tobacco began to appear. Pipes were reserved for the lower and middle classes, but taking snuff became highly fashionable—Venice at the time was awash with snuff even in the most refined circles. Although in England there was a social taboo on ladies taking snuff, this was virtually ignored, and a fashion for elegant snuff boxes arose in the 1770s. Society imposed strict rules on the habit: one writer described in detail the fourteen movements required for taking snuff in polite society.

In the early eighteenth century, the cigar returned—men were sent to a special smoking room called a divan to indulge. Between the 1830s and 1870s, consumption in Britain went up from 400 grams (14 ounces) a head to nearly 650 grams (1½ pounds).

But the world was heading towards the democratic, go-anywhere, smoke-anywhere, smoke-more delivery system—the cigarette. It is unclear whether the first cigarettes were made in Europe or the Middle East—many stories are offered. The French historian Fernand Braudel suggests that the cigarette entered Spain during the Napoleonic Wars—which broke out around the beginning of the seventeenth century—and spread from there to France, but it would be surprising if some form of tobacco wrapped in paper had not been tried before that (the Native Americans certainly used a form of cigarette). Other historians report that the Brazilians made the first modern cigarettes, called *papeletes*, from about the seventeenth century, and it was from Brazil that they were imported into Spain, Portugal and Italy.

The British were introduced to cigarettes during the Crimean War (1853–1856); their Ottoman and French allies smoked them. A veteran of that war, Robert Peacock Gloag, set up the first cigarette factory in Bristol, and made his cigarettes—branded Sweet Threes—from ground tobacco, yellow paper and a cane mouthpiece.

Cigarettes did not become popular in England until around 1870 (some reports says that Gloag stopped making cigarettes and began rolling cigars). At that time Phillip Morris, the Bond Street cigar maker, started making cigarettes. A Wills factory was set up in Bristol in 1871, and Players began manufacturing in Nottingham in 1878.

At first, cigarettes were seen as both effeminate and, among the aristocratic classes, more vulgar even than the pipe. There was a curious antagonism between tobacco and women in Victorian England. At that time, men were under pressure to give up smoking when they married, but when many continued to smoke after marriage, they were accommodated by having to leave the room after dinner, and the smoking room once again became the male refuge, with mixed blessings.

Writer, traveller and confidante to the powerful, Lady Dorothy Nevill, wrote in 1910 that 'cigarette smoking after dinner has undoubtedly been a great factor in the cause of temperance'— although not, one would imagine, if the port bottle followed the chaps into the smoking room.

By the end of the nineteenth century, tobacco use had spread around the world. The explorer Richard Francis Burton (1821–1920) found the Bedouin Somalis taking snuff, and his partner and later enemy, John Speke (1827–1864), drank beer and smoked with the local queen mother in Uganda.

The Americans of the time in many rural areas still loved to chew tobacco, a habit involving much spitting, which annoyed many visitors. Novelist Frances Trollope wrote after a trip on a Mississippi steamboat, 'I hardly know any annoyance so deeply repugnant to English feeling as the incessantly remorseless spitting of Americans'.

Some doubts about the health aspects of tobacco use began to emerge as early as 1880; an anti-tobacco journal was published and connections were made in medical circles between cancer of the mouth and pipe smoking. In England in the 1930s, an Anti-Cigarette League began. But although many doctors by this time were aware of the dangers, they did little in taking the lead against smoking.

The first American study statistically linking smoking and lung cancer was published in 1950 by the epidemiologist Morton Levin in the *Journal of the American Medical Association*. It found that rates of lung cancers were ten times higher among smokers than non-smokers. Another study in the same edition of the journal found that 96.5 per cent of lung cancer patients were heavy smokers.

In 1954, the American tobacco industry issued a joint pronouncement headlined 'Frank Statement to Cigarette Smokers refuting the link between cigarettes and lung cancer', in which they stated it was 'not regarded as conclusive'; that 'medical research indicates many causes of lung cancer' and that 'there is no proof that cigarette smoking is one of the causes'.

In 1957, however, the US Surgeon General issued a joint report from a study group on smoking and health that stated emphatically that prolonged smoking was a causative factor in the aetiology of lung cancer. In the same year, the British Medical Research Council published the statement that there was a 'relationship of cause and effect between smoking and cancer of the lung'.

In England in 1962, the Royal College of Physicians published 'Smoking and Health' which was, they said, 'intended to prove the overwhelming case against tobacco'. Two years later, the US Surgeon General's office released its negative findings on smoking and health.

Unsurprisingly, the tobacco industry reacted strongly, pointing out repeatedly that all studies linking cigarettes and lung cancer were statistical, not causal. The fact of the matter is that there has not yet been a successful study showing a causal link between smoking and lung cancer—in spite of repeated attempts using mice and dogs. Cigarette advertising continued. The cowboy, a powerful symbol for one brand of American cigarettes, which ran from 1954 to 1999, went from press and magazines to television.

In 1992, one of the actors who portrayed the iconic cowboy in print advertisements, Wayne McLaren, died at the age of fifty-one of a cancer that had spread from his lung to his brain. McLaren had a pack-and-a-half a day habit. Before his death, he appeared in anti-smoking advertisements. Soon after health warnings were placed on cigarette packs in America in 1966, stating 'Cigarette smoking may be hazardous to your health', sales went through the roof—up $7.8 billion in that same year.

In Britain, the government took measures against television advertising of cigarettes in 1965. Again, sales lifted exponentially. The United States banned television advertising for tobacco products in 1971.

In 1967, an attempt to link smoking directly to lung cancer using smoking dogs failed. After 875 days of smoking, the dogs were cut open and, while some had tumours, the results were not strong enough to make a direct link.

What is known is that nicotine is a highly addictive drug. Research has shown that nicotine is present in the brain within a minute or two of smoking, but has disappeared within twenty to thirty minutes, when the addict needs to replace it. This is why the industry had advanced with mass-production techniques: more and more smokers were smoking more and more cigarettes.

Fortunes of the tobacco companies have waxed and waned since the assault from the anti-tobacco forces. In the mid twentieth century, the advent of rock n' roll and teenage rebellion saw smoking as 'cool'. One brand responded to health claims by promoting itself as 'healthier' than the others, an approach that did not last. In the 1950s, mentholated tobacco was promoted as 'healthier'. Then came filters. One company tried to solve the problem of filtering out taste by putting the tars and nicotine in the filter; in 1956, another introduced an asbestos filter (the first recorded death from asbestosis was in 1934). Yet another brand promised 'more taste' by using all the offcuts from the floor of the tobacco processing plant in their cigarettes.

By the 1980s, the cigarette companies were beginning to realise there was not a great future in tobacco. They began to diversify. Phillip Morris, which had come a long way from a cigar store in London's Bond Street, now owns food company Kraft; R J Reynolds bought Del Monte Fruit; and British American Tobacco went into insurance, which raises some interesting questions.

The tobacco companies understood that we were beginning to get the message. By 1982, the British smoking population had fallen from a high of 81 per cent of males and 39 per cent of women in the post-war years, to 40 per cent of men and 35 per cent of women.

In the United States, the number of cigarettes smoked per person per annum dropped from 2810 in 1980 to 1633 in 1999, down 42 per cent. Smoking is in decline in France, China and Japan—all the major cigarette consuming countries.

Gradually smokers are losing their 'rights'. Smoking is generally banned in such places as restaurants, hotels, aircraft and buildings, due to the rise in awareness of the supposed dangers of passive smoking—'supposed' because, like the link between lung cancer and tobacco, causal studies have failed to show the dangers of passive smoking. In California between 1988 and 1997, the government spent $634 million on reduction of tobacco use. During that period, lung cancer rates fell by 13 per cent. But science has yet to find a causal link, and in 1997, the American Cancer Society published its cohort study of 250,000 people, which found no significant relation between passive smoking and lung cancer. A World Health Organisation study in 2000 concurred.

Nicotiana tabacum (tobacco)

But even without the causal smoking gun, the statistics continue to tell the story: smoking is life threatening. In 2006, Australia, which has mandated health warnings on cigarette packs since 1973, introduced a series of graphically illustrated warnings about specific diseases which cover 30 per cent of the front of the pack and 90 per cent of the back; upper case messages read, for example: Smoking causes emphysemas; Smoking clogs your arteries; Smoking causes mouth and throat cancer. Countries as diverse as Venezuela, Romania, Hong Kong and India—sixteen in all—have followed suit. In 2008, cigarette packs in the USA still carried only small printed warnings.

In the 1990s, a number of American states began exploratory proceedings against the tobacco companies. They demanded access to their internal documents, and were supplied 35 million pages. One of the legal team said, after reading through them, 'we couldn't believe what we were reading. It totally verified everything we suspected'. The tobacco industry has subsequently agreed to cover the states' medical expenses treating sick smokers in perpetuity, to set up a foundation to reduce teenage smoking, and to investigate diseases associated with smoking. It has also agreed not to target under-age smokers.

Is there a future for the leaf that filled the pipe of peace? The wreaths of smoke beloved of writers, artists and musicians are now too often associated with funeral wreaths. What was a rite of passage from childhood to adulthood is increasingly seen as childish. Smoking—unlike smokers—may never die. But now, when we light up, we know what we're letting ourselves in for.

Aphrodisiacs

Aphrodisiacs

Imagine the mystery of the sexual act to ancient man and woman. At once elusive and joyful, at times disappointing, but always on the mind—except, perhaps, when being pursued by wild beasts through the forest.

Often, it might have been the only pure pleasure available, a momentary respite from the hardships and miseries of their daily lives. But so transient, momentary and unreliable was the act (especially of the male organ), very soon there arose another desire: to find ways to extend and even perfect those elusive moments—and to ensure an always responsive penis. There must be something I can take, primitive man asked himself (we're betting it was a man), which will make it longer and better and harder.

It's a safe bet that we moderns are not the first to be obsessed with more, bigger and better sex. In the seemingly endless quest for a truly effective aphrodisiac, we've tried and enthusiastically endorsed everything from aubergines to avocados, saffron to tomatoes, valerian to Viagra.

The last named deals with the long-vexing question of the quixotic functioning of the male erection. But is it an aphrodisiac? Not in the real sense of the word, which is defined as 'a drug or a food that arouses sexual desire' and is derived from the name of Aphrodite, variously described as the goddess of love, beauty, desire, sexual rapture and fertility.

In a tale that reverberates with the complexity of sexuality, one version of her birth has it that Uranus was castrated by his son Cronus, who threw the severed genitals into the sea, where they began to churn and foam. From that foam was born Aphrodite. She was the most promiscuous of the gods, and, although married, had many affairs.

As for aphrodisiacs, the original was neither drug nor food, but the cestus, or girdle, that Aphrodite wore, which aroused the passions of all. Of this cestus, Homer wrote:

All magic was contained therein,
All love and yearning for love and
* talk of love*
Which have so often robbed reasonable
* men of their senses.*

But for us ordinary folk, the truth of the matter is, perhaps, as Richard Alan Miller writes in *The Magical & Ritual Use of Aphrodisiacs*, 'there is no sexual organ more important than the human mind'.

Perfumes were the very first aphrodisiacs—and our own smell, when combined with them, even more so. In his book *Scents and Sensuality*, scientist of the senses Max Lake points out that 'without knowing it, people communicate sexual attraction to each other in greater or lesser degree by scent'. He goes on to say that although we have known about this since time immemorial, we had to wait until now for a name: pheromone, from the Greek for transfer and excitement. 'When the scents of flowers, fruit and so forth are attractive', he writes, 'you can be sure that this will further their propagation, and borrowed for our perfumes they are truly seductive'.

Are there aphrodisiac foods? Nothing as sure fire as we hope, but, as Harold McGee in *McGee On Food and Cooking* puts it, while 'the truffle is not a positive aphrodisiac ... it can in certain situations make women more tender and men more agreeable'.

Many substances were believed by the ancients—and not so ancients—to have aphrodisiacal properties. Myrrh, most commonly the dried sap of the shrub *Commiphora myrrha*, was believed to be an aphrodisiac, mostly for its perfume, which resembles a combination

of ginger, cinnamon and clove (these three spices have also been considered aphrodisiacs at various times and in various places). Another Middle Eastern resin, frankincense, from trees of the genus *Boswellia*, was believed to be an aphrodisiac, again for its agreeable aroma—reinforcing Lake's theory of the nose being the main organ of sexual attraction.

Nutmeg is another spice that was seen as strongly aphrodisiacal as well as being an abortifacient and a hallucinogen (the last it is, if taken in enormous quantities). The tomato was likewise considered an aphrodisiac when it first arrived in Europe (see page 80)—indeed, its use was frowned upon in Presbyterian Scotland until the middle of the twentieth century as a naughty little red fruit from across the waters. It seems that aphrodisiacs are more highly thought of if they come from exotic places.

There is a long list of aphrodisiacs in Chinese medicine, including Chinese foxglove, *Rehmannia elata*, and ma huang, *Ephedra sinica*, a plant of the dry steppes that contains ephedrine. This has been extensively researched, found to make people feel lively, and put in the class of 'if you think it's going to work, it just might'.

The ancient Chinese were aware of the importance of sexual activity to health and longevity, and the philosopher Tung Hsuan Tsu (500–700 AD) wrote 'those who understand the nature of sex will nurture their vigour and prolong their lives. Those who treat its principle with contempt will injure their spirits and shorten their lives'.

The people of India have also incorporated aphrodisiacs into medical practice. Ayurvedic *vajikarana* therapy is based on a prescribed list of aphrodisiacs and tonics to maintain physical wellbeing, sexual health and fertility in both men and women—although it should be said that the aphrodisiacs in both Indian and Chinese medicine are mostly concerned with male virility.

Will a true aphrodisiac ever be found? From the evidence below, from reading much of the literature, perhaps there is at least one. But it's for you to make up your mind.

MANDRAKE

'Oh Mandrake, green grass
Beautiful bird which is so crazy
As to sing to me in the moonlight of the evening.'
Romanian folk song

Mandragora officinarum is a curious plant. Unprepossessing above ground, with spear-shaped leaves, a pale grey-green flower and orange to red berries, it is famous for its root, which is long and brown, 1–1.3 metres (3–4 feet) and forked. The forked shape can be somewhat human-like, and it is said that when dug from the ground the plant screams and kills all who hear it. This was alluded to as recently as in *Harry Potter and the Chamber of Secrets*, where anyone at Hogwarts tending the plants had to wear earmuffs, and as long ago as in *Antony and Cleopatra*, where Shakespeare has Juliet wail just before taking the poison: 'Shrieks like mandrakes torn out of the earth/That living mortals hearing them, run mad'.

Mandrake is another plant of the enormous, varied and curious Solanaceae family (the nightshades), which also includes tomatoes, potatoes, eggplant, tobacco and belladonna. It grows in southern and central Europe and around the Mediterranean. There are more superstitions and stories about the mandrake echoing down through time than just about any other plant growing on the planet. It has been said to be variously aphrodisiac, anaphrodisiac, an aid to fertility, and a powerful narcotic.

Its principal ingredients are scopolamine, atropine (see page 158), hyosyamine and mandragorine—all parasympathetic depressants, except for mandragorine, which is narcotic and hypnotic. It has the effect of lowering the brain waves into a dreamy and visionary mode.

Of mandrake's use as an agent of fertility, the best known story is that of Leah and Jacob in Genesis 30, where, after taking mandrake, the long-barren and presumably eroticised Leah sleeps with Jacob and becomes pregnant.

Perhaps its most famous claim to be an aphrodisiac is that the goddess Aphrodite herself claimed it as her plant and it was used by her followers. Scholars have also suggested that mandrake was the substance given by Circe to Odysseus' men that turned them into swine, metaphorically if not literally.

Mandrake has long been a favourite in literature. It is mentioned in the Old Testament Song of Songs, and by the metaphysical poet John Donne (1572–1631) in one of his most enigmatic poems, simply called 'Song'. Shelley, mourning the death of the sensitive plant in the poem of the same name, 'The Sensitive Plant', plants mandrake on its grave:

When winter had gone and spring
  came back
The Sensitive Plant was a leafless wreck;
But the mandrakes, and toadstools, and
  docks, and darnels,
Rose like the dead from their ruined
  charnels.

A myth widely believed in Europe held that mandrakes grew where the semen of hanged men fell. In the first act of *Waiting for Godot*, Samuel Beckett gives this curious explanation for why the mandrake screams when you pull it up. Discussing the erections that they would get if they were hanged, Vladimir comments, 'With all that follows'—meaning ejaculation—'where it falls mandrakes grow. That's why they shriek when you pull them up. Did you know that?' Beckett obviously knew of this myth, and perhaps also that alchemists used to throw semen onto the earth to grow mandrakes.

The mandrake cult lives on in Romania, where it is known as the 'plant of life and death'. Its collection is surrounded by the sort of ritual custom and taboo we read of in the works of the Jewish historian Josephus (37–100 AD), who recommends digging a wide furrow around the plant, then sending in a dog to uproot it. When the dog dies, it will be safe for the humans to take the plant.

Mandrake, like belladonna (which also contains atropine) is associated with the abilities of witches to fly. They were said to rub the mucous membranes of their vaginas with an ointment containing mandrake, which would enable them to fly—or at least to think they did.

In reality, mandrake being a parasympathetic depressant, is actually anaphrodisiac (in other words, it diminishes sexual responsiveness). It was possibly used for sexual dreaming, to induce a light, trance-like sleep with vivid dreams, more useful for fantasising than realising. If, as Richard Alan Miller wrote, the mind is the most useful sexual organ, then mandrake takes you there.

Finally, as Arlette Bouloumié, Professor of Modern and Contemporary French Literature at the University of Angers, has written, mandrake 'has the cosmic sense of a profound correlation between nature and humanity and the possibility of their merging'. And that, perhaps, is its most important attribute. Perhaps mandrake is the Caliban—that symbol of humankind's instinctive, natural self—of plants; our way of seeing ourselves, for good and evil, in the

Mandragora officinarum (mandrake)

plant world. Such an interpretation is given weight by the myth that the mandrake was fashioned from the same clay as Adam.

SMILAX

'How much sarsaparilla do I have to drink to get a hard on?'
Anonymous cowboy, 1846

It might come as something of a surprise that sarsaparilla—the drink teetotallers get laughed at for ordering—contains substances remarkably close to the human sex hormones testosterone and progesterone.

Smilax officinalis is a member of the Sarsapparilla (Smilacaceae) family. It is a thorny, woody vine that can grow up to 50 metres (55 yards) in length. It produces small flowers and black to red berry-like fruits beloved of birds. The long, tuberous root is used medicinally. And it is from *S. officinalis* and a few closely related species that sarsaparilla is extracted.

The flavour of the soft drink known as sarsaparilla is from the bark and root of the sassafras tree; sarsaparilla from *Smilax* was used in the same drink only as a foaming agent.

Smilax is native to tropical and temperate parts of the world, and there are some 350 species around the globe, but it was taken back to Europe from South and Central America. The name comes from the Spanish *zarza*, for bramble or bush, and *parra*, vine, with the diminutive *illa* attached.

It contains a number of plant steroids, some of them the saponins, which can be synthesised to the human steroids estrogen and testosterone; it was one of the plants of interest to scientists looking for such steroids to manufacture a birth control pill (see Mexican yam, page 161).

As for its aphrodisiacal properties, there is much controversy. What is interesting to us is that the Native Americans used various species of *Smilax* to increase male potency, knowing nothing of the presence of the saponins. Richard Alan Miller recommends an internal dose 25 to 50 grams taken two to four times a day to combat 'the dreaded syndrome of ageing with the accompanying loss of sexual powers'.

It is still used as an aphrodisiac in Latin America, England and elsewhere, despite there being a lack of clinical evidence that it works. There is ample clinical evidence of its efficacy in the treatment of skin conditions such as psoriasis, eczema and acne, respiratory diseases, and even syphilis. Yet unlike ginseng root, for which there is clinically proven evidence of some efficacy, the case for smilax is circumstantial.

In the magazine *Better Nutrition*, journalist Virginia Dolby wrote in 1998: 'New research suggests that ginseng's long-held reputation as a virility enhancer for men may be related to this herb's enhancement of nitric oxide synthesis. As surprising as it sounds, ginseng may be justifiably called an aphrodisiac, on the basis of its ability to enhance vaso-dilatation, the widening of the diameter of a blood vessel in order to decrease the resistance to blood flow, in this instance to the penis to facilitate erection. This blood vessel effect also has a potential benefit for the blood vessels feeding the brain, heart, lung, and other areas of the body'. The article cited several clinical studies.

No such endorsement can be found for *smilax*. But that's why *smilax* is so interesting. Who do we believe—the Native Americans or the white-coated scientists shaking their heads in disbelief? In the meantime, sarsaparilla supplements are sold around the world, especially as herbal aphrodisiacs for women. The only way to find out is to try it—and be assured that no known side effects or toxicity have been documented for sarsaparilla taken in reasonable doses.

And what about those cowboys ordering sarsaparilla at the saloon? Well, it appears that its efficacy against syphilis was known at the time, and the cowboys of the Wild West would drink sarsaparilla after a visit to Miss Kitty's—but not before.

Smilax officinalis (sarsaparilla)

YOHIMBINE

*'Other pleasant effects are warm shudders along the spine backbone
which are especially pleasurable during coitus and orgasm.'*
Adam Gottleib, quoted in Christian Rätsch, Plants of Love, 1997

If there is an aphrodisiac that works for both men and women, could it be yohimbe? The evidence points to a cautious maybe—if, indeed, aphrodisiacs do exist outside the realms of speculation, mythology and yearning.

Yohimbe bark contains the active alkaloids yohimbine and yohimbiline, and is taken, mostly as inner shavings, from *Pausinystalia yohimbe* (previously *Corynanthe yohimbe*), a tree of 9–15 metres (30–50 feet) that grows in tropical West Africa, especially Nigeria, Cameroon and the Congo region. Although the scientists have, as usual, spent more time on testing its effect on male erectile function, one report says, 'Yohimbine hydrochloride (a refined powder processed from the bark) has been proposed to increase female libido (sexual interest). There is only limited poor-quality research in this area, and more study is needed before a recommendation can be made'.

That's no pill pusher talking—that's Medline, the website of the US National Library of Medicine. Evidence or no, the experience of the users of the drug in its place of origin would suggest it might work for both men and women.

Yohimbe is used by the Bantu-speaking tribes of the regions where *P. yohimbe* grows during their traditional wedding ceremonies, which have been described as 'orgy rituals' that can last up to 15 days. It has long been known to the tribespeople, bushmen and pygmies of the region, and beverages containing it are dispensed by magicians and fetish priests, especially to tribal chiefs who have to exhibit public potency (which would make them, literally, potentates).

The yohimbe story became known to the wider world in the late nineteenth century, when colonists living in German South West Africa (now Namibia) began experimenting with it and gave *P. yohimbe* the title of 'the love tree'. German merchant seamen took it home, where a researcher named Spiegel isolated the active alkaloids in 1896. It was tested on the male inmates of an insane asylum, all of whom, it was reported at the time, 'exhibited hard and long lasting erections'.

But it was not until the 1950s that the pure alkaloid was first synthesised, and not until the 1960s that it was studied scientifically. Laboratory research at the time confirmed that it was a demonstrably effective aphrodisiac and erectile function agent for men (no experimentation was done with women), but this was coupled with strongly psychoactive effects. It became very popular in the drug culture of the 1960s and 1970s, and Miller records one user saying 'it makes you high and horny—they'll have to ban it'. Curiously, they didn't: yohimbine hydrochloride is approved by the Food and Drug Administration in the United States, although yohimbe, the bark itself, is not.

A trawl through the Internet for scientific papers will reveal scores of tests on yohimbine, most agreeing that it does work on erectile dysfunction. The scientists, however, differ from the pleasure seekers in their opinions of the drug. Dr Julian Davidson of Stanford University, where the drug was trialled, said 'yohimbine does help men get an erection but they don't know what to do with it because they feel so lousy'.

On the other hand is the first-hand report from Adam Gottlieb in Legal Highs:

First effects after 30 minutes ... warm, pleasant spinal shivers, followed by psychic stimulation, heightening of emotional and sexual feelings, mild perceptual changes without hallucinations, sometimes spontaneous erections. Sexual activity is especially pleasurable. Feelings of bodies

melting into one another. Total experience lasts 2–4 hours. After effects: pleasant, relaxed feeling with no hangover.'

Gottlieb reported similar but not quite so intense reactions with yohimbine hydrochloride pills.

Yohimbe—or yohimbine—is also used in bodybuilding and weight-loss supplements, to sexually arouse animals for breeding, and in treating depression. In 2004, the UCLA Neuropsychiatric Institute released the findings of a study demonstrating that mice treated with yohimbine overcame their fear four times faster than those given a standard anxiety medication.

The result of all this is that the market in Cameroon and Nigeria is booming—and there is now a black market in 'fake' yohimbe bark, because, as the United Nations Food and Agriculture Organization has warned, 'the destructive harvesting methods employed and the rapidly-growing market for aphrodisiac remedies' are endangering the resource. The FAO, in cooperation with the Centre for Research in Agro Forestry (ICRAF), has reportedly begun a research program in Cameroon to investigate the potential of the tree for domestication.

But is it the long-sought aphrodisiac for men and women? The problem is that all the serious research on the drug has concerned erectile function or dysfunction; erotic pleasure has not been on the research agenda. And there is one big hurdle to any further research being carried out.

Dr Alvaro Morales is a distinguished urologist at Queen's University in Ontario, Canada, who has done extensive research into yohimbine's effectiveness with erectile function. In 2000, he wrote in the *International Journal of Impotence Research* that yohimbine 'has been used for over a century in the treatment of erectile dysfunction. In-depth, systematic studies in animals have shown that the drug has a remarkable positive effect on sexual performance. Meta-analyses of the few controlled, randomized human studies have consistently shown an advantage of yohimbine over placebo'.

The problem, as he points out later in the same article, is that because yohimbine is an 'old' drug, it does not enjoy patent protection or commercial viability. 'Until molecular/formulation changes can be brought about (as recently happened with two other agents: phentolamine and apomorphine)', he writes, 'serious

investigations of yohimbine will remain in limbo. It could be that the nay-sayers are right and yohimbine, indeed, lacks clinical activity as a treatment for men with erectile dysfunction. As long as it remains an orphan drug, we will never know'.

This is a modern twist on our relationship with the plant world. Unless someone can own a potentially useful naturally occurring substance, we will never know the extent of its usefulness—so science becomes the handmaiden of commerce. And the possibility of pleasure is left waiting in the wings.

Trees

Trees

It would be impossible to overestimate the importance of trees to Earth and to the development of humankind. The irony is that the species whose development depended, for a large part, on the tree, and whose continuation as a species depends almost entirely on the tree, seems determined to wipe out the forests.

Firstly, trees are the vital link in the process of photosynthesis: humans inhale carbon dioxide and exhale carbon monoxide; trees inhale carbon monoxide and exhale carbon dioxide. The waste of one is the breath of life of the other.

Secondly, in myriad ways, trees control and regulate climate. With forests, there is rainfall, and the evolution and maintenance of diverse flora and fauna. Without the tree, Earth dries out and deserts take over.

And thirdly, before humankind appeared, the Earth was covered in subtropical and tropical rainforests. One creature that evolved at this time was the prosimian, the ancestor of all primates, including *Homo sapiens*. There are prosimians still on Earth today, the lemurs the most prominent of them.

The first prosimian to climb a tree began a chain of events, which, sadly, has ended with the almost total destruction of the rainforest, their natural habitat. The ability to climb helped develop the prosimian brain, organs, limbs and reproductive system. To meet the challenges of climbing, paws were modified to grip; claws retreated, digits lengthened and, eventually, the opposable thumb of *Homo habilis* made its appearance around two million years ago. The eyes became larger and moved to the front of the head (see Fruit, page 88)— all this and more occurred as prosimian evolved into hominoid and finally came down from the trees.

This, perhaps, is why the tree has always held a central place in religion, myth and folklore—this and the myriad ways in which we use the tree and it products for our survival, shelter, warmth, knowledge (in the form of paper), for making music, for making ploughs, ships, carriages and, of course, first of all these, the wheel—all those things that make us human.

And how do we reward trees for giving us the air we breathe, nurturing us, then helping us build our civilisation? We cut them down, in their millions. We cut them down to give us living room, to plant more crops and to turn them into toilet paper.

We have cut down more than half the original rainforests on the planet. They now occupy less than 6 per cent of the Earth's surface, but account for more than half the species on it. It is estimated that we are losing 0.6 of a hectare (1.5 acres) every second of every day: about 2 per cent every year. By the year 2020, the number of species found in the rainforests will have dwindled by around 20 per cent.

In that light, and with the advent of global warming, the importance of the tree takes on a new dimension, and becomes a metaphor for the planet, a highly visible and easily calculated measure of our destruction of it—or otherwise. To save the Earth, we must save and expand the number of trees and forests on it.

COCONUT PALM

'The milk bottle on the doorstep of mankind.'
Hugh C. Harries, quoted in J G Ohler, Coconut, Tree of Life, 1984

You'd be hard pressed to find a more useful tree on the face of the Earth than *Cocos nucifera*. It provides shelter, food, drink—both alcoholic and non-alcoholic—water, utensils, ornamentation, cooking oil, sugar and soap, and, if cut correctly, its trunk can be used to build and make furniture. In the Maldives, they used to make boats of 100–200 tonnes from various parts of the tree, which were used in voyages to the Philippines and Arabia.

The origin of the coconut palm has been the source of speculation among scientists and botanists for decades and yet is still unknown. Some of that speculation has located its original home variously at the northern end of the Andes, in Southeast Asia, and in Panama. Coconut botanist Hugh C. Harries advances a strong case for Asian origin, based upon a number of arguments, including sea currents, the number of varieties and the number of names used for the fruit.

The pinpointing of the origin of the coconut is not helped by its ability to germinate after floating in the sea for up to 110 days. Using this information, Harries has further speculated that it may have originated on the atolls that emerged from the sea when Gondwanaland was divided (around 200 million years ago),

and was helped because plant and animal competition had been destroyed by volcanic activity. Evolution favoured the dominant wild coconut called the *kia nufa*, a triangular nut that has a thick husk to protect the fruit inside, and large cavities in the shell so that it floats well and germinates slowly, thus increasing the ability of the fruit to float long distances and remain viable. Today, this kind of nut is found from Palmyra Atoll, in the Pacific Ocean, to the Seychelles, in the Indian Ocean.

Harries also speculates that it was not until some 12 million years ago, when the coconut reached the coasts of Southeast Asia, that the ape-like *Ramapithecus* came down from the trees and developed a close relationship with the palm and its fruit, resulting in the emergence of man—an interesting idea, when you contemplate the motor skills required to crack a nut, thatch fronds and build with the trunk.

It is highly likely that self-seeded palms and human-assisted generation went hand in hand. Evidence suggests that 4000 years ago, colonising mariners began moving eastwards from Southeast Asia to the islands of the Pacific carrying coconuts for food and drink, and others which would also have been planted

where they landed. Perhaps these migrations are also responsible for the coconut-based cuisines of southern India and Sri Lanka.

More recently, Portuguese traders, beginning with Vasco de Gama in 1498, took coconuts from India and East Africa to the tropical eastern Atlantic islands like the Cape Verde Group. From there, coconuts travelled westward, as a source of food and drink for slave traders bound for Cuba. They then moved eastwards to West Africa, Senegal and Angola.

One curious sidelight in this tale of coconut migration is that while they were certainly eaten by Indigenous people in the north of Australia, no coconut palms grew there prior to European occupation. They were either eaten as soon as they washed up or, just as likely, the white-tailed rat *Uromys caudimaculatus* gobbled the rest up before they had a chance to germinate.

The coconut kingdom is divided into 'Talls' and 'Dwarfs', the Talls having thicker trunks, a larger crown and heavier fruit. The Talls cross-breed (the female flowers are fertilised by pollen from nearby trees), while the Dwarfs self-fertilise (each tree contains both male and female elements). The result of this is that a grove of wild Talls might appear fairly mixed in shapes and colours.

Within the Tall group, there are two major subgroups. The subgroup with a large, rounder fruit and a thinner husk is the domesticated palm, which has evolved as a result of selection; the fruit of the wild Tall is smaller with a thicker husk, and a lower volume of nut water. There are three main varieties of Dwarf: the stumpy or compact tree of the South Pacific, the village Dwarf scattered throughout the Pacific, and the Malay or Nias Dwarf, found in Indonesia.

The fruit of the domesticated coconut palm germinates while hanging on the branch—there is no chance of it being dispersed by the ocean, as it wouldn't survive immersion in salt water.

In both the domesticated and the wild fruit, the embryo of the seed is concealed beneath the 'soft' eye at the top of the nut. The emergence of a green shoot signals germination, with the first growth inside being a soft, expanding lump of white tissue. There is a three-month gap between germination and the first green leaf, then for 12 months the baby plant feeds on the kernel, after which it is transferred by a palm farmer to the field or garden. At the end of five years, a Tall palm will be approaching its maximum height of 7 metres (22 feet), while a Dwarf will reach 3–5 metres (10–16 feet). Both begin to flower and fruit at about 10 years old, and can live for 100 years or more—although nut production drops severely in older trees.

The coconut palm can be exploited on a small level or industrially. On a small village scale, it can be 'tapped' for its sap to make toddy. A slice of tissue is taken from the tip of the emerging but not quite open flower sheaf, and a bottle is placed beneath to catch the sap—one tree can yield up to 1 litre (4 cups) over night. Fresh from the tree, it makes a drink rich in sugar and vitamin C, or it can be fermented to make an alcoholic drink, sometimes called arrack. It can also be made into coconut vinegar.

The frond can be woven into hats, baskets, panels for huts or, as in Bali, fashioned into offerings for the gods. Palm wood, which is easily cut and fashioned, can be used for anything.

Industrially, coconut cream and milk are canned and exported around the world, mainly from Thailand. But the most important use for the flesh of the coconut in the nineteenth and early twentieth centuries was as copra—easily transportable blocks of dried flesh, used to make soap and coconut oil.

Copra production began to fall in the depression of 1929–1935, then production was severely interrupted by World War II, during which time the United States boosted production of maize and soy bean oil and found copra substitutes. By the end of the war, determined to continue production of these oils, the United States marketed them as safe and healthier than coconut oil.

Later, the marketing of poly-unsaturated fats (coconut oil is 90 per cent saturated fat) was so successful that coconut consumption fell, even in traditional coconut cultures such as southern India. At the same time, according to Mike Foale in *The Coconut Odyssey*, 'the rate of coronary heart disease rose!'

More recently, there has been a turnaround. Coconut oil is being mixed with diesel as a fuel in the tropics, virgin coconut oil is being marketed as a health food, and coconut juice is being shipped to Vietnam and China and canned as a soft drink. The coconut-producing countries are again looking favourably at the products of this graceful palm tree.

Cocos nucifera (coconut palm)

CORK

'Some weasel took the cork out of my lunch.'
W C Fields

The bark of the cork oak *Quercus suber* has been the wine lover's friend since ancient times. Today, however, a small molecule has seen the corks pulled from millions of bottles and replaced with aluminium screw caps or synthetic corks, and is devastating the cork oak industry. That molecule is 2,4,6 trichloroanisole, commonly known as TCA, and it is the latest chapter in the long history of this useful bark.

The cork oak is an evergreen tree which, while it can grow up to 20 metres (65 feet), usually stops well short of that, and is indigenous to the western Mediterranean and north-west Africa. Portugal is the most important cultivator of cork oak, accounting for more than half of the world's harvest, but Spain, Morocco, France, Italy and Tunisia all have commercial forests. Cork forests today cover about 2.5 million hectares (6.2 million acres) and Europe produces some 350,000 tonnes of cork a year.

Although the earliest written account of cork is not until 400 BC, it is highly likely that cork had been used for shelter and flotation long before. Soliloquising on the golden age of the ancients in Cervantes' novel, Don Quixote said of cork oaks that they would 'without the asking, shed their broad light bark with which men began to cover their dwellings ... as a protection against the inclemency of the heavens'.

The 400 BC reference is in the *Life of Camillus* (Marcus Furius Camillus, 446–365 BC) and relates the story of a young soldier carrying a message across the Tiber when Rome was besieged by Gauls and the bridges were held by the enemy, using cork to keep him afloat.

Horace (65–8 BC) refers to wine casks sealed with cork. Pliny the Elder (23–79 AD) described the tree and wrote that its bark was used for 'ship's anchors, drag ropes, fishermen's dragnets, the bungs for caskets and also to make soles for women's shoes', all of which it is still used for today—with the exception of the drag ropes for ship's anchors. Today it is also used in building to insulate floors and, in those countries where the cork oak grows, as roofing.

After the invention of the glass bottle in the fifteenth century, cork production rose swiftly. The industrial exploitation of cork began in the seventeenth century, when an enterprising German resident of Spain first rented cork forests, cleared the undergrowth, supervised the harvests and sold the cork in Germany. By 1830, cultivation had spread to Portugal, Italy and North Africa.

This attractive and hardy tree—it will survive fire, flood and drought—is monoecious (has both male and female flowers) and bears yellow flowers in spring. It fruits (acorns) at between twelve and twenty-five years, and is ready for the harvesting of its bark at twenty years. It is stripped in the summer, when the foliage is new and the sap is flowing, which helps separate the bark from the tree. A tree can live for up to 200 years, and can be harvested of its bark every ten years.

Circular cuts are made to the base of the tree and just below the first branches. Vertical cuts are then made and, using the natural voids in the bark, it is removed by skilled workmen using traditional stripping hatchets.

A young cork oak tree can produce 16 kilograms (35 pounds) of cork, while a mature tree is more likely to yield around 135 kilograms (300 pounds). One large old tree is recorded as having yielded 1000 kilograms (2300 pounds). A skilled stripper can gather from 135 to 350 kilograms (300–800 pounds) a day.

Traditionally, the stripped bark was hauled from the forest to a central station

CHÊNE LIÈGE.

Quercus suber, L.

Quercus suber (cork oak)

and stacked to season for some weeks, then boiled in copper tanks in which it was submerged for thirty minutes to remove tannins and other water-soluble materials and loose dirt. This softens the outer surface (called 'hardback'), which is then scraped off. After boiling and scraping, the cork was cut, trimmed, baled and sorted into many grades of quality and thickness. That was how it was done traditionally—before the scourge of TCA arrived.

TCA is produced as a result of the contact between cork and chlorophenol compounds, which may come about as a result of the higher level of such compounds in the atmosphere (they are used in pesticides and wood preservatives) or perhaps as a result of the chlorine bleaching of corks to sanitise them, a process that is less and less in use (most modern cork manufacturers pump water heated to 70° Celsius (160° Fahrenheit) through the cork to clean it.

A 'corked' wine—the name given to a wine whose cork has been infected with TCA—has an unpleasant, musty, wet-dog smell that overpowers any attractive characteristics the wine may originally have had. The estimate of wines affected by TCA vary from 1 to 15 per cent, and it is the reason why more and more wine makers are abandoning natural cork for aluminium screw caps and synthetic corks. The Portuguese government is doing everything in its power to reinstate cork as the safe, dependable stopper it has been for centuries.

Apart from stoppers and the uses noted earlier, cork is used in various engineering applications, including cork gaskets and polishing wheels. No doubt cork will eventually recover from the TCA problem, and continue to provide useful material and deliver wine in good condition for us for many years to come.

OAK

'Heart of oak are our ships,
Jolly tars are our men.
We always are ready,
Steady, boys, steady,
We'll fight and we'll conquer,
Again and again'
David Garrick, Heart of Oak, *1759*

There are hundreds of trees in the genus *Quercus*, among them the little-loved willow oak *Q. phellos*; the post oak *Q. stellata*, whose wood supplied the posts and railway sleepers that enabled the colonisation of North America; and the holm oak *Q. ilex*, under whose canopy the Perigord truffle grows in symbiotic relationship with the roots (see Truffle, page 117) and whose acorns, in Spain, feed the indigenous black pigs that supply the world with Spanish cured ham, *jamón*, one of the world's great foods.

But the tree we see in our mind's eye when we say the word 'oak' is the common or English oak, *Q. robur*, the tree that supplied the English people with bark for tanning, planks and beams for building—the panelling in the debating room in the House of Commons is oak— and the wood for the ships that helped Britannia rule the waves for hundreds of years.

Q. robur is not confined to England. It grows in Ireland, across Europe into Scandinavia, and all the way through the Caucasus to Asia Minor. It comes in many forms but is mostly a rugged, branchy, deciduous tree that can grow to 30 metres (100 feet). It has hard, grey, fissured bark, short-stalked variably-lobed leaves and

acorns—also good pig feed—that ripen in a single season.

The secret of the longevity of the oak tree—they commonly live to 200 years, with some reported up to 1000 years—is the high tannin content of the wood, which renders it impervious to insect and fungus attack, and the density of its wood, which provides the hardness and desirability for building houses, furniture and ships.

Oaks are usually a lowland species, growing on clay or gravel soils, and preferring slightly damp and acid sites with good drainage. In the Earth's temperate band, oaks generally have been the primary trees of the forest. In England, studies over 500 years have shown regional variations depending on where they grow.

The Sanskrit terms for 'tree' and 'oak' are the same, *duir*—a word that also gives practically every language with Indo-European roots the name for a 'door': *tur* (German), *puerta* (Spanish) and *porte* (French) are three examples.

Many surnames such as Aikman, Oakley, Cashe and Del Encina are associated with the oak tree. The name of the historic Buddha, Sakyamuni, means 'sage of the oak tree people'.

On the other hand, important and ancient oaks are often themselves named: there was the Cowthorpe Oak, which stood on the edge of the English village of Cowthorpe, near York, and was said to have had a girth of 18 metres (60 feet) before its death in the middle of the twentieth century. A branch that fell from this venerable tree in 1718 contained five tons of wood, and its branches, according to a nineteenth century account, spread across half an acre (0.2 hectare). There was the Charter Oak near Hartford, Connecticut, where the colonists hid their charter from the English Redcoats; and the Royal Oak in Boscobel Wood, where King Charles II hid to escape the Roundheads following the Battle of Worcester in 1651. The tree there now is a descendant of the original. You will find famous and named oaks in every country where they grow.

In ancient times, the oak tree was even a source of food. In 800 BC, Hesiod wrote that acorns prevented hunger: 'honest people do not suffer from famine, since the gods gave them abundant subsistence, acorn-bearing oaks, honey and sheep'. In 160 AD, in his history of Greece, Pausanius described the founding of the kingdom of Arcadia by Pelasgus who, he said, invented the use of houses, the wearing of sheepskins and the eating of acorns. The oak was Zeus' tree to the Greeks, and Jove's tree to the Romans. Prophesying the redemption of Israel, Isaiah wrote 'they will be called oaks of righteousness, the planting of the lord to display his glory' (Isaiah 61:3). And in Tunisia, an ancient word for oak translates as 'meal-bearing tree'.

A culture of acorn eaters (today called balanophages), the Native Indians of northern California, survived into modern times. Described by the early settlers as 'sleek and indolent', they were remarkable for the size of their population, which was organised into one hundred tribes, each of which had tribal oaks. They gathered acorns across the whole of northern California in autumn, and would either eat them out of hand at the base of the trees, or take them to their villages where the wives and daughters of the tribe (and only they) milled them into flour with mortar and pestle. The flour from the acorns of the valley oak *Q. lobata* was soaked in water until it became a little mouldy, thus improving its flavour. From this flour they made soup, mush or bread. Today, acorn eating has all but disappeared, with only the Koreans and Japanese using them to make flour, and a tofu-like acorn jelly.

Oak was always the first choice of shipwrights because of its strength and comparative lightness, and because it was watertight, bendable and easy to work. The legendary ships of the Vikings were made mostly from oak: the keels from one or more slender boles, the planks split from whole logs, and a strong plank at the waterline, the *meginhufr*, made by gradually reducing a half log to the desired shape and thickness, and the frame, added last, from chopped and shaped pieces of oak wood.

From the fifteenth to the nineteenth centuries, the powerful nations of Western Europe dramatically increased their dominions and colonies. A great part of the reason was a revolution in shipbuilding. Unlike the Vikings, who built their boats and then added a frame, this new method began with the frame, or skeleton, and then covered it with a shell. This method called for hundreds of differently and carefully shaped structural pieces. But tall forest oaks were still needed. 'Only with such a stout skeleton and with well-caulked planks could ships sail the open ocean and around the Capes', wrote William Bryant Logan in *Oak: The Frame of Civilization*.

Such ships had to have large holds, or 'bottoms' as they were called, to stow their cargo, and this is when the word began to be used for part of the human anatomy. The British merchant navy had the biggest bottoms and traded around the globe, while the British navy ruled the waves, and their ships of oak were called 'the wooden walls of England'.

The age of oak ended in the American state of Virginia in 1862. An ironclad ship, the CSS *Virginia*, did battle with two wooden English ships, the *Congress* and the *Cumberland*, in the Battle of Hampton Roads. The *Cumberland* was rammed, but damaged the *Virginia*. Seeing what had happened to the *Cumberland*, the captain of the *Congress* ordered his ship to be grounded in shallow water, where he exchanged fire with the *Virginia*. The *Virginia*'s red-hot shot set the *Congress* ablaze.

The next day, another ironclad, the USS *Monitor*, arrived, and the world's first battle between ironclads took place. The result of the battle was inconclusive—it was declared a draw—but it had changed the world. Now there was a new race—to build more ironclads.

The age of oak has left magnificent buildings, crumbling documents and memories of adventure and warfare on the oceans. But oak remains an important adjunct to our civilisation. Wines are aged, still, in barrels of American and French oak, as are whisky and sherry, the acorns feed the pigs, and the magnificent oak trees of European forests continue to inspire and delight us.

Gall of oak

A remarkable product of the oak tree, with a tragic end to its story, is oak-gall ink. Some trees are infested with a parasitic wasp, which lays its eggs and injects an irritant substance in the leaves which causes a gall (swelling) to occur. Its larvae feed on the galls, which contain an excess of tannic and gallic acids. When crushed, the galls give up powerful dyes, especially those of the kermes oak *Q. coccifera*, whose gall dye is scarlet, and the Aleppo oak *Q. infectoria*, which gives a blue-black dye.

The recipe published in Martianus Capella's fifth century *Encyclopaedia of the Seven Arts* for oak gall ink called for iron sulphate solution, crushed and boiled oak galls, water or wine, and gum arabic. This powerful ink—basically a combination of tannin and ferrous sulphate—binds to the paper and is not water soluble. From the twelfth to the nineteenth century, it was much used where clarity and permanence were needed.

The United States Constitution was written with it, as was much of Bach's music. Dürer, Rembrandt and Van Gogh all drew with it. It was only after several centuries had passed that it was discovered that the iron sulphate would eventually react with the medium on which it was used—vellum, papyrus or paper—eating away the surface below the ink, leaving nothing but empty space where the drawings, music or words had been. Over the past several decades, the efforts of paper conservators and art historians have been brought to bear with considerable success on the problem of oak gall ink corrosion.

Quercus robur (English oak)

MAGNIFICENT MAHOGANY

True mahogany, the wood beloved of cabinetmakers, is *Swietenia mahogani*, West Indian or Cuban mahogany. It was classified botanically in 1760 and named for the Dutch physician and botanist Baron Gerard von Swieten.

Later the name mahogany was also used for *S. macrophylla*, which became known as Honduran mahogany (or big-leaf mahogany), and for the African trees of the genus *Khaya*, close relatives of *Swietenia* and known as African mahogany.

Mahogany was gathered in the West Indies, Cuba, Santo Domingo (now the Dominican Republic), Mexico, Guatemala, Belize (formerly British Honduras), Brazil and Peru. In Africa, it was and is found on the Ivory Coast, the Gold Coast (today Ghana) and Nigeria.

Sadly, like all trees which yield desirable wood, *Swietenia* is endangered and all its species are on the CITES (Convention on International Trade in Endangered Species) register in most countries in which they grow.

Perhaps the earliest use of mahogany still to be seen is a rough-hewn cross dated 1514 on a church, itself dating from 1549, in Santo Domingo in the Dominican Republic. The conquistador Hernán Cortéz saw mahogany used in boat building in Santo Domingo and adapted it for his own use. It was first brought to Europe by the Spanish in the sixteenth century, with the English hot on their heels.

A tale is told of Sir Walter Raleigh's mahogany boat being admired by Queen Elizabeth I when he returned from his travels in 1595.

As the story goes, he instructed the ship's carpenter to make her a mahogany table. When it is first mentioned in England in 1662, the French word *acajou* is used.

In 1654, a record from the Colonial History of New York notes a Spanish ship captured laden with mahogany, copper and canella (cinnamon). And a sale in the *London Gazette* in 1702 noted 'mohogony' wood for sale.

By 1724, mahogany had found its way into the royal household of George I, in the form of 'desart tables upon brass wheels', also 'clothes chests' and a 'mahogany supping table'.

The increased prosperity of the British and North American Atlantic port cities in the eighteenth century is illustrated by the expansion of the trade in luxury furniture, and by the middle of the century, mahogany from the Caribbean had become the standard of quality. This, the golden age of mahogany, was the period of the great Georgian master craftsmen: Chippendale, the brothers Adam, Hepplewhite, Shearer and Sheraton, and their American contemporaries Duncan Phyfe and William Savery.

So great was the wood's reputation that by 1934, Aldous Huxley could write (in *Beyond the Mexique Bay*), 'when I was a boy, there was hardly, in all my acquaintance, a single reputable family which did not eat off mahogany, sit on mahogany, sleep in mahogany. Mahogany was a symbol of economic solidarity and moral worth'.

But of course it was not just the ingenuity of the cabinetmakers that contributed to the value of this timber, but the thousands of unnamed and forgotten Afro-Caribbean slaves who were taken to the Central American camps to fell and drag the massive logs—and those in Africa who performed the same tasks.

There are no mahogany forests. The tree grows scattered, and an average of eight trees per hectare (two per acre) would be considered a good stand. The first trees found on river banks were easily transported, but then the spotters needed to go deeper and deeper into the forest to find more.

When worthwhile stands were discovered, main trails leading to the river were cut, then trails leading to each tree. The trees were felled and pulled by slaves (or later, in America, by oxen), formed into rafts and floated down river.

Mahogany trees can grow to 46 metres (150 feet) in height and 1–2 metres (3–6 feet) in diameter. The bark is grey-brown, varying from rough to fairly smooth. The flowers are small, yellowish and tulip shaped, and the seeds are packed in thick-walled capsules which are, curiously, the colour of well-aged mahogany wood.

S. mahogani, which has the reputation among cabinetmakers and boat builders as the finest of woods, has the finest grain, a silky texture and beautiful colour. It saws yellowish-white but rapidly changes with exposure to sunlight to a rich and deep red-brown. It is heavier and harder than the other mahoganies and resistant to rot.

Mahogany has been used to make everything from beds to boats, to the struts of early aircraft and drums, most notably Ludwig drums. Luthiers use it for the backs and sides of acoustic guitars, and Gibson's Les Paul range of electric guitars are made of mahogany.

And yet such a beautiful and useful tree is in danger of extinction through our own actions and our greed. Of the Bantu habit of clearing a small patch of forest to plant crops, the early forest conservationist Richard St Barbe Baker wrote in *Men of the Trees* in 1932, 'this devastation of the countryside may seem like wanton destruction yet the tribesmen did not act in any spirit of mischief, they were merely ignorant of the consequences of their recklessness that, by destroying the forests at this rapid pace, they would one day leave themselves without fuel to cook their food or building materials for their buts and granaries'.

Nothing has changed. Only we no longer even have the excuse of clearing the land to plant food.

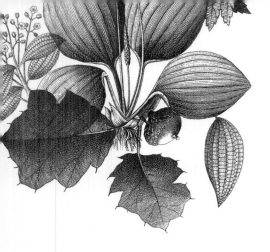

OLIVE

'The "olyve of pes" [olive of peace] is, then, a symbol, and I love it for what it stands for. I love it also for what it is, in itself, aesthetically; for what it is in relation to the Mediterranean landscape in which it beautifully plays its part.'

Aldous Huxley, The Olive Tree, 1936

If there is one tree that has marched down the millennia in step with humankind, easing the way, bringing peace and joy, that tree is the olive.

Oil pressed from the fruit of *Olea europaea* was used to anoint the kings of Israel, from Saul to Christ, although the olive tree was around long before any king ever trod the Earth. The first olive-leaf fossils have been found in Pliocene deposits (5–2 million years ago) at Mongardino, in Italy, and pieces of wild olive trees and stones have been uncovered in excavations from the Copper and Bronze Ages in Spain. The first olive press, used to squeeze the oil from the fruits of the tree, was found on the island of Crete, and dated to 1600 BC.

Olive oil lit the night, beautified the bodies of the naked athletes in the ancient Olympic Games, cured ills, was part of religious rituals and blessings and fed the body and the soul. Where did the olive tree come from? No one knows precisely, but we can follow its path westwards from Asia Minor.

Originally it was a wild tree that grew abundantly in wild forests, nothing like today's majestic tree. It is believed to have spread from Syria to Greece via

Anatolia or—for this is all conjecture—via Lower Egypt, Nubia, Ethiopia and the Atlas Mountains of Morocco. Professor Tiziano Caruso from the Department of Arboriculture in the University of Palermo believes the wild olive to have been indigenous to the entire Mediterranean Basin, and that it was first cultivated 6000 years ago in Syria.

What is known is that the Phoenicians (more or less corresponding to today's Lebanese), great seafarers and explorers, began disseminating the olive throughout the Greek islands in the sixteenth century BC, and onto the mainland between the fourteenth and twelfth centuries BC. By 600 BC, the Athenian statesman Solon (638–558 BC), in the world's first written legislation, passed the Olive Protection Law, which prohibited cutting down olive trees.

From 600 BC on, the cultivated tree spread throughout the Mediterranean, reaching Tripoli, Tunis and Sicily and from there to southern Italy. Once more there is a division of views. The author of an authoritative 1794 book on olive cultivation, Giovanni Presta, claimed that the olive tree's presence in Italy dated back to 1200 BC—three centuries before the fall of Troy.

Whenever the trees arrived in Italy, cultivation moved from south to north, from Calabria to Liguria. When the Romans arrived in North Africa about 455 BC, the Berbers already knew how to graft wild olives and had developed cultivation throughout their territories. (Today, the Berbers are unique in that some dry their olives on the roofs of their houses before pressing them.)

The Romans continued spreading the olive tree around the Mediterranean, using it as a peaceful weapon in their efforts to settle the people. It arrived with them in Marseilles about 600 BC and spread to the rest of Gaul.

Spain's olive trees arrived somewhat earlier, with the Phoenicians around 1050 BC, but olive agriculture did not develop until the arrival of Scipio in 211 BC and the advent of Roman rule in 45 BC. These dates coincide with folklore on the Balearic island of Majorca, which holds that some trees still standing, planted by the Phoenicians, are 1000 years old. When the Arabs arrived in 711 AD, they bought some of their own varieties with them and so influenced the spread of cultivation that the Spanish words for olive (*aceituna*), oil (*aceite*) and wild olive tree (*acebuche*) all have their roots in Arabic.

The first olive trees to leave the Mediterranean arrived in the Americas after 1492, and by 1560, olive groves were being cultivated in Mexico, then later in Peru, California, Chile and Argentina.

The olive tree arrived in Australia in 1805, when the first groves were planted in Parramatta, near Sydney. Groves are now planted right around the country, especially in South Australia, whose climate is most often described as Mediterranean.

So deeply have the roots of the olive tree reached into the soil and culture of the Mediterranean that the image of the tree, the leaf and the oil may be found everywhere, and would need a book far larger than this to even begin to catalogue its art and symbolism. A few examples will give the idea.

From the Twentieth Dynasty of the New Kingdom (1200–1090 BC), Egyptian mummies wore garlands of olive branches on their heads; in Greek mythology, Hercules was protected by an olive branch; the dove released from the Ark by Noah in the book of Genesis returned with an olive branch, thus permanently linking both the olive branch and the dove with peace (although Huxley noted that as Roman soldiers were awarded olive branches for victory in battle, 'the peace it proclaimed was the peace of victory, the peace which is too often only the tranquillity of exhaustion or complete annihilation').

And it wasn't only the kings of Israel who used oil in their holy rites: King Clovis, the first king of the Franks, was crowned in 481 AD when a dove appeared with a flask of oil. That flask was used to anoint another 34 French kings. The prophet Mohammad advised his followers to use olive oil on their bodies, and used it on his own head. He compared the light of Allah's being to the radiance of burning oil from 'the Blessed Tree, neither of the East nor the West'.

And today, the olive tree runs along the fault lines of the clashes between Arab, Jew and Christian in the Middle East.

The word olive is from the Latin *oliva*, and as it and the words from which it derives—the Greek *elais*, the Mycenaean *elaiwa*—are not Indo-European in origin, it is generally accepted that they came via Greek from some eastern Mediterranean language, most likely Semitic. But most modern European languages (except, as previously noted, Spanish) follow English in using variations on *oliva*.

The olive tree provides food and oil, defines the Mediterranean landscape and is a thing of beauty in the grove. Scientifically, it belongs to the *Oleaceae* family, which includes such odd relatives as jasmine, lilac and ash. Thirty different species of the *Olea* genus are found around the world, among them *O. europaea*, which has two subspecies, *oleaster* (wild olive) and *sativa* (olive). The adult tree has a large, clustered root system and a trunk whose shape will largely depend on local pruning techniques. For example, in many areas of Spain, the tree will have more than one trunk, whereas in the rest of the olive-growing countries, trees will be mostly single trunked. Even this characteristic is disappearing, as trees everywhere are pruned and shaped for mechanical harvesting, the manner of which will influence the shape of the tree and the pattern of its planting: some trees are kept deliberately low, and some even espaliered along a trellis.

The flower clusters originate from buds located on shoots from the previous year. The olive bears hermaphrodite flowers with tiny white petals, which produce both fruit and seeds. Because it is hardy, the tree produces a large number of flowers, only 1 to 3 per cent of which produce harvestable fruit.

The olive is technically a fruit known as a drupe; that is, a fleshy fruit with a single stone (like a peach or an apricot),

more or less round, whose shape depends on its variety. There are at least fifty-one varieties (a number confused by different names used for the same varieties in different countries) scattered around the olive-producing world, most having been selected using agronomic and technical criteria, others having sprung up as 'clones' in parts of the world where they have been transplanted.

Of 10 million tonnes of olives produced worldwide, 9 million are used for oil production, and only 1 million for the table. The International Olive Oil Council lays down strict regulations on the quality and naming of oils produced in Europe.

In the past, olive oil was extracted in hydraulic presses, which applied pressure to crushed fruit to squeeze out the oil. From that time stems the term 'cold-pressed' for the first pressings with best flavour, which were extracted at low temperature. Subsequent pressings were assisted by hot water being poured over the crushed fruit to extract the last drops.

Today, olive oil is almost exclusively obtained using a press that operates centrifugally, which allows much better yield without applying elevated temperature. Consequently, almost all olive oil in the food sector is 'cold-pressed'. The very best quality, which 'drips' from the fruit without squeezing, is produced without centrifugation, by sedimentation only; it is rare and expensive.

The best quality produced on a mass scale is today called 'native olive oil extra' in the countries of the European Union, and 'extra virgin' elsewhere. Both 'native olive oil extra' and the next quality class, 'native olive oil', must be produced without applying heat, and must not be refined. Products called simply 'olive oil' or 'pure olive oil', however, have usually been refined—that is, the oil is extracted by distillation using petrochemical solvents—and often contain small amounts of native oil (extra virgin) to improve the flavour. The lowest grade of olive oil is 'olive pomace'.

In spite of its historical importance and its position as the only oil used in cooking in the Mediterranean region, after World War II sales of olive oil declined in the face of the aggressive marketing tactics of the manufacturers of much cheaper products—soy, 'vegetable blended' and peanut oils. Even in countries as steeped in olive oil as Spain, the household oil was changed.

In the late 1980s, however, the International Olive Oil Council, an association of all the olive-producing coutries, began its own aggressive marketing campaign, aided by studies into the 'Mediterranean Diet', spearheaded by the publication of *Ancel Keys' Seven Countries Study* in 1970, which postulated that the high rates of coronary heart disease rates in Western countries were caused by a diet high in saturated fats. Olive oil was the right polyunsaturated fat in the right place at the right time.

In the face of this campaign, aimed mainly at food writers, chefs and other food professionals, consumption has risen sharply, from 957,000 tonnes in 1990–1991 to 1,615,000 tonnes in 2006–2007.

Today, olive oil is the romantic as well as the practical choice of cooking and eating oils in the affluent West, attended as it is by images of idyllic Mediterranean landscapes, tranquil village life and simple wholesome food. It may be manufactured in large factories in bustling industrial cities, but marketing never allows the truth to get in the way of a good story.

Nevertheless, olive oil and table olives are a welcome addition to American and Australian tables—and the IOOC has recently turned its attention to India—no doubt to the detriment of coconut oil (see page 215).

Olea europaea (olive)

RUBBER

'It was not until 1898 that any serious attention was paid to plantation development. Then came the automobile, and with it the awakening on the part of everybody that without rubber there could be no tires, and without tires there could be no automobiles.'
Harvey Firestone Jr, The Romance and Drama of the Rubber Industry, *1932*

The Spaniards returned with many wonders from the Americas, but the significance of one of these wonders passed them by for many years. The historian Antonio de Herrera Tordesillas (1559–1625) described a game played with a rubber ball at the court of the Aztec Emperor Montezuma II. The game was called *tlatchli orbatey*, and the stuff from which they made the dark bouncy ball was called *cauchu*, a milky fluid that wept from a tree—the French still call rubber *caoutchouc*. The Spaniards also noted, without much interest, that the natives made shoes, jars, torches and musical instruments with it. Yet it hardly made an impression on the West until 150 years ago.

The first description of latex extraction was made in 1615 by Juan de Torquemada. He noted that if a receptacle was not at hand, the Indians would mould the latex on their bodies.

But the first reliable reports on the substance were made when, in 1735, as part of a reawakened interest in their colonies in the New World, Philip V of Spain gave permission for a French scientific expedition to pass through South America, its aim being to measure an arc of the meridian line on the equator. One of the expedition's members, the mathematician Charles de la Condamine (a disciple of Voltaire), decided to explore Peru and Brazil on the way home. Among other observations, he learnt how to coagulate latex, made a case of it, and sent it back to France. The first description of the tree and latex tapping was made in 1749 by military engineer François Fresneau, who had met de la Condamine and become intrigued by latex. He was the first to recognise its industrial potential.

The French scientific community, hearing of the discoveries of these two, was also intrigued by the possibilities, and attempts were made to discover a solvent that could turn the crude rubber into a more workable and useful substance.

It was the British clergyman and amateur inventor Joseph Priestley who gave latex the name by which it is known in English, 'rubber'. In 1770 he wrote, 'I have seen a substance excellently adapted to wiping from paper the mark of a black lead pencil'.

As there are more than 200 plants in the world that contain the rubber hydrocarbon, it took scientists years of observation and experimentation to ascertain that the best producer was *Hevea brasiliensis*. Other species have been harvested, but were less successful.

After much skulduggery, plotting and seed smuggling, the *Hevea* tree is today cultivated in many countries and produces almost 100 per cent of the world's supply of natural rubber.

A tree with smooth grey bark, and greenish yellow flowers, it can, in the depths of the jungle, grow to 50 metres (160 feet), although farmed trees are much smaller. The latex is a milky sap that seeps out when an incision is made (a process known as tapping). The *Hevea* will begin to produce latex at between five and seven years of age, and can then be tapped every two or three days for up to thirty years.

In rubber plantations, a spiral-shaped groove is cut halfway round the tree, the latex flows down the groove to a spout and is collected in a cup hanging from the tree. It used to be gathered, rolled into a ball, and placed on a stick over a smoky fire to prevent fermentation and mould. In the more modern method, the latex is sieved, then mixed with water and formic acid to produce a uniform coagulation. It is left to stand for up to 18 hours, squeezed through rollers to remove any water, then dried in smoke

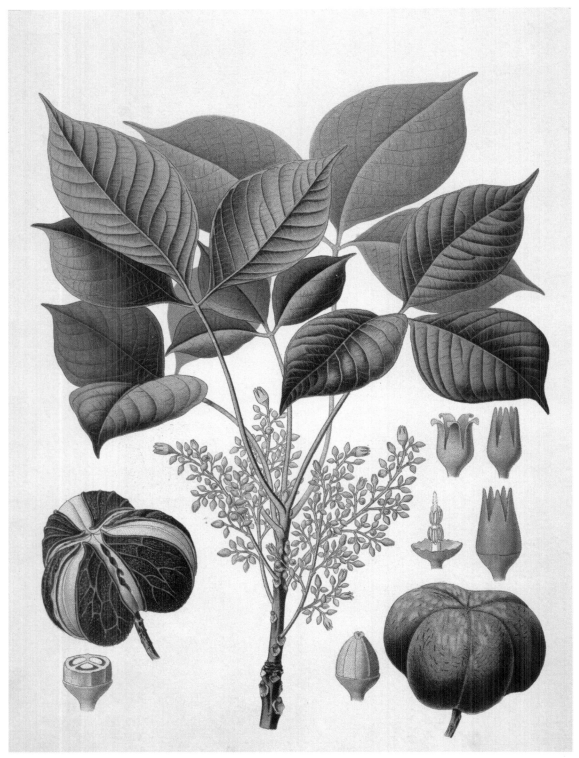

Hevea brasiliensis (rubber tree)

houses and distributed as smoked sheets ready for finishing and shaping.

Rubber's arrival in Europe coincided with the Industrial Revolution, and various manufacturers began to incorporate it into their goods. In 1775, the Portuguese began to manufacture rubber shoes; in 1791, Joseph Peel spread it onto cloth. In 1920, Thomas Hancock, an English manufacturer of rubber belts, rollers and hoses, invented a machine for chewing up waste strips for re-use, and discovered that this type of rubber was more malleable. And in 1823, Charles Macintosh discovered and patented a method of infusing cloth with it, thus bringing into the language the Macintosh. Hancock and Macintosh joined forces in 1834, and, later, Hancock alone invented a machine for spreading rubber on material.

Rubber was solving the problem of moving the goods of the Industrial Revolution. Machines ran with rubber belts, and very soon, carts rolled on rubber wheels. In 1839, the American hardware store owner and amateur inventor Charles Goodyear mixed sulphur with latex while heating it, which stabilised it. Sadly for Goodyear, he didn't attempt to patent this process until 1847, by which time the enterprising Hancock had obtained a sample—from Goodyear— and beaten him to the punch. He called the process 'vulcanisation'.

In 1888, after 18 years of solid rubber tyres, an Irishman, John Boyd Dunlop, invented the first pneumatic tyre. This was a real breakthrough, and by 1895, they were being used on motor cars. The rubber industry was established.

Everything from car tyres to condoms was made of rubber. But where this enormous success should have been shared with the country from which the raw material was sourced—Brazil—this was not the case. As was so often the case, the British, after some monumental bungling, managed to smuggle 70,000 seeds out of Brazil in 1876 to that clearing house for the Empire's pillage, Her Britannic Majesty's own Royal Garden of Kew, and into the hands of its director, Sir Joseph Hooker. The smuggler, a failed rubber planter called Henry Alexander Wickham, was knighted for his services— and then ignored, no matter how hard he tried to follow the seeds to the East and supervise their planting.

The seeds were raised as plants then sent, eventually, and over a number of years, first to Ceylon, then Singapore. In 1899, more than 100,000 seedlings were raised in the botanic gardens of Singapore thanks to the tireless efforts of Henry W. Ridley, the superintendent of the gardens, who took up the post in 1888 and took on the task of propagating and promoting rubber with zeal and determination, even slipping seeds into the pockets of plantation owners for them to take 'up country'.

By 1900, 2000 hectares (5000 acres) had been planted to *H. brasiliensis* in Southeast Asia, and over the next decade this increased to 400,000 hectares (1 million acres). The climatic conditions were perfect, there was an abundant supply of cheap labour and the techniques for production caught up quickly with the plantings. The Brazilians, whose economy had once received 40 per cent of its income from rubber, had supplied— unwittingly and unknowingly—the seeds that built the mighty industry which, by 1934, was producing 1,090,000 tonnes of rubber a year. By then, Brazil was producing, from its wild trees scattered through the rainforest, only 5 per cent of the world's rubber.

In 2006, the International Rubber Study Group's figures show production of natural rubber had increased more than eightfold, reaching 9,224,000 tonnes, with Indonesia, Thailand and Malaysia being the three largest producers. No doubt the increased production of latex condoms following the AIDS epidemic has helped considerably. The rubber tree is alive and well and being tapped in Southeast Asia.

Weeds

Weeds

Weeds are like terrorists, in that one person's terrorist is another person's freedom fighter. Whether we look upon a plant as a weed or not is, again, dependant on our point of view. To the home gardener trying to keep their rows of vegetables neat, the tiny common daisy *Bellis perennis* is a weed; to the homeopath, it is a remedy for muscular soreness.

The transformation of a plant into a weed can depend on place. The grass that grows as lawn will become a weed when it invades the garden plot. Lucerne or alfalfa, *Medicago sativa*, is an important fodder crop for livestock, but a troublesome weed in the vineyard. In Australia, *Echium plantagineum* is a weed damned as Paterson's Curse in well-watered areas, and looked upon with relief as stock feed in drier climes, prone to drought conditions, where it is known as Salvation Jane.

The word itself is of mysterious origins, and could have come from 'woad' via *woed*, the dye woad *Isatis tinctoria*, which is somewhat invasive, or the Old English *weod*, from Old High German *wiota*, fern. The reality is that its origins are unknown. Not many languages have a specific word meaning 'weed': in Spanish, they're *malhierbas*, bad small plants; the same in Italian, *malerbe*.

To be classed as a weed, a plant must be successful in exploiting its environment—too successful. Thus the popular definition 'a plant growing in the wrong place' is not correct: if the weed grows well, it is indeed growing in the right place—for the weed. This points us to the problem: humans.

As the human population grows and we colonise more land and turn it to our own needs, we come into conflict with more and more plants that stubbornly refuse to do what we want them to do—go away. Consider the global battle going on at the moment between those who want to plant genetically engineered crops—the vast majority of which are engineered for one thing and one thing only, to allow farmers to use as much glyphosate (a non-selective systemic herbicide) as they want without harming their crop—and those who think this is a bad idea. It is, at the moment, an argument about weeds (see Where next? page 242).

So definitions of weeds can be subjective: 'any vegetable or fungus interfering with the objectives or requirements of people', or ecological: 'any plant with a special ability to take advantage of human disturbance of the environment'.

And weeds can be re-evaluated. The burr medic, *Medicago polymorpha*, gets stuck to the fleece of sheep and is a real problem to the wool farmer, but provides good winter and spring fodder. Ragwort, *Senecio jacobaea*, is an important plant for the ecological balance of fungal and microbial organisms in some areas where it grows, yet is cursed as a weed anyway. And many weeds are being re-evaluated.

Petty spurge, *Euphorbia peplus*, a weed common in Australia and Europe, has recently been discovered to be an effective treatment against certain types of skin cancer, specifically basal cell carcinomas. Such 'weeds' would agree with another attempt to define them: 'any plant whose virtues have not yet been discovered'.

In so far as we can point the finger at any plant and call it a weed, where did they come from? Just as the Middle East is the cradle for many of the cultivated plants of the world (nine cereals, seven pulses, 15 fruits and nuts, 16 vegetables, and four root and tuber crops), the southern fringe of the Mediterranean and the adjacent Mediterranean–Iranian–Turanian steppes are the largest centres for weeds and the cradle for many of the weeds common to temperate and warm temperate zones.

The Bible, especially the book of Matthew, is very specific about weeds, which are there called tares: they are the work of the Devil. 'The field is the world; the good spring seed are the children of the kingdom; but the tares are the children of the wicked one' (Matthew 13:38).

In Breton mythology, the Devil boasted to a local saint that he could create a valuable crop, but in his clumsiness created darnel, *Lolium temulentum*, the tares of Matthew, a rye grass also known as 'false wheat', which tends to colonise wheat fields.

In 300 BC, Theophrastus wrote 'they say wheat and barley change into darnel and that this occurs with heavy rains ... and flax, too, they say, turns into darnel, the work of the Devil'. This belief was common in medieval times and right up to the fifteenth century, when Sir Francis Bacon (1561–1626) wrote in his 1622 book *Natural History* of corn 'degenerating' into wild oats.

His contemporary, the metaphysical poet John Donne (1572–1631), reiterated the belief in his poem 'To the Countess of Bedford': 'Good seed degenerates, and oft obeys / The soil's disease, and into cockle strays' ('cockle' was another name for darnel).

In Spanish there is a saying, *sembra la cizaña*, which means to sow discord—*cizaña* being Spanish for darnel. There are similar phrases in other languages, all agreeing with the general proposition that weeds are the Devil's work. The weed abounds in proverbs: in Argentina's *malahierba nunca muere*, 'a weed never dies', and the English 'one year's seeding, seven year's weeding', for example.

The Buddha said 'in the same way crops and fields are spoiled by weeds, men are spoiled by human desires'. And St Augustine told us that 'anger is a weed, hate is the tree'. The Japanese poet Hō Ru Tsa-Na wrote a wry and wise haiku on weeds:

Bowing to the mower
Yet they know nothing of classification
Happy little weeds.

In Sweden, there is a saying that 'he who sows thistles better not go barefoot'. This thought is included in the Scottish story that explains why the thistle is the emblem of that country: in the eleventh century, a raiding party of Danes were attacking a Scottish castle, as quietly as they could—until one trod on a thistle, cried out and woke the defenders.

And finally, before looking at the classification of these elusive plants and some examples, we would suggest that every gardener knows the truth of Michael Pollan's observation in *Second Nature* that 'thousands of weed seeds lie dormant in every cubic foot of soil, patiently waiting for just the right combination of light and moisture before setting on your plants'.

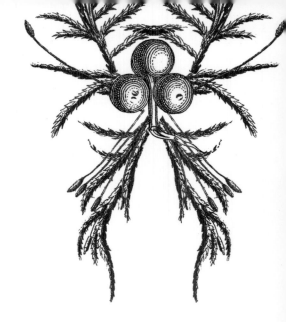

CLASSIFICATION

Agrestals: Weeds of tilled, arable land. Many plant cultivations have their own 'weeds'; for example, there are tea-weeds, coffee-weeds, banana-weeds and others. Agrestals can be perennial or annual.

Ruderals: Weeds or plants occurring on 'ruderal' sites (from the Latin *rudus*, debris), meaning earth heaps, dunghills, roadsides, railway lines and the like, all of which have been subjected to severe human disturbance. There is currently much study of these ruderal sites in a discipline called Urban Ecology.

Water weeds: In modern times, eutrophication of waterways in highly developed environments has created massive problems with water weeds. Eutrophication means an enrichment of nutrients, most commonly caused by sewage effluent and dissolved fertilisers discharging into waterways. This causes growths in blue-green algae (see page 238) and other weeds that block passage and slow down the flow of rivers, with disastrous effects.

Forestry weeds: These are weeds (mainly annual agrestals) of tree nurseries, weeds of afforestation, perennial sometimes shrubby species, 'weed' trees with pioneering colonising characteristics— they invade existing forests and replace native trees—and vines and other climbers dangerous to young trees. Even 'normal' forestry herbs and shrubs are now under suspicion of stealing nutrients and water from cultivated trees. And then there are the trees belonging to the forest vegetation designated by foresters as being 'undesirable' for various reasons, including that they are slow growing, or their wood is difficult to sell.

Environmental weeds: Introduced aggressive species that colonise natural vegetation and suppress native species. Worldwide, the problem of this type of weed infestation is increasing as we globalise and introduce plant species where they are not native. In Australia, this has been a problem for some hundreds of years, because of the introduction by the English colonisers of vegetation perfectly acceptable 'at home'—for example, the privet and the camphor laurel—which, when transplanted, turned into environmental disasters. Both have been declared weeds in Australia. This has also happened with imports to and from North America.

A good example is kudzu, *Pueraria lobata*, a vine introduced to the United States from Japan in 1876 at the Philadelphia Centennial Exposition, when farmers were encouraged to plant it as a forage crop and ornamental. In 1953, long after it had overrun the south-eastern United States it was declared a weed. Interconnectedness and ecology had to wait hundreds of years to be understood.

It should also be remembered that weeds, like all living things, have a definite place in the ecology of our planet. Let's examine this place briefly.

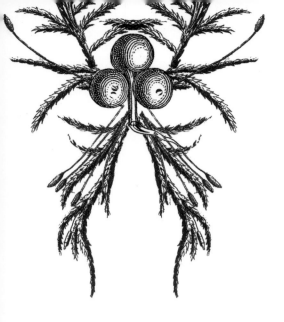

WEEDOLOGY

Firstly, it should be noted that even weeds that have not been found to be useful (petty spurge, ragwort) do have their usefulness: in creating a favourable microclimate for soil organisms; as protection against erosion; in transporting nutrients to the surface, in the case of deep-rooted weeds; and in the preservation of advantageous insect populations.

In some cases, severe interference with the natural order of weeds by removal with herbicides can lead to the disturbance of a delicate equilibrium. The scientifically and environmentally minded Austrian vintner Lenz Moser, who investigated vineyards in the 1920s, found some 'vine favourable' and others 'vine hostile'. Organic farmers today make similar distinctions on their land.

It's a subject that needs a good deal more work and investigation. Belatedly, with our growing understanding of interconnectedness, we are discovering that many of the things we have attempted to eradicate—such as sharks, weeds and snakes—have important roles to play on Earth.

Secondly, we have learnt that too much herbicide use is not beneficial to the farmer or the soil. Before herbicide use, weeds competed with each other in a richer weed environment, which kept their lives short and their impact lower: the weed environment was part of the natural order of a place. With the use of herbicides, we have created niches for the invasion of ruderal plants, causing fresh weed infestations.

Gardeners and farmers are currently advised to aim for a weed population rich in species but poor in strong individuals. Such a population can be more easily controlled by mechanical means and by crop rotation; the goal being management rather than total eradication, using the tolerable species to control the noxious ones.

Undisturbed natural vegetation is resistant to invasive plant species; weed colonisation is a sign of human interference. The question that has to be asked is: are such infestations natural or unnatural? Humankind is here. Weeds may be a metaphor for human presence: where we are, weeds are.

Looked at in that way, weeds can be used as natural indicators to give a 'feeling' for the complex of environmental factors in a certain location: a great aid to the cultivator. For example, annual weeds react quickly to alterations in the environment—a good farmer or gardener can 'read' a weed population to calculate the best time to sow, and the most beneficial and least harmful herbicide to be used.

More recently, studies have been done on the mycorrhizal interactions between roots and subterranean fungi. Fungi invade the root cells of many plants and exchange nutrients such as phosphorus for sugar—a beneficial exchange for plants that need phosphorus. A full-size long-term fungus might cover half a hectare (1¼ acres), and the application of herbicides could kill all of it.

Weed biographies

BLUE-GREEN ALGAE

Among the most dangerous and invasive organisms on the planet, blue-green algae are not algae (chlorophyll-containing plants ranging in size from a single cell to seaweeds), as they were thought to be for many years, but cyanobacteria, the collective name for a primitive microscopic organism that releases toxic substances into aquatic environments. It is now clear they have primitive cellular features that are closer to bacteria than to algae, but the name 'blue-green algae' has persisted.

While these organisms are always in the water, under certain conditions they get out of hand or 'bloom'—and engulf a river system or a backwater. Those conditions are when there is sunlight combined with high nitrogen and phosphorus levels; the light penetrates the water, discolours it and can turn it into a thick 'soup'. This normally occurs in summer, and in rivers, such blooms are related to river flows.

They also respond to nutrient levels. Like any weed, they are closely connected to human activity—to the phosphorus and nitrogen run-off from detergents and chemical fertilisers. When the cyanobacteria die, they decompose, using up the oxygen in the water so that nothing else can grow, and toxins are released.

But it's not all bad news for this strange bloom. Spirulina is a well-known health food supplement that is made from some types of blue-green algae, either cultured in alkaline fresh water or naturally grown and harvested. It is used to prevent and treat cancer and viral infections, to lower cholesterol and for weight loss.

Although there is no human clinical data to support its effectiveness, some studies suggest that spirulina has chemo-protective and radio-protective effects in animals. And while supplements of spirulina provide protein and small amounts of vitamins and minerals, there is no research to support their value. Research is also ongoing in the use of blue-green algae to treat HIV-AIDS, and in inhibiting the Ebola infection. Again, there is nothing conclusive—which is not to say there will never be.

WILD OATS

Avena fatua and *A. sterilis* are among the most successful weeds on the planet, with such a long history that they have entered into folklore. In English, 'sowing your wild oats' relates to a man's youthful promiscuity; in Sweden, it means to beget illegitimate children.

A. fatua probably originated in the Pamir Mountains in Central Asia, and *P. sterilis* in Asia Minor. These species are unsuitable as grain crops because their seeds fall as soon as they ripen, so they can't be harvested in bulk. In addition, their seed dormancy (the length of time a mature seed can last before germinating successfully) means they will be ploughed in with the grain and may not germinate in the field for months or years. *A. fatua* can be cleared out of a field, but *A. sterilis* is too similar to wheat. *A. fatua* appears in spring, *A. sterilis* in autumn and winter. They are disseminated either in contaminated cereal stocks (in this way they have been transported to the New World and Australia), or in the field, where they are highly self-fertile and will self-pollinate before their flowers open, so that even an isolated plant can cause an infestation.

Before effective herbicides appeared, the only way to control them was by date of sowing, crop competition and removal by hand. The first herbicides used against them were 2,4-D—a successful but contentious herbicide, now banned in many countries—and MCPA—another herbicide in use since the 1940s. But in the end, their use on wild oats only increased the weed's density as the plants developed immunity to the herbicides. There are now some twenty-five herbicides needed against them.

LANTANA

The genus *Lantana* contains some 150 species that have paradoxical traits. Their leaves are poisonous to many animals, including livestock, but their berries are delicious to birds, hence they are widely distributed. Their flowers are pretty and they are grown as ornamental plants, even in countries like Australia, where they are classed as a weed.

Lantana is native to tropical regions in the Americas and Africa, and has spread by one means or another throughout the Asia-Pacific region and Australia. In the mid 1970s, this writer climbed the active volcano Gunung Batur in north-eastern Bali, which rises some 2500 metres (8000 feet) above sea level. A mist covered the volcano, and only cleared at the top to reveal—a tangle of lantana.

A ruderal newcomer, lantana invades cleared bushlands and other disturbed landscapes. In East Africa, the invasion of lantana into cleared bushland has encouraged the resurgence of the tsetse fly population.

Especially in Australia, biological control has been tried without success. The lantana bug, introduced in 1995, made no impact and has become a pest in its own right. Lantana-feeding moths

Lantana camara (formerly *L. mistra*) (common lantana)

have also failed. Only dedicated removal and replacement with native understorey plants is successful.

Lantana is now classified as a weed in sixty countries, and is considered one of the ten worst weeds on the planet. An Australian government brochure on lantana calls it 'a weed of national significance', and 'one of Australia's most debilitating exotic invasive weeds'. Not so much pretty as pretty dangerous.

EDIBLE WEEDS

If you ask a Greek about weeds, he or she will perhaps launch into an enthusiastic description of grandmother's *hortapita*—wild weed pie—rather than bring up the subject of herbicides. Weeds, for the Greeks especially, but for many Europeans, are first and foremost free food.

Greeks have two names for weeds—*horta*, or wild greens, and *radíkia*, plants with beneficial roots and leaves. From *radíkia* comes the Italian radicchio: originally referring to a wild chicory, the term is now specific to a red-veined or blanched white-leaf chicory, *Cichorium intybus*. Before that, radicchio was the name given to all bitter wild edible plants, as opposed to the delicate salad weeds, called erbe or erbucce.

Edible weeds served the poor well in winter, when food was scarce, and in times of famine and poverty, when gathered and hunted food was often the only certain supply. But more than that, edible roots were a kind of wild medicine. There is an Italian saying from the town of Carrara that goes: *'Chi vo far 'na bona zena I magn'un erb' d'tut la mena'*—who wants to eat a good supper should eat a weed of every kind.

Edible weeds appeared in herbals (early books on the use of herbs medicinally) from the very first treatise on medicinal plants written by Cratevas (123–63 BC) in the first century BC, and stayed there until the seventeenth century. Monks grew the weeds in their monastery gardens, dried the leaves and roots and used the powder in medicines of all kinds. Edible weeds are still used by homeopathic practitioners.

The most widely distributed of these edible weeds are dandelions, *Taraxacum officinale*; wild endive, *Cichorium endivia*; all of the wild herbs, such as thyme, *Thymus* spp; mountain savory, *Satureja montana*; rocket *Eruca sativa* (now cultivated); any of the nettles from the genus *Urtica*, as well as other wild-growing plants, including asparagus, garlic and fennel (a prolific ruderal weed). The list goes on, and there are local specimens in many countries.

There are two warnings to be issued for any who would gather this bounty from nature—make sure they have not been sprayed with poisons, and be sure, as in gathering wild mushrooms, you know what you are gathering: there are poisonous as well as edible weeds. There are specialist books on the topic.

Where next?

Where next?

'Why is it that across cultures and through these long centuries of ecological awareness ... human practices [have] focused on the maximum utilization and degradation of the environment instead of pursuing the view of the human community as belonging to a biotic ecosystem of interdependent relationships guided by a "land ethic"?'

Sing C Chew, World Ecological Degradation, 2001

In the northern winter of 2007, the bees began to disappear. In America, between a half million to a million of a total of 2.4 million colonies died. Since the 1980s, two mites (*Acarapis woodi* and *Varroa destructor*) have caused similar die-offs in US bee populations. But this time, about a quarter of the deaths can't be attributed to mites.

As at time of writing, a cause for what has become known as 'colony collapse' had not been found. At first, US scientists thought that Australian bees exported to America could have caused the problem by bringing in a virus. But that was quickly and largely discounted. So far, scientists have looked at genetically modified plants, pathogens, pesticides and electromagnetic radiation from cell phones as possible causes—all of which only underlines in just how many ways we are endangering our planet.

Why are bees so important? In his book *How Flowers Changed the World*, botanist William C Burger outlines 'The Big Picture in Ten Major Stages', providing his view of what were the most important milestones in getting us to where we are today.

The eighth of these, Burger contends, was the development of flowering plants, enabling animals—mainly bees, but also birds and other insects—to carry pollen from plant to plant. The angiosperms (flower-bearing plants), as we have seen (page 140), supported the diversification of these insects and animals, and made the world as we know it today—rich, diverse and colourful. But for how much longer?

The difficulty with writing a chapter entitled Where Next? is that wherever we turn, we see the disastrous results of humankind's brief sojourn on this beautiful planet.

What can we blame for this blatant disregard for the wellbeing of our home? Some lay it at the feet of the Christian God's injunction to man in Genesis 2:28:

And God blessed them, and God said unto them, Be fruitful and multiply, and replenish the earth, and subdue it: and have dominion over the fish of the sea, and over the fowl of the air, and over every living thing that moveth on upon the earth.

We took to heart the commands to 'subdue' and 'to have dominion' but did not heed the warning 'to replenish'. Instead, we have steadily depleted.

Sing C Chew answered her own question, posed at the head of this chapter, by suggesting that 'the world historical process of incessant acquisition and consumption has advanced the denaturalization of the human community'. And that process of denaturalisation has gained pace relentlessly since the Industrial Revolution and the increasing urbanisation of humankind as we have moved away from nature and into the created environment.

So before we look at what is needed for the future, we must look at some of the problems we have already created.

Bumblebees and oriental lilies

Threats and Challenges

AGRICULTURE

'… recent discoveries suggest that the adoption of agriculture, supposedly our most decisive step toward a better life, was in many ways a catastrophe from which we have never recovered.'
Jared Diamond, American evolutionary biologist

In 2008, University of Wisconsin-Madison scientists used satellite images and crop and livestock production data to ascertain that nearly half the Earth's land surface—40 per cent—is taken up by food production. An area roughly the size of South America is used for crop production and an even larger area—between 3.2 and 3.6 billion hectares (7.9 and 8.9 billion acres)—is used to raise livestock. The US Food and Agriculture Organization suggests that total farmland has been increasing annually by five million hectares (12.4 million acres) between 1992 and 2002. To put those figures in perspective, it has been calculated that only about 7 per cent of the Earth's land was used for farming in 1700.

But the real problem is that this increase in land under cultivation has little to do with feeding the world and much to do with feeding industry. In Brazil, for example, in the five years from 2000 to 2005, soy bean producers increased their cultivation by 9.3 million hectares (23 million acres), producing an estimated (by the US Department of Agriculture) 60 million tonnes.

Soy beans are not a part of the traditional diets of the inhabitants of Brazil and America—another major soy bean producer. What happens to these beans is similar to what happens to the other crop taking up vast amounts of the Earth's surface, corn: it is fed to pigs, chickens and other livestock. And, increasingly, it is used in processing industrially produced 'food'. As Michael Pollan writes in *The Omnivore's Dilemma*, 'you'd be hard pressed to find a late-model processed food that isn't made from corn or soybeans ... The longer the ingredient label on a food, the more fractions of corn and soybeans you will find in it'.

Corn and soy beans—along with chemicals, artificial colours, flavours and preservatives—are the building blocks for all the processed foods you'll find in the central aisles of the supermarkets in developed countries. They are doing nothing to 'feed the world', only adding to the overfeeding of an already overfed sector of it.

Which is also the case with the even greater amount of land used to raise beef which, especially in America, is 'finished' on corn for 100 days in a feedlot—that is if it doesn't spend up to 400 days in the same feedlot.

According to David Pimentel, professor of ecology and agriculture in Cornell University's College of Agriculture and Life Sciences, 'If all the grain currently fed to livestock in the United States were consumed directly by people, the number of people who could be fed would be nearly 800 million'. In tracking food animal production from the feed trough to the dinner table by analysing US Department of Agriculture statistics, Pimentel found beef cattle production requires an energy input to protein output ratio of 54:1. America leads the world in producing beef in this highly inefficient way, but depending on prevailing grain prices and export demand, other beef-producing countries like Australia, Uruguay and Argentina are following suit.

Conventional agriculture currently creates problems in many other areas. Huge monoculture (one-crop) farms clear large tracts of land of trees and require excessive amounts of herbicides, pesticides and, perhaps most detrimentally, chemical fertilisers.

We know of the long-term effects of these chemical fertilisers because of an experiment that has been running continuously since 1856 at Rothamsted Manor in Hertfordshire in England. The experiment was begun by entrepreneur

and scientist John Bennet Lawes on his estate, Rothamsted, in partnership with chemist Joseph Henry Gilbert to test the impact of various organic and inorganic fertilisers on crop yield. Lawes had established one of the first artificial fertiliser factories in 1842.

One of the plots at Rothamsted, Plot 9, had been receiving regular doses of ammonium sulphate for 150 years when it was assessed by British ecologist Jonathan Silvertown, author of *Demons in Eden*. Silvertown arrived at two conclusions about Plot 9.

Firstly, any fertiliser that increases the total yield of hay—or anything for that matter—quickly leads to a corresponding reduction in the number of species present in the plant community.

And secondly, long-term use of fertilisers in the soil increases the acidity of the soil—the reason for the reduction in species. Most plants have difficulty living in acid soils. In Plot 9, only one species had survived its diet of 150 years of ammonium sulphate: sweet vernal grass (*Anthoxanthum odoratum*) which, when crushed, releases the odour of newly mown hay.

As Silvertown reported, the diversity has disappeared, along with the earthworms. All that remains is 'the essence of hay meadow', which had become 'a sweet vernal ghost'.

And all that land cleared for agriculture has been instrumental in advancing global warming: grasslands and crops absorb less light than forest canopy, increased reflected light above them warm the air, making the landscape warmer and drier, and when it does rain, because the land has been cleared, it erodes.

This is not a comprehensive critique of modern agriculture, only an overview of some of its problems. A little further on, we will be looking at some solutions to these problems.

THE AIR

In addition to creating greenhouse gases, nitrogen pollution in the atmosphere—from the burning of fossil fuels, exhaust fumes et cetera—produces nitrogen.

Plants cannot directly absorb the nitrogen gas—one of the reasons nitrogen fertilisers are used. Plants get their natural nitrogen by a process called nitrogen fixation, which converts nitrogen into usable nutrients. Once used, and in various ways, the nitrogen gas is recycled into the atmosphere. In pre-industrial times, nitrogen cycling was roughly in balance. But in the last 200 years, human activity has upset this balance. Nitrogen is deposited into the air from the burning of fossil fuels: exhaust fumes from cars, home heating, and air travel. In the 1930s, two million people travelled by air every year; today, the figure is 200 million.

In America, more than 3.2 million tonnes of nitrogen are deposited from the atmosphere every year. Areas of the country with the greatest rainfall and worst atmospheric pollution are at greater risk.

And this changes the balance of the plant's nutrient intake, and can change a pristine environment which is kept so by the balance of nitrogen and the other key elements for plant nutrition (potassium, phosphorus and magnesium). A twelve-year study in Minnesota showed that added nitrogen decreased species richness by 50 per cent. In England, diversity in meadow plots dropped from thirty species to three at higher nitrogen levels over ninety years. At Rothamsted it was calculated that as much as 45 kilograms (99 pounds) a day of nitrogen is deposited daily into soil from the air. In Sweden, where nitrogen deposits can reach 45 kilograms per hectare (100 pounds per 2 ½ acres) the results are equally alarming: in some areas, beneficial mycorrhizal fungi have produced no fruit (mushrooms) for six years.

DEFORESTATION

Nowhere is human greed and disregard for the long-term environmental effects of our actions more evident than in the continuing carnage committed against forests worldwide.

Is there any need to reiterate the central role that trees play in the continued health of the planet? Trees are the largest and longest living organisms on Earth. A tree is at once a miracle of engineering and a complex chemical factory. Through photosynthesis they clean the air that we breathe, and remove carbon dioxide from it.

As Thomas Pakenham writes in *Meetings with Remarkable Trees* (of the giant oak, ash and beech trees of the British Isles):

Each year the tree pumps several tons of water about 100 feet into the air, produces a new crop of 100,000 leaves, and covers half an acre of trunk and branches with a new pelt of bark. Yet the tree is alive. There is no mass production: every tree, sexually conceived, is built to a different design—as we see at first glance.

Tropical rainforests in particular are of great significance to the health of the planet. Yet despite our continued destruction of them—we've destroyed roughly half of the original rainforests on Earth, and they now occupy less than 6 per cent of the land surface—they still manage to sustain more than half of the planet's biological species. Let's just look at a handful of cases of the destruction of forests of all kinds.

Forty per cent of the forests existing in Indonesia in 1950 were cleared in the following fifty years. Forest cover fell from around 162 million hectares to 99 million hectares (400 million acres to 245 million acres). Since 1996, deforestation has been happening at around 2 million hectares (almost 5 million acres) a year.

More than 20 million hectares (50 million acres) have been cleared since 1985, the majority of which have not been re-used. For example, although 9 million hectares (22 million acres) have been approved for conversion to estate crop plantations, only 2 million hectares (5 million acres) have been planted.

According to the organisation Global Forest Watch, this has come to pass through a combination of a 'corrupt political and economic system that regarded natural resources, especially forests, as a source of revenue to be exploited for political ends and personal gain', and because 'Illegal logging has reached epidemic proportions as a result of Indonesia's chronic structural imbalance between legal wood supply and demand'.

Similar stories can be told in Papua New Guinea, and in the Amazon Basin in Brazil, where, between May 2000 and August 2006, nearly 150,000 square kilometres (58,000 square miles) of forest—an area larger than Greece—has been cleared, and since 1970, over 600,000 square kilometres (232,000 square miles) of Amazon rainforest have been destroyed. This has been brought about by a combination of clearing for cattle pasture, farming, colonisation of the Amazon Basin and legal and illegal logging.

But it is not only developing nations that are cutting down their forests at an alarming rate. In the Australian state of Tasmania, only 25 per cent of the original old growth forests remain. And yet logging of these forests continues, with trees up to 60 metres (almost 200 feet) in height being cut down to be converted into wood chips, mostly sold to Japanese companies which turn them into domestic and industrial products, like cartons and toilet paper.

But let's now turn to some of the solutions that can provide or are providing ways out of the problems we have created for ourselves.

CYCADS: THE SURVIVORS

The cycads are survivors. They have been around since Paleozoic times—at least 250 million years ago, perhaps even longer. They were, some scientists believe, the favourite food of the slow-moving herbivore *Stegosaurus* in the Jurassic period. They have survived the tectonic shifts of splitting continents, the Ice Age, meteors and catastrophes aplenty. Yet sadly, in just one hundred years, we humans have driven many of them close to the edge of extinction.

In form, they are like a small tree fern or palm, a typical cycad being the Mexican *Dioon edule*, with a short stocky trunk covered in an 'armour' of old leaf base and surmounted by a crown of dark green fleshy leaves. Perhaps the best known is the Japanese sago palm *Cycas revoluta*, from which the Japanese do extract a form of sago (although most sago comes from palms not related to the cycads).

Cycads are usually called palms in the countries in which they grow. The name cycad comes from the Greek *kykas*, meaning palm.

Cycad fossils, the evidence for their longevity on Earth, have been discovered on every continent, as well as some of the larger islands, and in several areas where current climatic conditions would not be favourable to them, such as Russia, Alaska and Antarctica.

This can be explained by the theory of continental drift, first proposed by geologist and meteorologist Alfred Wegener (1880–1930) in 1912, and now widely accepted in a modified form. This posits that at the beginning of the Mesozoic era, the Earth's landmass comprised one single vast continent, which he named Pangaea. About 150 million years ago, the theory goes, it began to split in two: Laurasia in the northern hemisphere, Gondwana in the southern.

When cycads are mapped, they generally occur between 30 degrees north latitude and 34 degrees south, with the majority occurring in the subtropics and a handful in equatorial habitats but at higher altitudes. There are a few that can tolerate frost or freezing, and some are tolerant of humidity.

There are some 300 described species of cycads, in 10 to 12 genera and two to three families—the reason for the imprecision being confusion regarding the true identity of many of them, a problem which continues to perplex botanists and taxonomists.

Few other groups of plants, with the possible exception of palms, rival the cycads for variety of foliage, size and general habitat. They are, as pointed out in an article in the *New York Times* magazine, 'seriously weird plants ... They produce outsize, often garishly coloured cones—lemon yellow, scarlet, maroon, pumpkin orange, apricot—that can weigh as much as 90 pounds [40 kilograms] apiece'. The odour of the cones produced by one species in Indonesia is so offensive they have to be buried. They can be highly poisonous to humans and animals, yet after careful treatment are used as food in many parts of the world.

Insects facilitate their pollination. The cones generate heat that releases a scent to attract weevils that burrow into the cone and carry the pollen to female plants in the search for food, shelter and a place to mate.

It is perhaps their 'serious weirdness' or their primeval quality or both that has triggered enormous interest in the cycads. People bitten by the cycad bug are said to have been infected by the 'green needle'. There are collectors determined to collect a specimen of every single known plant: ominously, the rare cycads they want cannot be obtained legally. Mature plants of certain species can be sold for more than US$50,000 each. This and habitat encroachment are the main reasons that cycads are now listed as endangered by CITES (Convention on the International Trade in Fauna and Flora).

In 1998, the World Conservation Union concluded that 12.5 per cent of the world's seed-producing plans and ferns—nearly 34,000 species in all—were threatened with extinction. All forty cycad species found in South Africa are endangered. A serious problem arising from the desire of collectors for mature plants is that the cycad is very slow growing indeed, and may take 100 years to grow 1 metre (3 feet).

As food

Charred remains of cycad seeds have been found in Australia and carbon dated to 7000 years ago. Some Indigenous Australians still eat the extracted starch, which they form into thin loaves and bake in ashes.

The raw or cooked seeds taste palatable, but are highly poisonous unless treated to leach out their toxins. The members of many early European exploration parties, ships' crews and settlers fell victim to cycad poisoning, including the crews of de Vlamingh in the early seventeenth century, Cook, La Perouse and the companions of the explorer Leichhardt. One imagines that these haughty Europeans would not have stooped to ask the locals how to prepare them.

The starchy kernels were (and are) cracked and crushed (often cooked first) then soaked in water for days or weeks, after which the fragments are ground to paste, cooked and eaten. Although different tribes in Australia and others around the world have slightly different methods of preparation, they all follow roughly the same processes.

Aboriginal gatherers (usually women) can also 'sniff' out which seeds are edible without preparation, and trigger seeding by setting fire to the groves. The abundant seed produced would feed enormous gatherings for weeks at a time. Early European bushmen, learning from the Aborigines, sometimes extracted the starch and used it as a flour to make bread.

Cycad flour is also used in Kenya, New Guinea and Japan (where it is a famine food, used only when the soy crop fails) and on many South Pacific islands.

As starch

The Native American tribes of Florida produced starch commercially from the abundant *Zamia integrifolia* species. From 1845 to 1920, it was also produced commercially by settlers, who set up mills to extract it using much the same technology as the tribespeople. Stems were ground, the ground material was sifted, repeatedly soaked, then washed and dried before being packed into barrels and shipped as 'arrowroot flour'. This extensive exploitation, added to urbanisation, swamp drainage and land clearance, has resulted in a dramatic reduction in the number of native cycads.

As alcohol

In the Ryuku Islands of Japan, an alcoholic drink similar to sake (but slightly poisonous) is made using *Cycas revoluta*. In various parts of Africa, a beer-like drink is made from the stem pith of various species of the *Encephalartos* genus, and in Sonora in Mexico, stems of *Dioon sonorense* are used to make a drink which, predictably enough, is said to be like tequila.

As medicine

In Japan, the seeds of *Cycas* were used for the treatment of diarrhoea, tuberculosis and neuralgia. In Indonesia, cycad starch and water is used to treat skin lesions.

It is to be hoped that our newfound awareness of and respect for these ancient and remarkable plants will alert the world to their precarious existence, and we will nurse them back to environmental health and abundance for another million years.

Solutions

AGRICULTURE

Apart from—and alongside—repairing the damage done by hundreds of years of extractive agriculture, we face a new challenge: how to feed the estimated increase in humans expected on the planet. US Census Bureau figures show that the world's population doubled between 1959 and 1999 from 3 billion to 6 billion. Their latest projections suggest that we will grow from that 6 billion to 9 billion by 2042, a figure that many say is conservative.

Others say that the problem of feeding the world is not one to be solved by agriculture—we can very easily grow enough food—but of politics and distribution. The wealthiest nations are hogging the lion's share of food grown (see soy beans and corn page 246) and the emerging and poorer countries are being starved. Now, however, technological and practical solutions are being offered to solve problems both real and perceived.

GENETIC MODIFICATION

Can genetically modified agriculture feed the world? Its proponents—particularly the four biotech companies which stand to gain substantially from its adoption (Monsanto, Syngenta AG, Bayer CropScience and DuPont) say it can. Opponents say it can't.

Depending upon whose research you read, the yields of GM crops are either higher or lower than for conventional or organically farmed crops. The fact remains that the main benefit of GM crops so far is their ability to withstand herbicides whose active ingredient is glyphosate, the most popular brand of which is Roundup, manufactured by Monsanto: indeed, Monsanto's seeds engineered for this purpose are called 'Roundup ready'. It's pretty hard to find a balanced account of the GM argument, as most writing on the subject is passionately anti or passionately pro. But in his book *Demons in Eden*, Jonathan Silvertown, professor of ecology at England's Open University, attempts an even-handed overview.

He begins, however, by casting doubt on the concept of 'substantial equivalence', as it has been used by the US Food and Drug Administration, a concept applied to determine whether a food shares similar health and nutritional characteristics with an existing familiar food with a history of safe use.

The FDA has approved many GM foods (and other so-called 'novel foods') using this concept. Silvertown's question is a simple one: if they (the GM foods) are the same, how can a patent be taken out on them? Because this is the aim of the biotech companies—not so much to feed the world, but to own the rights to sell the basic means of food production: seeds.

Silvertown points out that the three major problems cited by GM sceptics are:

1. *Potential threats to human health from consuming GM food.*
2. *Possible adverse environmental effects including the possibility that they (the GM crops) become invasive weeds.*
3. *Contamination of non-GM crops by GM crops.*

The arguments are long and complex and would take up far too much space in this book, but let's look at a couple through Silvertown's analysis. He first turns his attention to GM canola, a Roundup-ready product from Monsanto.

Anyone looking at a ripe canola field—yellow flowers waving in the

breeze—will realise that it is an insect-pollinated plant. Insects, and wind, carry canola pollen from field to field. 'It should have come as no surprise', he writes, 'when reports began to come in that canola (plants) tolerant of more than one herbicide were showing up in Canadian fields (most canola grown in Canada is GM—and that which was not planted as such is almost certainly contaminated by GM), a worrying development that threatens to produce a serious weed problem in prairie provinces in Canada'. And in other countries, a very serious problem is arising for the farmer who prefers to remain GM-free for marketing or health reasons: it just isn't possible.

Silvertown believes that 'properly regulated releases of GM crops could bring environmental benefits', and that 'transgenes (genetically modified crops) have to be studied in a natural environment to prove they're safe'.

There were such farmland trials in Britain using maize, beet and spring oilseed rape, the result of which were released in 2003. The results were that the rape (canola) and beet didn't pass muster, but the maize did. Maize seeds were released onto the market, then taken off: no one wanted to grow it. Major supermarket chains in England said they would not stock GM food.

Silvertown suggests one solution for looking at the pure science—that national and international agencies should take over the trial and breeding of GM crops. This proposition seems neither practical nor possible. In *Seeds of Deception*, author Jeffrey M Smith reports on a biotech industry conference held in 1999, where a representative from a company consulting to Monsanto told the audience that they (Monsanto) saw a world 'with 100 per cent of all commercial seed genetically modified and patented'. It is difficult to see what such a goal has to do with feeding the world, and to imagine the biotech companies relinquishing the control they now have (and hope to have) over their patented seeds to work for the betterment of humankind.

The real problem so far with the introduction of GM crops is not the science, which, as Silvertown points out, if applied carefully to testing for both environmental and human safety, might prove beneficial. The real problem is the bulldozing tactics used by its proponents.

In a forward to the Australian edition of *Genetic Roulette* (also by Jeffrey M Smith) a book outlining the scientific research available on the health aspects of GM food, Australian nutritionist Rosemary Stanton writes, 'As a scientist, I don't have a problem with technology as such, and this includes genetic modification ... but as a scientist, I would expect that all products of a new technology should be fully investigated for their effects'. And in Stanton's opinion, this has not happened. 'Appropriate tests have generally not been done and agribusiness companies have mostly refused to allow adequate and independent testing of their products.'

So, to the question can GM feed the world, the answer must be: we don't know yet, as we don't have sufficient information from independent scientific testing. Perhaps we should look to another concept before releasing GM into the world: the precautionary principle.

DEEP ROOTS

A more promising technological solution—but still hypothetical—to the problems posed by monoculture was laid out in the August 2007 edition of *Scientific American* in the article 'Future Farming: A Return to Roots?' by JD Glover, CM Cox and JP Reganold.

One of the most serious problems associated with monoculture's intensive land use is that it tramples over natural biodiversity and natural ecosystems in relying on the continued planting of annual crops, which is energy intensive and detrimental to the health of the soil.

The idea being investigated is called deep root planting, which replaces these single season crops with perennials with large and deep root systems capable of preserving the soil.

This radical (in the very real sense of the word) proposal came from plant geneticist Wes Jackson, who noted that the perennial grasses and flowers of the Kansas tall grass prairies remained highly productive year after year, without the use of herbicides, pesticides or artificial fertilisers, and wondered why.

He believes the difference is their longer roots—2 metres (7 feet) or more—which allowed them to dig deeper for moisture and nutrients and boosts their ability to sequestrate carbon (lock it into the soil). Two further benefits, if such a technology can be applied to food crops, would be lower emissions of carbon dioxide, since there would be no need to plant every year using tractors and trucks, and the ability to farm on now marginal lands.

SMALLER FARMS

There is a global movement against large-scale intensive farming, much of it centred on the organic movement (see below), but it is at its most powerful and organised in Europe and especially France, where its key organisation is the Confédération Paysanne, described as the 'radical French farmers union' (which now encompasses all Europe as Via Campesina). Its leader, sheep farmer Jose Bové, will be best remembered outside France for leading a team that 'dismantled' a McDonald's franchise in 1999.

Bové and his fellow members lead the world in agitating for a socially progressive future for farming. Rejecting the premise behind agribusiness increasing intensification and industrialisation of agriculture, the Confédération argues for the need for local food production by small, independent farmers—both for the sake of the quality of the food we consume and to support the kind of societies we want to live in.

They believe in small farms, locally produced food and in dismantling the mechanisms of the European Union that favour large agriculture—for example, the Common Agricultural Policy, which they see as a disaster. In the book articulating the Confédération's ideas, *Food for*

ORGANIC FARMING

Thought, authors Patrick Herman and Richard Kuper write that 'a de-intensified agriculture is called for, one that produces less but better, one that keeps the countryside people and respects nature, one that integrates agricultural policy into rural policy ... to move away from the policy of enlargement, concentration and industrialisation and to put small farms back into the heart of agriculture'.

In this, they are in lock step with the international organic movement. But, just as we had to ask whether GM food feed the world, the same question has to be put to the organic movement: can organic farming feed the world?

There has been some movement on this front. In April 2008, the International Assessment of Agricultural Knowledge, Science and Technology for Development, an initiative of sixty-one countries, brought down its findings after several years of deliberation on the problems of agriculture and feeding the world.

Their detailed report concluded that small-scale, environmentally responsible agriculture, including global organic farming, held the key to solving many of the problems. There were only three abstentions from signing off on this report: the United States, Australia and Canada.

For many years, conventional farmers have derided organic agriculture as a romantic, reactionary movement, harking back to a time before scientific farming showed the way.

But recent alarm over the damaging effects of an agricultural regime based upon the monocultural raising of crops using repeated applications of herbicides, pesticides and petrochemical fertilisers has forced a massive rethink.

If current farming practices form one of the main problems facing the environmental health of the planet, can a global switch to organic practices be a remedy? As information and research is amassed, it would appear that the answer is a cautious but encouraging yes.

The Rodale Institute is the research arm of Rodale Press, the pioneering American publishers of organic farming and gardening magazines. Jerome Irving Rodale, the founder, published the first magazine, *Organic Farming and Gardening*, in 1942. In 1971, his son Robert bought a 120 hectare (305 acre) farm in Pennsylvania to conduct research into organic farming.

For twenty-three years, a side-by-side (organic versus conventional) study was conducted by the Rodale Institute.

One of its major findings was that the carbon levels of organically formed soils increased while there was little change in the soils under the conventional system.

How it works is simple. Chemical fertilisers, most often derived from petrochemicals, strip the soil of nutrients and need to be re-applied, often in greater and greater amounts, to be effective. Organic fertilisers—mulch, compost, manure and other organic waste materials—build up the soil, are more efficient at retaining water (from 15 to 20 per cent more) and carbon (up to 981 kilograms per hectare in the organic system as opposed to 293 kilograms per hectare in the conventional—or 2162 pounds per 2½ acres as against 645 pounds per 2½ acres)

And the more carbon in the soil, the less there is in the atmosphere.

The other interesting thing about the Rodale trials was that yields were the same for both crop systems—except in drought years, when the organic yields were much higher.

And the study showed that organic farming used just 63 per cent of the energy required by conventional farming. Based upon its findings, the Institute calculated that if just 10,000 medium sized farms

REFORESTATION

converted to organic production, they would store so much carbon in the soil that it would be the equivalent of taking 1,174,000 cars off the road.

Organic farming appears also to be of benefit in much less fertile environments than Pennsylvania. According to Tewolde Berhan Gebre Egziabher, the Director General of the Environmental Protection Authority of Ethiopia from 1991 to 1994, a village in the Tigray region of Ethiopia that had converted to organic agriculture continued to harvest crops during a severe drought, while the crops of neighbouring villages using conventional chemical fertilisers failed.

This was again because using compost rather than chemical fertilisers meant that the soil contained more humus and organic matter, and could also store around twenty times its own weight in water.

Tewolde reported that this and other success stories has encouraged the Ethiopian government agricultural departments to adopt organic techniques. In 2003, the government announced it would support the development of organic agriculture, and a task force was established to draw up an Ethiopian Organic Agriculture Regulation, which

can become law, and a Regulation for Organic Agriculture Products to describe how organic products are defined, and what may or may not be used in their growing and processing.

Finally, after studying evidence like this coming in from all around the world, in 2002 the United Nations Food and Agriculture Organization (FAO) in its report *Organic Agriculture and Food Security*, stated categorically that organic agriculture can address local and global food security challenges. The report found that: 'Organic agriculture performs better than conventional agriculture on a per hectare scale, both with respect to direct energy consumption (fuel and oil) and indirect consumption (synthetic fertilisers and pesticides)'.

It is increasingly hard to look at organic agriculture as a 'niche market' supplier, with organic farms now to be found in 120 countries, covering 31 million hectares (77 million acres) of cultivated land.

Another area showing considerable progress globally is the move to re-plant the trees lost to what Sing C Chew in *World Ecological Degradation* points out is 5000 years of land clearing: for building, ships, firewood, charcoal, agriculture, paper and pulp milling, and today, as previously discussed, illegal logging for forest hardwood furniture production (as the price of hardwood rises, this is no longer confined to the East—reports of illegal logging in North America are growing). As Chew points out, trees have fuelled the socioeconomic transformation of every societal system, and as societies become wealthier, they find more extravagant uses for what is becoming increasingly rare timber: rainforest teak garden furniture is just one example.

But over the last twenty or thirty years, a number of strategies have been developed to reverse the trend and to re-forest on a large scale. Here are some examples. Note that websites of the non-government organisations mentioned in this section are listed on page 265.

American software billionaire Bill Gates has already contributed US$126 billion to his Bill & Melinda Gates Foundation, established in 2000, although US$25 million of that has gone to develop

GM crops to feed the world's poor. In 2006, the foundation appointed a former Monsanto vice-president to run their African division. This spells out some of the problems inherent with philanthropic conservation: the directives of the donor are often at odds with the best use for the funds.

Since 1996, the Forest Stewardship Council has been setting standards for responsible forest management, certifying forest and forest products and allowing those that measure up to carry their trademark. Products include garden furniture, pulp and paper. In that time the council has accredited over 90 million hectares (220 million acres) of forest in over 70 countries, with Canada the leading country.

The organisation People And Plants International (PPI) introduces the new science of ethnobotany (the study of the relationship between plants and people) to the field. They recognise that 'wild, managed, and domesticated plant resources represent a vital "green" social security to the majority of the world's people in the form of food, fuel, housing, textiles, medicines, and income from their processing and sale. Around the world, traditional systems of managing these resources are put under great stress by forces such as global markets for wood, non-timber forest products, and other biological or mineral materials'.

PPI, in bringing together local and international experts, helps to combine traditional knowledge and biological sciences to develop sustainable local solutions to improve the relationships between the human cultures and their natural environments and to train local people in these skills.

Debt-for-nature swaps are designed to free up a nation to allow them to spend money on conservation projects. The debt can be paid off by governments or by individuals through conservation groups or, as often happens, a combination of both governmental and non-governmental organisation sources. The idea was born of the findings of the organisation Conservation International that half of all threatened plant species and a third of mammals, birds, reptiles, et cetera are to be found in just 25 'hotspots' around the globe, adding up to less than 1.5 per cent of the Earth's surface. Buying that amount of land would cost, they estimated, US$23 billion dollars.

The US government, in concert with conservation groups, has initiated a Debt-for-nature swap in Costa Rica. Possible problems in these transactions revolve around whether or not the agreement will be honoured. In Costa Rica's case, it seems to be working. One of the environmental agencies in the arrangement, the Nature Conservancy, noted that Costa Rica has reversed a deforestation trend that saw it lose almost 80 per cent of its original forest cover. It has since replanted areas, with 52 per cent of the country now reforested.

Part of that successful reforestation in Costa Rica can be attributed to the pioneering and innovative work of one individual: evolutionary ecologist Dan Janzen, at what later became the Santa Rosa National Park, the nucleus of a larger area covering, the Area de Conservación Guanacaste, 120,000 hectares (295,000 acres) of regenerated tropical dry forest.

The area Janzen began on had been cleared for grazing, and aggressively populated by an African grass from the Serengeti called *jaraguá*, which had two characteristics that made it a formidable opponent; it is both highly flammable and fire resistant. The ranchers would burn it, and it would replace itself, thus stopping the forest from returning—and supplying crop fodder.

Janzen knew the trees would come back when the burning stopped, but he needed some help from grazing animals. He invited ranchers to put a few cattle on the land, so that tree seeds in their manure would germinate. He wrote 'the challenge is to turn the farmer's skill at bio-manipulation to work for the conservation of biodiversity ... restoring complex tropical wild lands is primarily a social endeavour: the technical issues are far less challenging'. Ethnobotany in action.

SPACE

And if all else fails, we can abandon ship. NASA and bodies like the NASA-funded Wisconsin Center for Space Automation and Robotics have been looking, for some time, at overcoming the problems of growing plants in space. Firstly, as food for astronauts on long space trips, but also as a way of overcoming the problems of cultivation in microgravity—for a possible future 'off-planet'. In 2003, space biologist Dr Bratislav Stankovic ran an experiment at the Wisconsin Centre using *Arabidopsis thaliana* (thale cress), a species often used in botanical experiments, planted in an Advanced Astroculture growth chamber about the size of a shoe box. For the first time, the microgravity growth experiments also included a process to rid the atmosphere of ethylene which had, in the past, caused plant sterility.

The experiment was pronounced a success. Against a control of plants grown normally, researchers found almost no differences between the two. Although, as Dr Brankovic said, 'we are still in a heroic age of understanding how plants and other organisms grow and develop in microgravity' such early successes mean a move toward the ability to grow food for long space voyages and the possibility of plants growing from the Moon to Mars—and beyond, according to a report in the *Wisconsin Engineer*.

There is hope for the future, but it rests in the hands of humanity. Whether we can work together across geographical and political borders and outside self interest—or even harnessing self interest as in Debt-for-nature—to bring the planet and all that grows on it back to good health is the most important challenge of our age.

Just as the solution to environmental degradation—and the future of the flora and thus the fauna of the planet—is in the hands of its human inhabitants, so are the seeds of its destruction.

The pessimistic view is best stated by American public health physician Warren M Hern. In two papers (in *Population and Environment* and in *Bioscience*), he has outlined his hypothesis that human occupation of the ecosystem is showing increasing similarity to a malignant cellular process.

Using figures for human population doubling—he estimates it passed its thirty-third doubling in 1998—he compares it to a malignant tumour, which usually results in the death of its host organism at between 37 and 40 doublings. Why does he make this comparison? Hern cites the following signs. Firstly, the signs, giving the symptoms of a malignant tumour, and then, in parenthesis, the corresponding symptoms in the effects of humanity on the planet:

- *rapid uncontrolled growth (of global population)*
- *destruction of adjacent tissues (invasion and destruction of planetary ecosystems, for example deforestation, air pollution)*
- *de-differentiation, that is loss of specialised appearance and function at individual cell level (homogenisation of cultural forms via the dynamics of the global economy)*
- *metastasis or distant colonisation (colonisation and urbanisation).*

He goes on to say that in medical diagnoses, confirmation of any two of these characteristics would establish the conditions for malignancy.

So where do we turn for hope? How can we save the diversity of growth—the flowers, fungi, trees, shrubs and vines that spring from the earth?

Increasingly it is becoming obvious that we must set limits to growth if we

The Roots of Civilisation

are not to fulfil our destiny to become a malignant tumour on the planet. To push Hern's metaphor a little further, the only other mechanism that thrives on unlimited growth is free market capitalism. How can we expect to deliver infinite growth on a planet with finite resources?

If our forest grows by two per cent a year and we harvest two per cent of its trees each year, we will still have a forest. If we harvest more, eventually we will have an empty field.

Secondly, and this is more difficult and perhaps even paradoxical in a book dedicated to those living organisms that have been useful to humanity—items of what is called economic botany—perhaps we have to accept and revel in nature simply for its own sake. In his short book *The Tree*, British novelist John Fowles wrote:

The subtlest of our alienations from it (nature), the most difficult to comprehend, is our eternal need to use it in some way, to derive some personal yield. We shall never fully understand nature (or ourselves) and certainly never respect it, until we dissociate the wild from the notion of usability—however innocent and harmless the use. For it is the general uselessness of so much of nature that lies at the root of our ancient hostility and indifference to it.

There is another way to look at our growing environment, as suggested by Michael Pollan in *Second Nature*: a conservation ethic based on the garden. He sets out ten points, what he calls 'provisional notes', towards the idea of treating the natural environment as a garden.

Pollan's central thesis is that we, with our brains, our desires and our interventions, are as much a part of the growing environment as the trees and the bees. But what we must do is curb our desires, and work with nature. He quotes Alexander Pope's advice to landscape gardeners:

Consult the Genius of the Place in all.

And Pollan reminds us that:

Even wilderness, in both its satanic and benevolent incarnations, is an historical man-made idea. Every one of our various metaphors for nature—wilderness, ecosystem, Gaia, resource, wasteland—is already a kind of a garden, an indissoluble mixture of our culture and whatever it is that's already out there.

Is such an idea in conflict with Fowles' 'general uselessness'? No. Take what is seen as farming on 'marginal land' in Australia, land where the farmer is often bailed out by government handouts in times of drought.

There are calls for some of these farmers to walk off the land. If we accept that Earth is a garden, that would be counterproductive. Another solution would be for the farming families to stay on the land and, perhaps with help from the Indigenous inhabitants of the area, both paid by the government to look after—to garden—the land back to the state it was in before it was cultivated for crops.

Such custodianship would, in the long run, save the land from the problems (and expense) of neglect: erosion, salinity, being overrun with opportunistic invasive plants and trees. It might no longer be 'productive' as a sheep station or a wheat farm, but it would be useful in the wider context of the environmental health of the landscape.

Perhaps as long as we look upon every plant, every forest, every flower and fungus as an item of consumption and profit, we are in danger of destroying the entire system. The answer to the question

Where next? then, relies entirely on our ability to overcome our own nature, our own flawed humanity.

To return to Genesis 2:28, quoted at the beginning of this section, and God's injunctions to humanity: we have been fruitful and multiplied; we have subdued it (the planet); now is time we obeyed the forgotten directive, and replenished it.

To do this will depend on the ability of our leaders to redefine their roles from those of exploiters and conquerors of the planet and its flora, to becoming stewards and saviours.

For the sake of our children and our children's children, we hope they can manage the change.